63|- 06|-

$$\frac{5}{60}$$

CROP PRODUCTION AND ENVIRONMENT

G. V. Jacks and R. O. Whyte

THE RAPE OF THE EARTH

*

R. O. Whyte and M. L. Yeo

GREEN CROP DRYING

*

R. O. Whyte, G. Nilsson-Leissner and H. C. Trumble

LEGUMES IN AGRICULTURE

*

R. O. Whyte

THE GRASSLAND AND FODDER RESOURCES OF INDIA

*

R. O. Whyte

PLANT EXPLORATION, COLLECTION AND INTRODUCTION

*

R. O. Whyte, T. R. G. Moir and J. P. Cooper

GRASSES IN AGRICULTURE

CROP PRODUCTION
AND
ENVIRONMENT

by
R. O. WHYTE

FABER AND FABER

24 Russell Square

London

First published in mcmxlvi
by Faber and Faber Limited
24 Russell Square, London W.C.1
This new edition mcmlx
Printed in Great Britain by
William Clowes and Sons Ltd
London and Beccles

CONTENTS

ILLUSTRATIONS

PLATES

ILLUSTRATIONS

8

FIGURES

A*

FIGURES

10

FIGURES

Chapter I

THE CENTRAL PROBLEM OF
PLANT SCIENCE

Introduction

Plant ecology, the study of the plant in its οἶκος, home or habitat, has two major subdivisions: autecology, the knowledge of the interrelations between the individual and its aerial and edaphic environment, and synecology, the knowledge of the structure, development and causes of distribution of plant communities. This book is mainly concerned with certain fundamental aspects of autecology, in particular, the interrelations between the individual plant and those primary factors of the aerial environment, temperature, light and darkness, which, at appropriate times, sequences and intensities, govern the maintenance of a vegetative condition, or a change from a vegetative to a reproductive state. All other factors, such as soil fertility and reaction, availability of water, and weather conditions like drought, cold, hail or excessive winds, may from this point of view be said to be of a secondary nature, controlling or influencing the type and extent of the manifestations of growth and reproduction, but not the relationship between these processes themselves.

It is, of course, rare for a crop plant to be grown as a solitary individual, away from the competition or other influences of neighbours of the same or other species. Proximity to neighbours in an association of wild plants or cultivated crops may introduce competition for factors such as light. For this reason, it is necessary also to consider what effect varying degrees of congested growth may have on the perception of the primary and secondary environmental factors by the growing points, leaves or other parts of the individual plants.

The results obtained from the study of the relations between the primary factors of the environment and plant growth and reproduction are of outstanding importance in the distribution, cultivation and management of all economic crops. In delivering his opening address to

13

the 14th International Horticultural Congress in the Netherlands in 1955, the Director of the East Malling Research Station adapted an earlier statement by Prof. F. G. Gregory to say that 'the central problem of horticultural science remains that of the growth and reproduction of the plant as a whole' (Tubbs, 1955).

Stoughton (1955) points out that at least two functions are covered by the term 'growth' in general usage: 'elongation growth', which is suppressed by high light intensities, so that variations in light may profoundly modify growth habit; and 'accumulation of dry matter' determined primarily by the amount of light energy received by the plant (a conclusion based on the work of Blackman and his collaborators). Some crops are a manifestation of growth processes either *per se*, or in the form of storage organs associated with a period of vegetative growth, others represent reproductive development, and others an optimal combination of the two. The yield and quality of the economic produce from lettuce, cabbage and sugarcane are highest when conditions favour growth rather than reproduction. Herbage plants provide the greatest amount of nutrients for livestock, the highest yield of green matter combined with high protein content, when they are at a certain stage intermediate between growth proper and the sexual maturity which is an expression of reproductive development. The many crops of which the fruits or seeds represent the economic end-product, the cereals, industrial crops, oil seed crops, fruits, give the highest yield when conditions have been optimal for reproduction.

The literature on the subject of growth and reproductive development has, as Dr. Tubbs states, become almost unmanageable in quantity. 'How can we best coordinate and build together the many small bricks of knowledge, whose number and diversity now threaten either to engulf our understanding or to drive us in retreat to an increasingly specialist, and finally inadequate, approach to horticultural science as a whole?' On photoperiodism alone, Borthwick, Hendricks and Parker (1956) state that there are over 1,000 papers. There must be more on hormones, auxins, and related biochemical studies. Many papers were presented to Section 11 of the 8th International Botanical Congress in Paris in 1954, in special sub-sections dealing with vernalization, photoperiodism and the phasic theory of development. In the Proceedings of the 14th International Horticultural Congress, there are some 40 papers on the basic principles of the subject, on the type of response to environmental factors obtained in many horticultural plants, or on the control of the environment in commercial production.

For these reasons and also probably because of the immaturity of a rapidly developing subject, it is frequently difficult to draw anything approaching conclusions which might have a practical application or explain phenomena experienced in crop production, either from the individual articles themselves or from the many reviews, some of a high degree of complexity, which have been published on different aspects of the subject. There is a great need for reviews of this relatively new branch of plant science of the type recommended by Tubbs (1955) and supported by delegates to the Horticultural Congress from U.S.A., the United Kingdom, New Zealand and Mauritius. Provision should be made from time to time for a series of comprehensive monographs, with as their central theme the phases of growth and morphogenesis, such as root and shoot growth, flower induction, flower bud differentiation, flower or fruitlet development. The study of the particular phase treated in each monograph should, according to Tubbs, be based upon (and illustrated by copious reference to) the fundamental and applied research on the individual crops and upon the relation of that phase to other growth phases and to environmental factors. These views are expressed with particular reference to fruit trees, and it is believed that the monographs would reveal great gaps in our knowledge. 'If such emphasis led to even one or two long-term, and possibly very ambitious, field studies upon the whole growth of mature trees in the field by pomologists, physiologists, biochemists and analysts working as a team, it would be ample recompense.'

These remarks could, of course, be applied just as well to all the other major groups of crops. Whether the proposed monographs should be on the suggested subject matter basis, or on the developmental physiology of individual crops or groups of crops is a matter for debate. Most of the existing reviews deal with different aspects of the physiology of growth and reproduction. In many experiments, important crop plants have been used as the guinea pigs for exposure to different environmental factors, but it is extremely difficult for the agronomist or plant breeder specializing in a particular crop to bring together all the results which are scattered over a wide literature, frequently in scientific journals to which he may not have ready access.

The present book is not an attempt to provide one of these monographs, but to review, within previously agreed limits of space, some of the important facts arising from research on growth and reproductive development which are seen to have a practical application in agriculture and horticulture. This volume deals only with seed plants; for a review of the literature on the physiology of reproduction among the fungi (including sex hormones), the Algae, Bryophyta and Pteridophyta, see Naylor (1952); also Bentley (1958) on the role of plant hormones in algal metabolism and ecology.

This review is not intended so much for physiologists as for agricultural botanists, agronomists, crop ecologists, plant breeders and general biologists. Since crop specialists generally work with a specified crop or group of crops, a great part of the book is presented in that way. The initial chapters deal very superficially with certain aspects of research from which new and important results of wide scientific or practical significance may arise. Chapters on reactions of plants to temperature and light alone or in combination have been omitted from this edition; the effects of these factors are dealt with under the crops. The chapter on winter-hardiness has also been omitted. Neither in the subject matter chapters nor in the crop section can anything approaching a comprehensive review be attempted. All that has been done is to indicate the directions of current research, the nature of experiments and the type of results which are being obtained, and their possible application in practice. An attempt has been made to list the important reviews which have appeared to date, and to select those papers for reference which are recent and which will through their bibliographies lead the reader to the more important past literature on a specific subject or crop published by workers in many countries and types of specialization within the broad subject.

There are only relatively few references to the work of Soviet physiologists, partly as a reaction to the somewhat exaggerated attention given to them in the first edition, but also partly because there do not appear to have been any outstanding developments in the Soviet Union. The same physiologists are still working in their own specializations, and the literature still contains references to phasic development, thermo-phases, photo-phases and so on. There is a need for an up-to-date review in English. In this connection, the anonymous article on 'Plant Physiology in the Soviet Union during the last forty years (1917–1957)' published in *Fiziologiya Rasteny*, 1957, states:

'The Michurin doctrine had a great influence on the development of plant physiology. It created an increased interest in the questions of plant growth and development, especially in connection with development of the theory of stages of development (T. D. Lysenko) and also in connection with the effective nature of the Michurin trend in biology. From the point of view of the Michurin doctrine plant physiologists have more completely appraised the statement of K. A. Timiryazev that the investigator must not only study living phenomena but must also direct them in a way desired by man. The efforts of physiologists have been directed towards changing such plant characteristics as drought resistance, salt resistance, frost resistance, aiming to increase productivity of photosynthesis, to give to the plant optimal water conditions, mineral nutrition and so on.

'However, it should be noted that this enthusiasm for the ecological and agronomical approach carried in itself several negative features regarding the development of plant physiology. One of several was the decrease in attention given by scientists to the use of more exact methods of investigation, thus shifting the load to more gross and rapid comparative methods. A series of problems in which Russian and thus Soviet plant physiology had always led, that is, problems of biochemical direction in research (respiration, fermentation, photosynthesis), began one at a time to fall behind foreign research. Therefore, the Institute of Plant Physiology of the Academy of Sciences of the U.S.S.R. in recent years, under the direction of A. L. Kursanov, has posed itself the task of developing and disseminating new methods of research. Such methods as the use of tagged atoms, paper chromatography (qualitative and quantitative), electron microscopy, paper electrophoresis, the partition of mixtures with ion-exchange resins and others came from the arsenal of the many Soviet laboratories of plant physiology. The Institute of Plant Physiology of the Academy of Sciences of the U.S.S.R. is also giving great attention to the biochemical basis of plant physiology, which in the Soviet Union during the last 20 years was given a secondary place. . . .

'The doctrine of physiologically active substances was created by the work of N. G. Cholodny. . . .

'With the great overall success of plant physiology (during the last 20 years) the approach to understanding plant life may be considered sound. In this regard Soviet plant physiology is going along the course set by K. A. Timiryazev. The individual physiological processes previously separately studied are now flowing together into one great, integral whole. Everything is clearly founded on the profound interdependence and interrelation of the paths of physiological processes in the plant organism. For the understanding of plants as a whole, a big part was played by the knowledge of plant development, to the study of which our country particularly contributed, although as if plant development were isolated from the physiology of growth and reproduction.

However, it should be recognized that founding of a truly evolutionary plant physiology, which includes the theory of ontogenesis, of variability and of heritability, is still a job for the future and is only beginning to be visible in outline. The vigorous efforts of present and future generations of investigators must be directed toward the creation of this theoretical trend in our science. . . .

'In the realm of plant development a great role was played by the phenomenon of photoperiodism, which was discovered in the U.S.A. in 1920 and which received its illustrious development later in the Soviet Union. One such major discovery in this area of investigation was the determination by B. S. Moškov and M. H. Čaïlahjan that photoperiodic perception is localized in the leaf. This discovery led to the appearance of a great number of works, which expanded and broadened our knowledge of plant photoperiodism. It should be mentioned that the role of growth variations in development, which was generalized by N. P. Krenko in a theory of cyclic ageing and rejuvenation, in spite of a number of deficiencies, played a decided part in the physiology of plant development. The theory of stages of development also had a special influence on the science of plant development. On the basis of these theoretical considerations, methods for winter and summer vernalization were developed which produced a stage analysis for selection of pairs for inter-breeding, and provided a basis for altering the inheritance of native plants (T. D. Lysenko, A. A. Avakjan, V. I. Razumov, V. O. Kazarjan, A. A. Aginjan and others).' (Quoted from English translation published by the American Institute of Biological Sciences, Washington, D.C.)

It is not possible and would be presumptuous for one reviewer to express his views on the correctness of theories and interpretations over the vast field covered in the present book. It represents rather a report of a shadow conference at which the sayings and writings of specialists in this subject from different countries are presented, as nearly as possible in their own words. The result is a picture of how the voluminous literature appears to an economic botanist. This picture is unavoidably still somewhat shapeless and untidy.

It must surely be agreed that the relation between growth and reproduction of experimental and economic plants is an integral part of plant science, considered by many to be the nucleus to which all other branches of plant science are secondary or ancillary. In view of the rate at which literature on the subject is appearing, this may, however, be the last time that it will be possible even to attempt to cover the many ramifications and complications within one volume. In future, we may see either reviews of the work of a particular school or laboratory, such as Went's report on the Earhart Plant Laboratory at Pasadena (1957), or the reviews of growth and reproductive development in specific crop plants recommended by Dr. Tubbs.

It is probably true to say that physiologists studying growth and reproduction have used crop plants such as rye, wheat, barley, soybean, etc., primarily as convenient experimental material, and have not been so concerned with investigating the reactions of a typical range of varieties of a given crop to all possible combinations and permutations of the primary environmental factors. The economic botanist, plant breeder and agronomist may be forgiven for hoping that the world resources of plant physiological knowledge, techniques and equipment may in future be directed more towards studying the reactions of individual economic species, crop by crop. The complete picture for each crop which would be obtained would be of the greatest practical value in appreciating the behaviour of crops in the field throughout their respective ranges of distribution, and of adjusting breeding programmes, introduction activities and management techniques accordingly. For the major crops of wide geographical distribution, some form of international collaboration and planning would be necessary, experimenters adopting standard techniques and approaches for the study of a given group of varieties within a specific crop, under a range of conditions of latitude, altitude, etc. The alternative would be to concentrate the varieties of a crop at a phytotron, and recreate there the conditions of its natural range.

An indication of the importance attached to this subject in the U.S. Department of Agriculture is the fact that one of the thirteen 'pioneering groups' of scientists who are to be freed from all administrative duties for projects of special and urgent importance is to study how plants are influenced by their environment, with initial emphasis on the effects of light on the regulatory mechanism.

A brief reference must be made to the need for more investigations under tropical and subtropical conditions, and for the provision of adequate facilities for this research. The statement was made in the first edition that India was the only country other than the Soviet Union where vernalization was being taken seriously as a possible agronomic technique. In his review of the physiology of tropical plants, Sen Gupta (1952) states that there is little evidence of pronounced earliness of flowering following cold and hot treatments, nor has any crop been treated successfully for cultivation in the field.

Sen Gupta does, however, make a strong case for the provision of laboratories and growth chambers for studies on the growth and reproduction of tropical crops. Earliness and lateness of flowering caused by reduction or extension of the normal light period have been recorded with several crops in India; for example, jute flowers at the same time of year even when sown at different times. Thermoperiodicity, the relation between day and night temperatures, may also be important; Sen Gupta considers it not unlikely that the wide differences quoted in yields per acre of rice in India as compared with Japan, China and Italy may be influenced by this factor, apart from the more favourable overall temperatures of the subtropical and temperate climates.

There is no doubt that, in the tropics also, there is a need for intensified and co-ordinated research in this field of plant physiology, which should have so much to contribute to a better knowledge of the characteristics, requirements and relative sensitivities of the important food crops of these regions. Perhaps this is nowhere more urgently needed than in the field of rice production in South East Asia and the Far East.

Flowering and Environment

The early history of the study of flowering has been described briefly by Gregory (1948), who states that the modern approach owes its inception to Sachs; in 1865, he produced experimental evidence to show that leaves in light produce 'flower-forming' substances, and stated that specific substances may be accumulated in storage organs. The rigid analysis of the external and internal factors controlling flowering was initiated by Klebs (1918), whose work with *Sempervivum funkii* led to the postulation of a balance of carbohydrates and soil nutrients as a causal factor, the carbohydrate/nitrogen ratio of Kraus and Kraybill (1918). Gregory considers that the evidence indicates that the ratio is a consequence and not a cause of flowering.

The phasic development theories of Soviet physiologists are a natural outcome of Klebs' formulation of definite stages in development; he recognized three stages, (1) ripeness-to-flower, corresponding with the stage of puberty, (2) flower initiation, and (3) bud development and ultimate opening. The next steps in progress were made by Gassner (1918), on the effect of temperature during germination on the flowering behaviour of spring and winter cereals, Garner and Allard (1920 a and b) on the importance of the durations of alternate light and dark periods in controlling flowering, and Went (1928), who isolated plant hormones controlling extension growth and meristematic activity. Thus the three major aspects of modern research on the physiology of flowering were introduced, the reaction to temperature or vernalization, the reaction to light or photoperiodism, and the hormonal regulation of function in plants.

As already stated, the external factors which govern the origin, form and size relationships of leaves, the change from a vegetative to a reproductive state, related in cereals especially to a minimum leaf number, and the nature of the reproductive stage itself, are those of the aerial environment, primarily temperature and light (presence or absence), always necessarily supplemented or complemented by the secondary factors which govern to a great extent the size and quantity of the economic return. There is a marked increase in the number of experiments on timing the application of nitrogenous and other fertilizers in relation to the progress of growth and reproductive development. Important interactions do, of course, exist between several of the controlling factors, such as photosynthetic light and temperature, photoperiod and temperature, and soil moisture and relative humidity of the air. Relations between weather factors have been noted in studies of plants of groundnut grown under controlled conditions (Wassink, 1957). The growth of stems and an increase in the number of flowers are closely linked with soil moisture, optimal development being associated with relatively moist soil. When soil is allowed to develop even moderately high moisture tensions between successive irrigations, the rate of flowering falls, but there is a further rapid increase in the number of flowers 2 days after each application of water. Lack of harmony between soil and air temperatures is frequently the cause of depressed growth in crop plants.

In his paper to the 15th International Horticultural Congress, A. E. Canham drew attention to the fact that the environment of the root is often given less attention than that of the stem, particularly in respect of temperature; there are few experimental data available on the effects of soil temperature on plant growth. It is, however, an important factor in both the propagation and growing stages and, if it is sub-optimal, the efficiency of the processes of rooting and growth is diminished. Preliminary experiments with tomato plants grown under controlled soil temperatures show large differences in dry weight and nutrient uptake over the range of 45° to 66°F and similar variations have been obtained with sweet corn and gladioli. Field experiments with electrically warmed soil show that increased soil temperatures result in earlier flowering of bulbs. When grown in constant temperature tanks, strawberry plants require less fertilizer for the production of a given amount of dry matter at 45°F than they do at 75°F. Varieties differ in their requirements, a fact of importance when there may be as much as 30°F difference between soil temperatures under mulch and clean cultivation respectively. Similar varietal differences occur in apples; Malling IX produces roots at soil temperatures of 44°F or above, French crab produces none at 44°F but luxuriant root growth occurs at 77°F and above; Malling VII is adapted to a wider range, producing roots at 55° and also at 77°F. Root temperature can therefore have a significant effect on growth and is a factor which should not be neglected if partial environmental control is to have the maximum effect.

Even the velocity of winds is an important secondary factor. Wind-tunnel investigations on stands of *Brassica napus* show that growth rates increase with wind speeds up to an optimum near 30 cm/sec and fall off at higher speeds (Wilson and Wadsworth, 1958); this result is likely to be significant in the field. Data are available for wind speed recorded at various heights in crops, grassland, *Calluna* heath, and mountain summit vegetation.

Temperature

The temperature of the natural or artificial environment in which a plant is germinated and grown is in many species one of the dominant factors not only of mere existence, but also in controlling the growth and reproductive development of plants. In the latter connection, temperature may act alone or in association with other environmental factors, particularly light, and may be effective at low or higher figures. Chouard (1955) has reviewed the action of low temperature, as an agent of death of plants, as a factor checking growth, and as a stimulative agent. Under the last head comes cold in relation to the breaking of dormancy, vernalization and thermoperiodism.

Vernalization is the treatment and, in some writings, also the process which accelerates the onset of ripeness-to-flower, the term first used by Klebs (1918) to describe the transition from the juvenile state (inability to form flowers) to the adult state (ability to produce flowers). Ripeness-to-flower is therefore to some extent equivalent to puberty in mammals. Plants can receive their vernalization, their requirement of so many hours below a given temperature, either in the field over the winter or during the early spring months for spring varieties, or as an artificial treatment in the laboratory or barn. Those plants which can be vernalized

22

in an embryonic stage must be in a state of more or less active life before they can respond to the treatment. Seeds of cereals, for example, must be germinated and then held in a non-dormant but not a growing condition during the treatment for the requisite period; during this period the 'plants' must be kept moist and well aerated. Some plants cannot be vernalized effectively until a more advanced age (see p. 24); in many biennial rosette plants, this stage is that of a rosette of a few leaves. Wellensiek and his associates have made a special study of the juvenile state and 'maturity for vernalization'.

The acquisition of the adult state or ripeness-to-flower can be cancelled by a devernalization treatment, as shown by Gregory and Purvis. This involves either exposure to warm temperatures (32° to 35°C for a few days), or a milder temperature (20°C) in a nitrogen atmosphere devoid of oxygen, for the number of days the plant can resist this treatment without dying. It then becomes unable to flower, but can again be effectively vernalized by low temperature and devernalized again by the same treatment with high temperatures. If, however, the devernalization treatment is delayed for some time after the completion of vernalization, it is no longer effective, as the vernalization has become irreversible. Plants vary widely in their requirements for vernalization; in some biennial plants and winter varieties of annual plants it is almost obligatory, but in a great many plants the requirements are very low. Vernalization by chilling can be replaced entirely or partially by treatment with other factors, e.g. short days. Gregory has shown that, in Petkus winter rye, short-day treatment reduces the number of leaves which need to be formed before heading (minimum leaf number) from 25 to 16, but chilling can reduce it to 7. Short days can replace cold treatment in *Campanula medium* (Wellensiek). Chouard has observed that flowering of many short-day plants can be accelerated or conditioned by a previous long-day treatment which in itself cannot induce flower formation (Jerusalem artichoke and varieties of chrysanthemum).

The skeleton scheme on page 24 has been proposed for the roles of low temperature in flowering and as a basis for comparison with other examples (Stokes and Verkerk, 1951).

Only one or two species are cited from each type in the many references in the literature which apply to group 2. Species requiring cold for flower initiation are very few. It is probable that the action of low temperature in seed vernalization is of a different nature from the immediate action which is necessary for flower initiation in Brussels sprouts, for example. *Hyoscyamus* and beets treated as biennials respond to the immediate

23

action of cold in the adult stage, but when given seed vernalization the subsequent flowering is also affected by conditions of daylength; Stokes and Verkerk believe it may be general that those plants of which the seeds can be vernalized are also sensitive to daylength. 'Perhaps one might

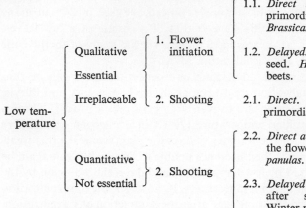

describe seed-vernalization as preparing the plant to react to the reception of a light effect acting on the leaves, whereas the direct action of cold is on the growing point itself."

Vernalization is a process of acceleration of transition from the juvenile to the adult state, usually by a cold treatment. The plant may have different temperature requirements at the beginning and end of the vernalization period, or as the Russians call it, the thermo-phase. Thus, Waterschoot (1957) has shown in *Dianthus barbatus* that it is often more effective to give the cold treatment not in one long cold period, but rather by giving high temperatures (30° or 35°C) first. Razumov has shown that low temperatures of $-4°$ to $-5°$C may be correct for the end of the period, but cannot initiate the response. Although the early Russian workers made recommendations regarding the practical application of the vernalization technique on a large scale for the cultivation of cereals and other crops, this does not appear to have become a routine measure in crop production. Vernalization is, however, frequently used in experimental work, as will be seen in later chapters.

The biochemical basis of the ripe-to-flower condition is not known, but some substance is assumed to exist, as the response can be transmitted to all the buds which are direct descendants of the vernalized bud, or may be transferred by grafting in certain dicotyledons, e.g.

Hyoscyamus niger, Dianthus barbatus and *Pisum sativum* (see Chapter IV).

Thermoperiodism

In the temperature responses of plants, a distinction should be made between seasonal and daily thermoperiodicity. Many perennial, deciduous plants from temperate or cold climates with pronounced seasonal changes in temperature exhibit seasonal thermoperiodicity, an adaptation to or requirement for cycles of cold and warm temperatures of several months' duration. Each morphological or physiological stage in bulbs has a different temperature requirement, necessitating the passing through a succession of higher and lower temperatures with a cycle of approximately one year's duration.

Since Sachs showed that growth in many plants occurs mainly at night, the temperature of the night, the 'nyctotemperature' of Went (1957) is of paramount importance. Went has found that, although the photoperiod is very important in the vegetative growth of the tomato plant, it is strongly thermoperiodic in its environmental response, and photoperiod is of little importance in its fruiting behaviour (see Figs. 18 and 19 in Went, 1957). Daily thermoperiodicity is also an important factor in potatoes, chillies, maize and other plants; frequent incidental reference to the significance of night temperature is made in later sections. (See also Went in Murneek and Whyte, 1948.)

Presence and Absence of Light

The literature on experiments on plant growth and reproductive development in relation to the presence, absence and quality of light is already voluminous, and has been the subject of a number of comprehensive reviews. Photoperiodism is one aspect of the subject of radiation biology (Hollaender, 1956), in which it is associated with questions relating to energy efficiency in photosynthesis, the mechanism of photosynthesis, the absorption, action and fluorescence spectra of photosynthetic pigments in living cells and in solutions, the formation and accumulation of chlorophyll in plants, the relation of light to nitrate reduction, phototropism, and the action of light in seed germination. Borthwick, Hendricks and Parker (1956) have reviewed almost 200 papers on photoperiodism in plants and animals, covering the organs of perception, the pigments involved, photoperiodic after-effects, flowering in relation to auxin, inheritance of responsiveness to photoperiod, and the influence of other environmental factors on photoperiodism.

Schmalz (1958 a) has made an interesting attempt to classify the current work by plant physiologists on the photoperiodic behaviour of plants, but without claiming that this is in any way a complete enumeration.

(1) Classification of species in different response types (long-day, short-day, daylength-neutral, long-short-day and short-long-day plants) through the determination of their critical daylength by means of variations of daylength (down to one second) for different periods, at varying ages of the plants and at different temperatures. Nutritional conditions, especially nitrogen nutrition, are also varied.

(2) Determination of the minimum number of inductive cycles needed for flower induction.

(3) Use of plants with varying number and size of organs (leaves).

(4) Study of the inhibitory effect of non-inductive daylengths, before and after flower induction, on the rate and degree of flower formation.

(5) Study of the influence on flower formation of the photoperiodically effective light spectrum and of light intensity.

(6) Exposure of experimental plants to cycles of varying length (sometimes very different from the 24-hour cycle), with absolute and relative variations of the alternation of light and darkness; for instance, light and darkness in proportions such as 12:12, 18:18, 24:24 or 8:16, 16:32, 24:48 hours, etc.

(7) Use of interrupting light at different times during the extremely long dark periods of cycles differing greatly from the 24-hour cycle (e.g. 72-hour cycles), an arrangement which makes it possible to check on Bünning's theory of endogenous diurnal rhythms (see p. 32).

(8) Study of the flowering response of plants in cycles with split light periods.

(9) Grafting experiments (with or without union of the partners) designed to determine the capacity of induced 'donor' plants to transfer the flowering impulse to non-induced 'recipients', either between similar or between different photoperiodic response types, including studies on the rate of translocation of the impulse.

(10) Study of the rate of translocation of the flowering impulse from one organ to another in complete plants, by means of partial induction, and on the possible effects of temperature, antibiotics, etc., on this translocation.

(11) Examination of the effect of total defoliation on the photoperiodic behaviour of experimental plants.

(12) Study of the effect of different substances (growth substances, triiodobenzoic acid, gibberellins, etc.) on flower formation at different temperatures and daylengths, partly in connection with systematic defoliation and grafting of leaves at certain places.

(13) Study of the readiness-to-flower of long-day and short-day plants after various biochemical and biophysical manipulations (during the light or dark period of inductive or non-inductive cycles), such as infiltration of sugars capable of being used up in respiration, supply of ferment inhibitors, maintenance of plants in anaerobic conditions or in a nitrogen atmosphere, or in air free of CO_2 or over-saturated with CO_2, as well as in different concentrations of carbon monoxide.

(14) Study of the biochemistry and metabolism of induced and non-induced plants.

(15) Study of the relationships between vernalization and photo-period.

One of the most intriguing aspects of the photoperiodic control of flowering, as Anton Lang told the First International Photobiological Congress in Amsterdam in 1954, is that one and the same environmental condition, the photoperiod, may affect one and the same process, flower initiation, in opposite ways. Long days promote flowering in long-day plants and inhibit it in short-day plants; short days act in the reverse manner. Grafting experiments indicate that the flower stimuli of long-day plants and short-day plants are identical; photoperiod controls the formation of the stimulus, but once a transmissible stimulus has appeared in the plant, it is the same in a long-day and in a short-day plant. Studies on the kinetics of photoperiodism show that the most important factor of photoperiodic action is the length of the daily dark period. Long dark periods promote flowering in short-day plants (Hamner and Bonner, 1938) and inhibit it in long-day plants. If a long dark period is interrupted in its middle by a small amount of light, its effect is nullified. The action spectrum of this 'light flash' is identical for long-day and short-day plants, and in either case the effect of the light flash can be reversed by

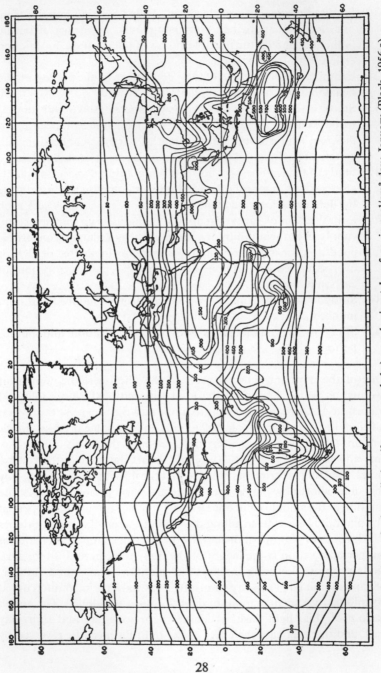

Fig. 1. Isopleths of solar radiation (from sun and sky) on a horizontal surface, in gcal/cm² day: January (Black, 1956 a).

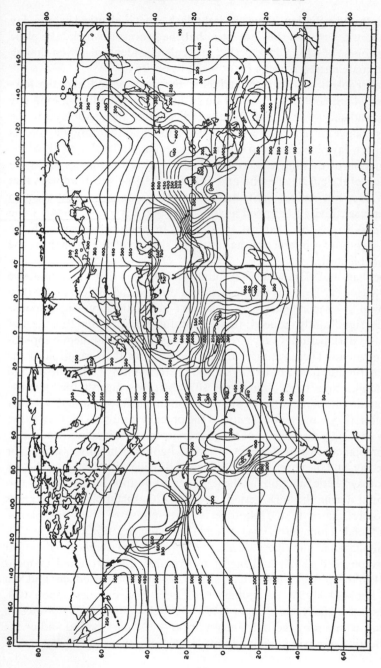

Fig. 2. Isopleths of solar radiation (from sun and sky) on a horizontal surface, in gcal/cm² day: July (Black, 1956 a).

near-infrared radiation. Thus, the light flash effect is identical in long-day and short-day plants; this indicates that the processes which take place in the course of a long dark period must also be identical—even though the ultimate response of the plant is the opposite.

The problem is to understand how the dark period and the low-intensity light control the formation of the flower stimulus in long-day plants and short-day plants. Results indicate that the auxin level in the leaves changes in the course of a dark period, and that long-day plants and short-day plants seem to differ in the leaf auxin level needed for the production of the flower stimulus. The question then arises as to the relation of the effects of auxin and of low-intensity light. It appears that auxin does not replace light, but that small amounts of light seem to increase sensitivity to applied auxin (Lang and Liverman, 1954); Lang considers it possible that we are dealing in photoperiodism with the same light/auxin interaction as noted in studies of the growth of the *Avena* coleoptile.

Lockhart and Hamner (1954) found in *Xanthium* that, if an inductive dark period (12 hours) is terminated by a brief period of light and is then followed by a second dark period of 5 to 6 hours, the flowering response may be significantly reduced; they found, furthermore, that this effect of a second dark period is very strongly increased by simultaneous application of auxin. These results indicate, firstly, that the formation of the flower stimulus proceeds in two stages: the formation of a precursor, and its 'stabilization' to the final flower stimulus; they suggest, furthermore, that auxin interferes with the stabilization of the flower stimulus, either by interfering with the conversion of the precursor stage to the final stage, or by causing a dissipation of the precursor to some inactive product.

For plants sensitive to photoperiods, light is generally essential for flowering, and the requirement for carbon dioxide with the light indicates a photosynthetic function for the light period. It appears that CO_2 is also essential during the dark period, and that CO_2 metabolism in darkness is closely related to the photoperiodic response of short-day plants. Spear and Thimann (1954) studied the interrelation between CO_2 metabolism and photoperiodism in *Kalanchoë* with reference to the effect of prolonged darkness and high temperatures; Langston and Leopold (1954 b) the dark fixation of CO_2 as a factor in photoperiodism; and Sen and Leopold (1956) the influence of light and darkness upon CO_2 fixation. Salisbury and Bonner (1956) treated *Xanthium pennsylvanicum* at various times by red light interruption of the dark period and/or the application of auxin (which inhibits the act of induction). The effects of these treatments on floral induction were measured in terms of rate of subsequent floral development, which is assumed to represent the amount of flowering hormone exported from the leaf. Salisbury and Bonner suggest that three reactions take place during the dark period: (*a*) conversion of photoreceptor pigment from a far-red to a red-receptive form (complete in 2 or 3 hours), (*b*) preparatory reaction(s), which together with pigment conversion determine the critical night length, and (*c*) actual synthesis of hormone.

The effect of prolonged culture of excised leaves of *Bryophyllum calycinum* either in darkness or in light is to set up a condition which Vickery (1956) interprets as representing a steadily increasing degree of

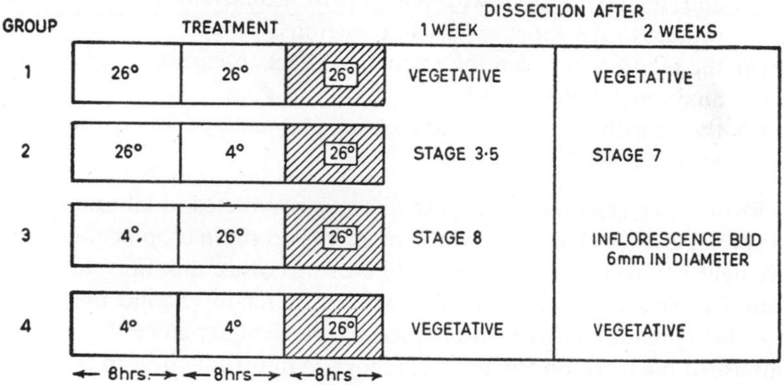

GROUP	TREATMENT			DISSECTION AFTER	
				1 WEEK	2 WEEKS
1	26°	26°	26°	VEGETATIVE	VEGETATIVE
2	26°	4°	26°	STAGE 3·5	STAGE 7
3	4°.	26°	26°	STAGE 8	INFLORESCENCE BUD 6mm IN DIAMETER
4	4°	4°	26°	VEGETATIVE	VEGETATIVE

← 8hrs.→ ←8hrs→ ←8hrs →

Fig. 3. The influence of different temperatures during the long photoperiod on the flowering response in *Xanthium* (De Zeeuw, 1957).

physiological stress. This condition is characterized by the diminishing speed at which the major chemical changes in composition subsequent to transfer are observed to take place as the culture period is prolonged. The data refer particularly to the synthesis and decomposition of starch and the correlated reciprocal changes in malic and citric acids.

The literature on light quality in relation to growth and reproductive development has been reviewed by Borthwick, Hendricks and Parker (1956) and by Wassink and Stolwijk (1956). The latter summarize the main increase of knowledge obtained in the period 1950–56 as follows:

(*a*) the discovery of photoperiodic and formative effects of near infrared radiation in fully-grown green plants and the indication of antagonism between the action of different spectral regions;

(b) the recognition that various, at first sight not closely related, effects show the same spectral sensitivity, suggesting close similarity or identity of the underlying pigment system; and

(c) the demonstration that this pigment system shows a reversibility between a red-absorbing and a near-infrared-absorbing form, the final form of which determines the ultimate physiological behaviour.

Some major points that have been tackled but require further study and are likely to yield interesting results in the near future would seem to be:

(a) the effects of the spectral composition of the 'main light period', and its interaction with day-length extension, especially with respect to the short wave length regions;

(b) the relation between the formative effects of spectral regions and auxin metabolism, and

(c) the identification of the underlying pigment system (Wassink and Stolwijk, 1956).

Most of the research referred to above is conducted in laboratories or in special growth chambers. Much more important in crop production is the light environment in which field crops, pasture mixtures and other stands of economic plants are grown commercially. Rapid progress is now being made in this field of research, particularly since Watson first published his work on the leaf area index. An introduction to the literature on this subject is given in Chapter III: Competition for Light.

Endogenous Rhythms

Bünning (1956 b) has evolved a theory of endogenous rhythms to describe biological processes which alter periodically although external conditions remain constant, for example, rhythms with short periods (e.g. flagellar or nutational movement), endogenous diurnal rhythms, endogenous rhythms with longer periods (e.g. cycles of ageing and rejuvenescence), and endogenous annual rhythms. Bünning states that, as in pendular movements, biological systems also require an impulse to set them in motion. A single impulse brought about by some external factor, such as a transition from darkness to light, or from a low to a high temperature, may evoke an endogenous rhythm which was previously unrecognizable. Frequently these external factors are also decisive as

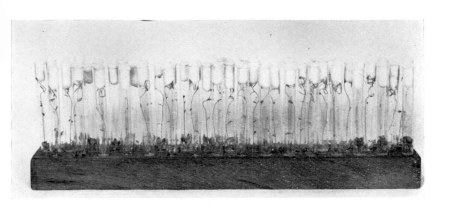

1. The aseptic culture of *Arabidopsis thaliana* (Langridge, 1952*b*)

(a)

(b)

(c)

2. Moscow. Station of artificial climate. (Photos by courtesy of I. I. Tumanov.) (a) General view (b) Thermostats for maintaining controlled soil temperatures. (c) Low-temperature chambers for studying cold resistance

time determinants, fixing the position of maxima and minima of the rhythm which occur following the single impulse while the external conditions are constant. The time required for one period of the endogenous rhythm, i.e. the duration of a single period, however, may depend upon external factors such as temperature.

An endogenous rhythm must not necessarily be considered as of hereditary origin, although it may often be so. It is in some cases obviously induced by some preceding external rhythm, for instance, by light/dark periodicity. In such cases a single impulse, such as transition from light to darkness, or darkness to light, is not sufficient to make the rhythm manifest. An endogenous rhythm can usually be maintained, under constant external conditions, only for a relatively short time. Sometimes only two or three periods can be registered if further impulses from some external stimulus do not follow.

In discussing the relation between endogenous rhythms and photoperiodism, Bünning states that it has become clear that two phases, each of about 12 hours, alternate during the course of the endogenous diurnal rhythm. These phases differ in a quantitative manner with respect to certain partial processes and in a qualitative manner to certain others. Thus it is nearly self-evident that during these phases, plants respond to external stimuli quantitatively or even qualitatively with different reactions. Primarily, they react differently to light and darkness. For normal development, a light/dark rhythm must be present and this rhythm should be in the period of the endogenous rhythm, i.e., in a 24-hour cycle.

The necessity of dark periods reminds us of the photoperiodic reaction. According to the reviewer's conception, the essential nature of all photoperiodic reactions consists in the fact that the two phases of the endogenous diurnal rhythm respond to light, with different reactions, often with antagonistic ones. This conception of the mechanism of photoperiodic reactions does not differ fundamentally from that developed by other authors. Photoperiodism was explained by postulating that light and darkness respectively induce certain reactions. Very soon this postulation had to be supplemented with the additional assumption that these induced reactions require a definite length of time. Moreover, it can be concluded that these reactions must be followed by other reactions which in turn are characterized by a definite time requirement. Bünning considers that these interpretations should be fitted into our existing knowledge of endogenous diurnal rhythm with the conception that the induced reactions are phases of the endogenous rhythm

B

33

regulated by the light/dark alternation. For example, it is possible to distinguish in short-day plants a high-intensity light reaction, a dark reaction and a low-intensity light reaction. The high-intensity light reaction may consist of photoperiodic processes. With its characteristic features, it corresponds quite well to that phase of the endogenous rhythm which is characterized by high photosynthetic efficiencies and which is also regulated by a light period, as is the high-intensity light reaction itself. The dark reaction starts several hours after the high-intensity light reaction and has features which are comparable to the other phase of the endogenous diurnal rhythm. Therefore, one is almost compelled to assume that the several reactions in the photoperiodic responses are nothing but phases of the endogenous diurnal rhythm.

Bünning considers that the endogenous diurnal rhythm may also be regarded as a cause for the diurnal variation of sensitivity to temperature characteristic of thermoperiodism (see also under soybean, Chapter XXI).

Phases in Reproductive Development

Considerable attention was given in the first edition to the theories and supporting evidence which had been produced on the existence of well-defined and rigid phases in the progress of a plant from seed to seed. In his classic work on the new science of developmental physiology, Klebs (1918) found that the process of formation of the inflorescence proceeds in three clearly separable phases, which he called the onset of the ripe-to-flower condition, the formation of the flower primordia, and the development of the flowering inflorescence. Not all Klebs' three phases are of the same nature. Ripeness-to-flower is not recognizable morphologically; on the other hand, the initiation of flower primordia and the formation of the inflorescence and flowers are recognizable morphologically.

The ripe-to-flower condition was regarded as the product of intensive C-assimilation with active transpiration and a relative limitation of uptake of nutrient salts. Klebs states that the idea that a one-sided increase of C-assimilation, especially of carbohydrates, governs ripeness-to-flower also explains the relation to temperature. Under intense summer light, temperature can be very high without adversely affecting the initiation of ripeness-to-flower. As the light intensity falls, however, the hindering effect of higher temperature on ripeness-to-flower increases. It is not the absolute strength of the light or the level of the temperature that is the decisive factor, but the quantitative relation of assimilation to the temperature effect, which is manifested more especially in an increase in dissimilation. Under the low intensity light of a German winter or even after months without light, the ripe-to-flower condition is maintained. The lower temperature can even induce the initiation of this condition in a well-fed rosette in darkness. Under such circumstances, light may to some extent be replaced by the lower temperature, a clear indication, according to Klebs, that under normal conditions light produces the ripe-to-flower condition largely through its assimilatory operation, which is dependent on its energy (see also Hänsel, 1949, and p. 320).

The second phase, the initiation of microscopically recognizable primordia, would appear to be dependent upon light, but it is not clear whether success may still be achieved when light is replaced by another factor. It is again the energy of the light that is operative. Continuous strong artificial illumination must last for several days before primordia appear. The time required depends upon the extent to which the ripe-to-flower condition has increased in the spring under the influence of daylight at a lower temperature. With interrupted illumination the number of light hours per day even at the higher intensities must be relatively great. A simple relation between the number of light hours and light intensity does not appear to exist, as the dark hours have an antagonistic influence at medium temperatures of 20° to 25°C. A special characteristic of the light effect is the contrast between weak and strong refracted rays. The red rays stimulate the onset of flowering within wider limits of intensity, under both weak and strong light intensity; the blue-violet rays hinder the process, and ultimately cause a reversion of the ripe-to-flower condition. Klebs concludes that it follows that the trophic effect of light is replaced by a blastic effect, and that this depends on a change of the ripe-to-flower condition into true flower formation or conversely into purely vegetative growth.

Klebs' third phase, the formation of the inflorescence, is completed in *Sempervivum* by the elongation of the axis, the formation of lateral branches and by the unfolding of the flowers. The whole process depends upon light, but in a way more similar to the acquisition of the ripe-to-flower condition. If the microscopically recognizable primordia are already present, the development of the inflorescence may proceed in the dark, particularly if a low temperature is applied (up to 6°C), but the formation of flowers is very poor compared with cultures in the light. The later in May the experiment on the absence of light was begun, the better was the flower formation, due to the influence of the earlier light effect. The light intensity necessary under continuous lighting and a temperature of about 20°C for the formation of more or less normal inflorescences is higher than that required for initiation of flower primordia. According to Klebs, flowering depends not so much upon the absolute light intensity as upon the relation of the nutrient-storing C-assimilation to the removing processes of dissimilation.

This early work contains at least a reference to most of the problems at issue in the study of the developmental processes in plants, and of the reasons for the transformation from a vegetative to a reproductive state: the effect of the decisive factors, light, darkness and temperature, alone and in combination, upon a series of phases or conditions, each one of which must be acquired before the next can begin; a hint of a light after-effect; evidence of reversal of development; the internal metabolic changes associated with vegetative growth or reproductive development.

Another notable paper published almost simultaneously with that of Klebs on *Sempervivum* was that by Gassner (1918) on the physiological characteristics of summer and winter annuals. Whereas Klebs was concerned primarily with light as the decisive factor, Gassner devoted special attention to temperature. As he considered that the shooting and flowering of winter cereals depend to a marked degree on their passing through a period of low temperature, experiments were conducted to determine (1) the principles underlying the effect of low temperatures on flower production, and (2) further details regarding (*a*) the co-operation of the temperature of germination, and temperature and other conditions during the course of vegetation, and (*b*) the significance of the vegetative period in understanding the relative peculiarities of summer and winter Gramineae. Gassner's conclusions regarding the physiological difference between summer and winter rye were as follows. Summer rye is practically independent of any need to pass through a cold period before it can achieve flower initiation (Blütenauslösung). The flower formation (Blütenbildung) of winter rye depends on its passing through a cold period either during germination or at some stage subsequent to germination.

Gassner remarked on the correlation between winter hardiness, sugar content and flowering:

(1) the growing of winter plants at a low temperature induces increased winter hardiness;

(2) low temperature is a condition for the 'flower formation';

(3) cultivation in a low temperature increases sugar content; it may be assumed that winter hardiness and sugar content are in a causal

relationship, while the 'flower initiation' depends on sugar content;

(4) winter hardiness and the cold-requirement, so important for flowering, are correlatively connected (see also Tumanov in first edition, p. 196).

Gassner was concerned more particularly with the first phase of Klebs. Some of his grain which germinated at a low temperature had acquired thereby the 'ripe-to-flower' condition. The grain or seedlings which had this property could not be distinguished morphologically from those which had not, but the difference between them became apparent in their subsequent flowering behaviour. Gassner did not specifically suggest that a plant must necessarily pass through any series of phases or conditions, each governed by a particular set of environmental factors. Neither Klebs nor Gassner seemed to consider that processional, regular development is inherent in a plant, but that this depends on the way (this being inherited and transmissible) in which a plant responds to the sum total of all external factors; that is, that the developmental rhythm is a product of the specific inherited reaction method of the organism and of the sum total of all environmental factors.

Continuing the work of Gassner, Maximov in U.S.S.R. treated seedlings with low temperatures and thereby influenced the whole of their further development. Winter cereals, which, when sown in spring, did not normally reach the heading stage, headed and flowered normally when the seedlings had been exposed to a short period of chilling. It was found to be possible to determine the further course of development during the early stages of the growth of a plant, by treatment of seedlings with appropriate temperatures and a given periodicity of light.

At the All-Union Congress of Genetics in the Soviet Union in 1928, two papers were read which appeared to bring the earlier research of Gassner into the realm of routine agronomic practice. It was realized that the germinating grains of winter cereals require a certain quota of low temperature for their optimal development, that they usually receive the requisite amount while growing slowly in the open in the winter, after autumn sowing, and that the more the sowing date is delayed the less likelihood is there of the plants flowering and reaching maturity sufficiently early for harvesting in the following season. Slowly germinating grain was given the necessary degree and duration of low temperature while in the laboratory or the barn. It so happened that the proceedings of the above Congress, published in 1929, contained, in addition to one of the early papers by D. A. Dolgušin and T. D. Lysenko on pre-treatment of seed with low temperature, another paper on the same subject by M. A. Tolmačev. This author almost achieved a simultaneous solution of the problem of vernalization of winter cereals.

Reviews of the theoretical bases of the method of vernalization and the hypothesis of phasic development were published by Whyte and Hudson (1933), Maximov (1934), the Imperial Agricultural Bureaux (1935), Whyte (1939), McKinney (1940), and other authors. Lysenko (1935) formulated the theoretical conceptions upon which this method of pre-treatment of seed was based as follows:

(1) growth and development are not identical phenomena;
(2) the entire process of development of an annual seed plant consists of individual *étapes* or stages;
(3) the stages always proceed in a strict sequence and a subsequent stage cannot set in until the preceding stage has been completed; and
(4) different stages of development of the same plant or crop require different environmental conditions for their completion.

In much of the English literature on this subject, the word 'phase' has been used in the place of the word 'stage', as the latter term appeared to be already in wide use in connection with purely morphological manifestations of growth, for example, tillering stage, stage of 50 per cent flowering, etc. Thus arose the term 'phasic development' to describe all aspects of the theory underlying the method of vernalization.

Although much research has been done during the past 20 years on the physiological basis of the vernalization response, the method does not appear to have acquired any agronomic value. The accompanying theory of phasic development has been found to be too rigid, and has therefore not received wide acceptance, although V. I. Razumov of the All-Union Institute of Plant Industry published a review of recent research on the theory in *Agrobiologija* in 1957. An example of the type of criticisms produced is given by the following extract from Melchers (1954 b).

Since in winter cereals, the biennial variety of *Hyoscyamus niger* and the biennial *Beta*, flower initiation can be accelerated or even induced by low temperature (vernalization) and subsequent exposure to long days, the generalization has been made that this is an invariable relation 'by law of nature'. The extreme example is the so-called doctrine of phasic development. The fact that these long-day plants with their low-temperature requirements have close relatives which are sometimes differentiated only in a few or even one pair of genes with regard to temperature requirements is regarded as proving that such a generalization is inadmissible. Petkus summer rye is a long-day plant but does not require low temperature. The same is true of the annual variety of *Hyoscyamus niger*. *H. albus*, which can be crossed with *H. niger*, although the F_1 hybrids are sterile, requires neither low temperature for flower initiation, nor the extreme daylength characteristic of *H. niger*. *H. albus* is essentially neutral. *Nicotiana silvestris* is a long-day plant. Most cultivated tobaccos are daylength neutral, although flower initiation is favoured slightly by long days. *N. tabacum* var. Maryland Mammoth is a short-day plant with only one pair of genes different from the neutral varieties.

Only one conclusion is possible, according to Melchers: varying temperature requirements, vernalization optimum, photoperiodic behaviour, degree of photoperiodic influence, position of critical daylengths, etc., are all controlled by genes, like flower colour, leaf shape and all the other characteristics of an organism. The combination of such genes in individual cases depends entirely upon natural selection in wild plants and upon breeding in cultivated plants. This explains why the northern European flora contains relatively numerous plants which combine a low-temperature requirement with a long-day character: they flower only 'in time' in northern or southern latitudes if they are neutral, or long-day plants. In the tropics, only neutral or short-day plants can flower. Low-temperature requirement coupled with short-day character is comprehensible from the point of view of selection in the case of high mountain areas in the tropics. However, short-day plants may occur in the northern or southern temperate zone if they also have other adjustment characters, e.g. the plants which flower in spring or autumn. Schwabe's analysis of *Chrysanthemum* has revealed a combination of low-temperature requirement with short-day character. A complicated sequence of different temperatures is required to produce optimal flowering in many bulbs.

Melchers finds no constant physiological relationship between vernalization and photoperiodism. Existing combinations are the result of natural or artificial selection. Critical daylength for plants with photoperiodic reactions is also controlled by genes (cf. *Xanthium*). Critical daylength is, however, also influenced by other factors, of which temperature has been most thoroughly investigated. In the long-day plant, *Hyoscyamus niger*, the lower the temperature, the shorter the critical daylength, a fact which may suggest that the annual variety of *H. niger* could also be 'vernalized' by low temperatures. Indeed, in those cases where low-temperature requirement and photoperiodic behaviour merely accelerate flower initiation, but where flower initiation is also possible without vernalization and with unsuitable daylengths, it is difficult to distinguish experimentally between the influence of temperature on the satisfaction of low-temperature requirements and that on critical daylength (e.g. winter rye). This is, however, possible without ambiguity with the two varieties of *Hyoscyamus niger*: the annual has no low-temperature requirement, but flowers when kept continuously at 20°C above critical daylength (although this daylength is dependent upon temperature). The biennial variety flowers only if its low-temperature requirement is met first and if it is subsequently cultivated at daylengths above the critical limit. Besides, photoperiodic reaction depends upon the presence of leaves, while vernalization can occur in the apical meristem of the shoot only. This means (*a*) that a clear distinction must be made between the satisfaction of low-temperature requirements (vernalization) and photoperiodism, and (*b*) that at least in the biennial race of *Hyoscyamus niger*, the low-temperature requirement must be met before photoperiodic conditions can influence flower initiation. It is, of course, true that photoperiod has an effect even before vernalization, in this case on leaf shape. Under short-day conditions the leaves formed in the rosette are relatively broad and have short petioles, under long-day conditions they are narrower and have long petioles. However, as far as flowering is concerned, it is immaterial whether the days before vernalization are long or short. Although an experimental distinction between vernalization and photoperiodism is not as easy for winter annual cereals, it is probable that the same principle applies to these species. Thus, Gregory and Purvis in their diagram indicate that the effect of daylength follows upon the completion of vernalization. Although to this extent, there is some truth in the phasic doctrine as applied to certain plants (biennial and winter annual long-day plants), there is no justification for the assumption of a 'thermophase' preceding a 'photophase' in the annual race of *Hyoscyamus niger*, which is differentiated from the biennial by only one gene.

The general consensus of opinion of biologists with regard to the rigid theory of phasic development and the distinction between growth (accumulation of dry matter or increase in size) and development (progress towards reproduction by externally recognisable or invisible stages), which is an integral part of the theory, has been expressed by Hamner (1948): 'According to the hypothesis of "phasic development", the plant passes through several distinct stages or phases in its development, and (in the original presentation of the theory at least) presumably one phase of development must have been completed before another phase is begun. It seems to me that the term "development" as defined above has very little real usefulness and that an attempt to separate development into several phases has served to confuse rather than to add to an understanding of the processes which occur within the plant and which eventually lead to the differentiation of reproductive structures. If we were to apply the term "development" to "short-day" plants, for example, it would seem essential to apply the term "development" to the maturing of the leaves, since flowering is dependent upon certain changes within the leaves. In some "short-day" plants, however, the generation of the stimulus for flowering is continuously dependent upon actual exposure to favourable photoperiods. The processes leading to the generation of the stimulus seem completely reversible, being operative only during the actual exposure to "short-day". The above is only one illustration of the difficulties encountered in attempting to describe the reactions which lead to flowering in terms of phases of development.'

Hamner finds the hypothesis of Purvis and Gregory (see p. 91) much more attractive; although their diagrammatic representation may be an over-simplification, 'it does seem to form a good working basis for discussion and experimentation.

'There is fairly conclusive evidence that the satisfaction of the "short-day" requirement results in the actual generation of the stimulus for flowering. It seems possible also that a stimulus is generated fulfilling the "long-day" requirement. We have relatively little evidence that the same stimulus is involved in both cases. In fact, the conditions which result in the generation of the stimulus in the two cases are so different that it seems not unlikely that two different stimuli should be postulated. There is no evidence that an actual stimulus is transferred when the low-temperature requirements are satisfied. The use of the term "florigen" to signify a flower hormone for all plants may be unjustified. Perhaps the term should be limited at present to describing or signifying the stimulus which causes flowering in the "short-day" plants. It seems possible that this stimulus might never successfully cause the initiation of flowers in any plant which has not reached the "ripe-to-flower" condition. It seems possible, also, that the stimulus could never successfully substitute for the low-temperature requirement. The use of the same term to describe the stimuli in both "long-day" and "short-day" plants should await additional evidence that they are transferable from one type of plant to the other' (Hamner, *loc. cit.*).

THE CENTRAL PROBLEM

Measurement of Time-to-Flowering

Various measures have been adopted for expressing time from sowing or emergence to the formation or the opening of the first flower (Hänsel, 1954 a). These may be grouped as follows:

(a) time measure in days,
(b) temperature/time measure = summation of temperature,
(c) temperature/time/daylength;

or

(d) measurement based on developmental physiology = number of sterile nodes;

or, in certain cases,

(e) caloric measurement = total radiation,
(f) measurement of the extent of metabolism (not yet used, as far as is known).

The constancy of the results obtained by the use of any one of these different measures will determine which of them is most suitable for a quantitative definition of time-to-flowering. Hänsel has compared the methods a to d using three varieties of peas.

The measurement of time-to-flowering in days from sowing showed greater dispersion than from 50 per cent emergence. Small varietal differences are better expressed as mean than as median time-to-flowering.

Temperature summations have the same type and extent of dispersion as mean or median time-to-flowering.

Temperature summation × mean daylength is probably more constant than temperature summation alone under natural conditions, but not if continuous day is provided by additional artificial lighting.

The regression (as between varieties) from the number of sterile nodes to mean time-to-flowering does not change.

Botanical Drosophilas

A number of plants have acquired a place in research on developmental physiology equivalent to that long occupied by *Drosophila* in genetical investigations. Many references will be found in the following chapters to the use of cereals, soybeans, peas, cocklebur (*Xanthium pennsylvanicum*), henbane (*Hyoscyamus niger*), *Kalanchoë blossfeldiana*, *Perilla*, *Bryophyllum*, and other plants, but the interest now appears to

42

be in species to which a mass production technique can be applied, thus giving greater statistical accuracy in interpreting results. In the early work in air-conditioned greenhouses in Pasadena, California (Went 1943, 1944, 1957), spring annuals were used for experimental material, as they grow and mature rapidly and take up little space. A few thousand plants have been grown, many of them to maturity, in only fourteen 20 × 20 in. seed boxes.

Laibach (1943) favours *Arabidopsis thaliana*, a small widely distributed Crucifer, with a low chromosome number ($n=5$) and a high degree of fertility (152 ± 11 seeds under aseptic conditions). The duration of development is short, 30 days in early strains under optimal conditions. When cultivated, the plant has extremely modest requirements and needs very little space. There is an extraordinary abundance of strains and, since the plants are self-fertile, pure lines can be obtained with ease. Summer and winter annual strains exist. In the winter annuals temperature, and in the summer annuals light is the most important factor for flower formation. All the strains are long-day in type. This species has been used by Gregory and Hussey (1953), who found that, given 8 hours of daylight each day together with supplementary artificial illumination, the number of days to flowering was progressively reduced the longer the total daily period of light. A further progressive acceleration of flowering was obtained with an increase in the intensity of the supplementary light up to 50 foot-candles.

Working in the Division of Plant Industry, C.S.I.R.O., Canberra, Langridge (1957 b) developed methods for the culture of *A. thaliana*, to meet the following requirements: (*a*) the medium should be nutritionally inert except for those inorganic elements or radicals necessary for growth, and (*b*) plants should be maintained in an aseptic condition throughout their life cycles (Plate 1). The small size and rapid growth enable the plants to be grown throughout their life cycles on sterile nutrient agar in ordinary test tubes. Alternatively, up to 50 plants may be grown on silica gel in crystallizing dishes. For optimal growth, the trace element cations should be chelated and light should be excluded from the roots. When supplied with sucrose, the plants absorb only the glucose portion. During growth, they excrete small quantities of vitamins and other substances into the medium, but not in amounts likely to prevent the detection of growth mutants through cross-feeding (Langridge, 1955). *A. thaliana* has also been used by Langridge (1957 a) in a study of the relationship between daylength and gibberellic acid (see Chapter VI and Plate 21). Physiological varieties of *A. thaliana*, natural summer annuals, flower more rapidly after seed vernalization, particularly under long-day conditions, but still noticeably under short days. In winter annual varieties, vernalization is effective only if followed by long days. High temperatures have a devernalizing effect, and even the treatment of unvernalized seed with these temperatures (30°C for 3 days) delays flowering. The effect of vernalization persists in spite of desiccation and storage of seeds, at least for 44 days. *A. hirsuta* is a perennial which needs cold treatment every year; the seed of this species could not be vernalized.

Chapter II

BIOLOGICAL ORGANIZATION

Form and Function

That branch of botanical science which deals with analytical and experimental morphogenesis is making a great contribution to our knowledge of the sequence of forms and functions which occur during growth and reproductive development. As a result, important techniques, data and interpretations are becoming available which are applicable in all aspects of crop production. An indication of the scope of the subject may be obtained from a statement of the botanical contributions to the 1948 Symposium of the Society for Experimental Biology on 'Growth in relation to differentiation and morphogenesis':

The control of flowering in plants. (F. G. Gregory.)

Factors governing the induction and development of reproductive structures in plants. (K. C. Hamner.)

Vegetative and reproductive development of *Kalanchöe blossfeldiana* as influenced by photoperiodism. (R. Harder.)

The geometry of phyllotaxis and its origin. (F. J. Richards.)

Differentiation in the primary shoots of *Lupinus albus* L. and of *Tropaeolum majus* L. (E. Ball.)

On the determination of leaves. (Mary Snow and R. Snow.)

Experimental morphology, with special reference to pteridophytes. (C. W. Wardlaw.)

Morphogenic factors as exemplified by the onion plant. (O. V. S. Heath and M. Holdsworth.)

Wardlaw (1952) defines the term morphogenesis as including all the activities involved in the development of an organism from the zygote, spore, gemma or bud rudiment to the distinctive form and structure of the adult state. It thus includes the inception, formation and development of organs or parts, and the differentiation of the tissues within; not least, the harmonious or regulated development or organization of the

45

individual is recognized to be an essential feature of the morphogenetic process. Those who study morphogenesis are concerned not only with the eventual form and structure (morphology), but also with the analysis of the factors which cause them to arise.

When an attempt is made to explain how familiar morphological features have come into being, it is found that the present state of knowledge is inadequate, and that no single branch of botanical science can provide the whole answer. 'The study of morphogenesis is thus seen to occupy a central position and to have an integrative function in botanical science—a matter of importance at the present time, when many new aspects are being developed and becoming highly specialized and almost separate branches of science' (Wardlaw, *loc. cit.*).

An adequate knowledge of morphogenesis in a species demands information on the genetical, physical, ecological and other factors which operate during structural development. In a flowering plant, one would be concerned with the inception and development of form and structure at different embryonic stages, in subsequent stages culminating in the adult leafy shoot, and in the flowering and fruiting stages. Various factors may be causally involved in the inception and development of an organism or its parts, and the relevant hypotheses should be susceptible of experimental confirmation. The specialized techniques of experimental morphology, such as the use of surgical treatments in embryonic regions, may have a wide application, but also their limitations. Since the structural developments are the result of growth, this process must also be analyzed.

The student of experimental morphogenesis must turn to the evidence provided in the study of general plant physiology, the morphogenetic or growth-regulating or activating substances, the effect of the environment, and perhaps above all in physiological genetics. 'The summation of contemporary knowledge indicates that the physiology of an organism . . . is gene-controlled; hence in studies of morphogenesis, the contribution of physiological genetics may be expected to become of ever-increasing importance. The fundamental hereditary units, the genes, are held to be biochemical agents, and, if so, their action during development must be in conformity with biochemical laws. . . . How do the genes, and all the biochemical processes which they invoke, determine or control, actually yield the observed form and structure? Once again our picture is seen to be incomplete' (Wardlaw, *loc. cit.*).

Any study of the factors influencing plant development, both structural and reproductive, must be based on the realization that no factor ever acts alone or in isolation; it is usually only one of a whole complex. Although some of the following chapters deal with experiments made primarily with a single factor, it is assumed that this statement will be borne in mind while reviewing the evidence and conclusions.

In his paper before the Royal Society of Edinburgh, 5 November 1956, Wardlaw stated that, in trying to understand the physiological mechanism that underlies and determines the orderly formation of floral organs, it is essential to consider the organization and functional activities of the apex of the antecedent leafy shoot. The general characteristic of its apical meristem is that it gives rise to a succession of regularly spaced leaf primordia, sometimes very variable in form and structure, these having their inception in loci of a special metabolism or growth centre. The latter typically originate in the subdistal region of the meristem. The initial state of this region, which consists of equivalent embryonic cells, may be such that the reacting metabolic substances are distributed homogeneously in it. A contemporary chemical theory of morphogenesis envisages the possibility that a reaction system of this kind can give rise to a distribution of growth centres according to a definite pattern, this constituting the chemical basis for the ensuing morphogenetic developments. This general property of the apex is maintained throughout the floral development. The positions of new primordia are affected by those already present around the meristem.

At a certain stage in the development of a flowering plant, and often in direct relation to exposure to some characteristic photoperiod, it is held that new metabolic substances, perhaps hormonal or enzymic in nature and action, enter the apical meristem system, and important and usually irreversible changes ensue. The allometric growth pattern of the apex is radically changed; in particular, the elongation of the axis is greatly curtailed, so that the growth centres, and the lateral organs to which they give rise, are now formed in closely associated groups, either whorls or condensed helices, or an abbreviated floral axis.

A characteristic feature of floral ontogenesis is that the apical reaction system passes through a sequence of well-defined phases, due almost certainly to physiological correlations. As a result of the initial change in the state of the reaction system, the action of specific genes, hitherto inert, is induced, the changes effected thereby lead to further specific gene action, and so on, until flower formation terminates with the utilization of all the residual distal meristem. Wardlaw considers that the formation of calyx, corolla, androecium and gynoecium should be attributed to the action of particular genes or groups of genes as components of the reaction system. These concepts are held to afford a basis for the conspicuous features of floral ontogenesis, namely, that

(a) the several floral organs are homologous with leaves,

(b) they are formed in a characteristic pattern on the meristem, and

(c) the successive groups of growth centres have each distinctive physiological properties and accordingly give rise to organs which differ in form and structure from each other.

The advantages of this theory are considered to be that:

(a) it attempts to bring the morphological facts of floral ontogenesis into direct relation with physiology, genetics and the dynamic geometry of the embryonic apical region,

(b) many of the former highly controversial issues, for example, of homologous and non-homologous floral organs, of organs *sui generis*, of morphological transitions, etc., disappear as consideration of the relevant phenomena is transferred from the morphological to the physiological plane, and

(c) it suggests important opportunities for new observations and experiments, in its more general and more specific aspects.

Differentiation of Flower Primordia

Differentiation of floral primordia is the first visible sign that a plant has passed from a purely vegetative to a reproductive condition; this transition does not take place in many plants until a certain minimal number of leaves has been acquired, but this does not mean that no internal advance has been made in reproductive development. The Russians assume that development towards reproduction begins as soon as a plant or germinating grain is exposed to the low temperature applied in vernalization. The 'ripe-to-flower' condition recognized by Klebs is also reproductive development. In neither case is the condition recognizable externally.

There are several studies of growing points of different plants. The work of Purvis is well known. The following are keys to Plates 3 and 9 provided by Sharman, who has elsewhere (1945) published a morphological and anatomical study of leaf and bud initiation in the Gramineae:

Plate 3. Apices dissected from various species of Gramineae.

A   Underground rhizome of couch grass, *Agropyron repens*.

B   Vegetative shoot of wheat.

C   Vegetative shoot of floating pond grass, *Glyceria fluitans.*
D   Aerial vegetative shoot of *Agropyron repens.*
E   Vegetative shoot of sweet vernal, *Anthoxanthum odoratum.*
F   Vegetative shoot of Italian ryegrass, *Lolium multiflorum.*
G   Young inflorescence of *Agropyron repens.*
H   Young inflorescence of sweet vernal.
I   Young inflorescence of six-rowed barley.

B and I are viewed in the plane of the leaves, the remainder perpendicularly to the plane of the leaves.

Plate 9. Dissection of vegetative shoot of privet, *Ligustrum vulgare.*

A. 2′ and 2″ indicate the second pair of young leaves overarching the apex; 3, 4 and 5 are the shoulders left where leaves of the third, fourth and fifth pairs were attached; *b* indicates the first two leaves of bud in the axil of one of the fifth pair of leaves.

B. The same as A, with the young leaf 2′ removed and the whole shoot turned round a little. The first pair of leaf primordia are visible as small protuberances; *b* indicates a bud beginning to appear in the axil of one of the fourth pair of leaves.

C. The remaining primordium 2″ has been removed and the shoot is now viewed from the side. Only the first two primordia and the flat apex remain. The shoulder 3 indicates the former position of one of the third pair of leaves. *b* is one of the first pair of leaves of the bud in the axil of a fifth leaf.

D. An aerial view of C from above, showing the apex as a shining more or less rectangular platform between the first pair of primordia. 2, 3 and 4 mark the positions where primordia of leaf pairs, 2, 3 and 4 were attached.

The early development of the spikes of barley and wheat has been studied by Bonnett (1936) and Anderson (1952, 1954). Under the conditions of Bonnett's experiment (variety and latitude), the growing point remains vegetative during autumn, winter and early spring. In the autumn, it produces only leaf initials, while in early spring, in addition to producing leaf initials the growing point elongates. The beginning of the reproductive stage is marked by the appearance of double ridges, the upper of which produces the spikelet and its parts.

The early stages of differentiation of the flowering spike of rye are demonstrated by Bremer-Reinders (1958) (see Figs. 4, 5 and 6). In agreement with Blaauw and his co-workers, Bremer-Reinders uses symbols to indicate the successive stages. Stage I (vegetative phase) and Stage II (beginning of reproductive phase) are used, while the following stages of the reproductive phase are designated by abbreviations of the botanical name of the organ characteristic of the separate stages:

Stage	*Differentiation*
I	Growing point vegetative; only leaf initials present.
II	Elongation of the growing point; beginning of the reproductive phase. Spike length ±1 mm.
Spi	Spikelet primordia developing.
Gl	Initiation of the empty glumes on both sides of spikelet primordia.

Stage	Differentiation
Pr	First flower primordia become visible. Spike length ±2 mm.
An	Primordia of anthers become visible.
Ar	Rapid elongation of the awn on the flowering glume of flowers of the first order. Flower primordia of higher order become visible. Spike length ±5 mm.
Th	Anther primordia of flowers of the first order are divided into two thecae. Spike length ±8 mm.

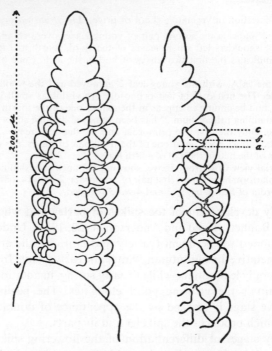

Fig. 4. Early stages of development of rye spike (Bremer-Reinders, 1958): (*left*) Stadium Pr. Flower primordia initiating. Length of young spike 2000μ. (*right*) Stadium An. Primordia of anthers initiating in flowers of the first order. Flower primordia of the second order developing in the spikelets of the central region.

a. Empty glume. *b.* Flowering glume (palea inferior). *c.* Flower primordium.

Observing at the Ohio latitude, Evans and Grover (1940) found that the growing point of perennial grasses such as timothy remains vegetative during late summer and autumn and until April or very early May of the following year. In annual grasses, seeds of which germinate in early spring, the inflorescences originate and develop somewhat later than in the perennials. In describing and illustrating inflorescence primordia of the one-branched type (*Agropyron repens* and *Lolium perenne*) and of the multiple-branched type (*Phalaris canariensis*, timothy,

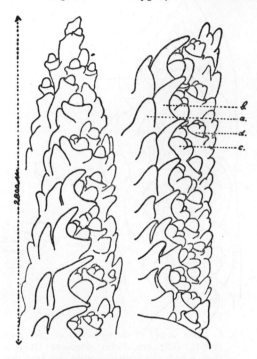

Fig. 5. Early stages of development of rye spike (Bremer-Reinders, 1958): Stadium Ar. Linear outgrowth of the flowering glume. Length of young spike 5 mm.
  a. Empty glume. *b.* Flowering glume (palea inferior). *c.* Flower of the first order.
  d. Flower of the second order.

tall oat-grass, cocksfoot, millet and *Euchlaena mexicana*), Evans and Grover note that the transition from the vegetative to the reproductive phase is usually marked by a sudden and vigorous elongation of the growing point and by an increase in its diameter. The further development of leaf fundaments ceases. The protuberances or lateral swellings initiating the inflorescence then appear. Each of these represents a lateral growing point and may be regarded as the homologue of the primordium of a vegetative bud.

As a rule, each protuberance on a reproductive primordium, whatever

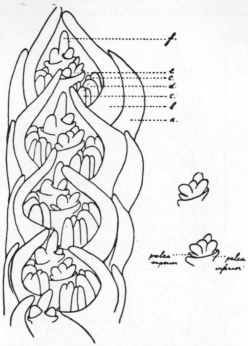

Fig. 6. Early stages of development of rye spike (Bremer-Reinders, 1958): Stadium Th. Anthers lobed; the anthers are divided into two pollen sacs. Length of young spike 8 mm. Side view.

a. Empty glume. *b.* Flowering glume. *c.* Anthers lobed. *d.* Central meristem of flower of the first order. *e.* Flower of the second order. *f.* Apex of the spikelet axis. *g.* Flower of the second order, showing flowering glume (palea inferior), palea (superior), three anther primordia and the central meristem.

its order, ultimately organizes a spikelet at its apex. There is a general tendency for spikelet formation to begin in the upper middle region of the young inflorescence, and to progress upwards and downwards. Further specialization is, however, more rapid in the distal region than in the central and proximal regions. Consequently, flowering and seed maturation progress from the apex towards the base of the inflorescence, in reverse order to the formation of primordia. The behaviour of growing points varies, of course, with the variety of grass concerned. Late pasture types will differentiate their primordia considerably later under natural conditions than early hay types.

The latest study of this type is that made by Jeater (1956) on bred strains of perennial ryegrass, cocksfoot, timothy and meadow fescue (see Plates 4 and 5). A random sample of tillers taken from plants sown in spring, 1952, was examined in the laboratory throughout the growing seasons of 1953 and 1954. Each tiller was separated from the plant as near the ground as possible, and each leaf removed with a sharpened dissecting needle. Every bit of leaf tissue had to be taken off to prevent any masking of the small apex. Although there is a wide variation in type of inflorescence in the Gramineae, the first development stages of the reproductive phase are similar. Scales for these stages in perennial ryegrass and cocksfoot are given below (Jeater, *loc. cit.*).

Perennial ryegrass (*Lolium perenne*)

Developmental stage	*Appearance of the apex*
1	Apex short. Normally 4 vegetative primordia.
2	Apex elongated. 5 or more vegetative primordia.
3	Transition stage. Double ridges at the base of the apex. Secondary reproductive primordia above the double ridges visible as rounded protuberances.
4	Secondary reproductive primordia from base to tip of apex. Primordia in the centre of the apex beginning to elongate.
5	Ridges of glumes visible in the centre of the apex.
6	Most secondary reproductive primordia elongated. Ridges of glumes visible at the base and top of apex. Glumes elongating in the centre with floret buds developing and ridges of lemmas visible.
7	All reproductive primordia elongated with lemma ridges showing on floret buds at base and top of apex. Lemmas elongating in the centre.
8	All glumes elongated. Lemmas of all basal florets elongating. Anthers budded off and elongating in the centre covered by developing lemmas.
9	Ear in boot stage, most of the developing florets covered by lemmas.
10	Ears emerged.

Cocksfoot (*Dactylis glomerata*)

Developmental stage	*Appearance of the apex*
1	Apex short. Normally 2–3 vegetative primordia.
2	Apex elongating. 4 or more vegetative primordia.

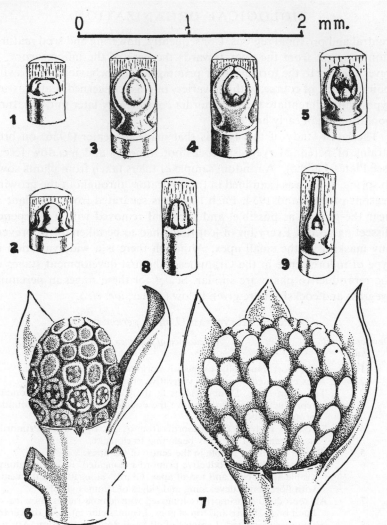

Fig. 7. Apical growing point of *Baeria chrysostoma*, with front leaf removed leaving semi-circular scar. Diagrams 1 to 5 show successive stages of flower primordia; in all cases, two youngest opposite leaf primordia are separated by flower primordium, which has just initiated involucral bracts in diagram 4 and florets in diagram 5. Diagrams 6 and 7 show later stages; the two highest foliage leaves and two or three involucral bracts are removed to show flower head. Diagram 8 shows the growing point of a purely vegetative plant; only two leaf primordia are visible and the small apical meristem is hidden between them. Diagram 9 shows a growing point which has been kept at 28°C in continuous light; the flower primordium has been initiated but is not developing further owing to unfavourable environment and has become overgrown by leaf primordia (Sivori and Went, 1944).

54

Cocksfoot (*Dactylis glomerata*)—cont.

Developmental stage	Appearance of the apex
3	Transition stage. Apex conical. Double ridges developing with secondary reproductive primordia at the top of the apex.
4	Apex conical. Secondary reproductive primordia visible on apex, elongating in the middle.
5	Apex conical. Secondary reproductive primordia developing at top of apex and elongating at middle and base with tertiary reproductive primordia developing on them.
6	Apex conical. Secondary reproductive primordia developing at the top. Tertiary and quarternary reproductive primordia visible in the middle of the apex and at the base. Glume ridges just visible in centre of the apex.
7	Apex elongating. Glumes developing on the basal and middle parts of apex and ridges of lemmas developing in centre of apex.
8	Inflorescence internodes elongating. Glumes visible on most of the apex. Lemmas elongating on the middle part of apex and anthers developing in the centre.
9	Apex elongated. Developing floret buds covered by developing glumes and lemmas. Anthers elongating within floret buds. Boot stage.
10	Ears emerged.

The number of distinguishable stages between the transitional or double-ridged stage and ear emergence is not necessarily limited to seven. Anderson (1952, 1954) distinguishes nine stages in barley, oats and wheat between the time of change over to reproductive primordia and heading.

In his study of floral histogenesis in three species of the Cyperaceae Barnard (1957 b) found the organization of the tissue of the apex of the spikelet to be similar, and also to resemble that in the Gramineae (Sharman, 1945; Barnard, 1957 a) (see Plate 6). The principal differences between the two Orders are in the size and arrangement of the glumes and flower primordia. The mode of origin of the flower primordia is also essentially the same in the two Orders. Floral structure in the Gramineae is remarkably uniform, but shows considerably more variation in the Cyperaceae. Variation in inflorescence and spikelet form associated with a reduction in the number of florets per spikelet seems to have been the principal feature of evolutionary development in the Gramineae; in the Cyperaceae it would appear that floral structure has evolved along a number of distinct and separate pathways.

Number of Leaves as Indicator of Ripeness-to-Flower

An important aspect of this research is the need for discovering some outward expression of the inner physiological state of a plant. The condition of ripeness-to-flower postulated by Klebs was not thought to be recognizable morphologically. However, Purvis (1934) and later Purvis and Gregory (1937) have put forward their interpretation based on number of leaves. First, in a study of the reaction of Petkus winter rye to temperature at germination and to varied daylength, Purvis reached the following conclusions regarding the exact time in the life history of a plant at which the change from vegetative growth to reproduction takes place;

(a) in assigning a plant to its correct photoperiodic category, the time of formation of the flower primordia should be considered rather than the time of emergence of the inflorescence;

(b) in winter rye, the differentiation of flower primordia is subject to an interaction between daylength and the temperature during germination, which factors determine both the minimal number of leaves formed before differentiation of flower primordia begins, and the rate of growth of the meristematic tissue.

The concept of ripeness-to-flower suggested by Klebs was accepted and was identified with the stage in development at which the 'minimal leaf number' had been laid down. This number was stated to be seven or eight in spring rye, and was thought to be about twelve in unvernalized winter rye. In both the spring and winter varieties grown in short days, it reached twenty-two, as it did also in unvernalized winter rye grown in long days. These conclusions were modified in a second paper; it was then seen that a quantitative relation exists between the duration of the vernalization treatment and the length of the vegetative phases, and that the number, twelve, applied only to winter rye vernalized for the particular period (4 weeks) used in those earlier experiments.

In the experiments reported in 1937, the effects of varying preliminary periods of low temperature and short days on subsequent development were observed. Both treatments resulted in acceleration of flowering. With the low-temperature treatment, an exposure for 4 days leads to a definite response and the magnitude of that response increases with the duration of treatment up to a limit of 14 weeks, after which winter rye is indistinguishable from spring rye in its flowering behaviour. With increasing exposure to low temperature, the 'minimal leaf number' necessary before the ripe-to-flower condition is achieved is reduced from about twenty-five to seven. With preliminary treatment with short days (10-hour), the magnitude of the effect on flowering increases with length of treatment up to 6 weeks, but longer exposures retard flowering. The

56

minimal leaf number falls to sixteen after 6 weeks' treatment and increases again with longer exposures.

In both spring and winter rye there is a minimal leaf number, seven, which cannot be further reduced, and a maximum, twenty-five, which cannot be further increased. The primordia between the 8th and 25th are indeterminate and can produce either leaf or spikelet; this is related to the structure of these initials, which are double, consisting of a flowering branch (spikelet) with a subtending bract, either of which may be inhibited according to the length of day or the temperature during germination.

Melchers also uses leaf number as an indicator of flower initiation (Blütenauslösung), stating that the method as developed by Purvis should be generally useful for plants with terminal flowers or inflorescences, such as *Hyoscyamus*. The advantage of this indicator lies in the fact that the values compared depend primarily upon the initiation of the primordia as such, and not on such indefinite characters as the appearance of visible buds or flowers and other growth phenomena. *Hyoscyamus* has also the advantage, as compared with several other plants such as the cereals, that leaf primordia and flower primordia are distinguishable at the earliest stages of development. Melchers determines the number of leaves newly formed from the beginning of the experiment up to the first flower, or to the end of the experiment, and describes this value as leaf increase.

Although counting the number of leaves on the main tiller provides a quick and reasonably accurate method for determining the developmental stage of spring cereals in the field, this method is unsuitable for perennial grasses. Their nature makes it impossible to pick out any one main tiller or even a number of primary tillers. Counting the leaves is difficult because of their dying off over winter (Jeater, 1956).

Morphological and Physiological Age

Reliable information on the physiology of ageing is scanty; the physiological changes which occur and their causes are ill-defined and poorly understood (Robbins, 1957 a). Even the definition of age varies; it may be measured from the last gametic reproduction or from the establishment of an individual plant by any means, gametic or agametic. A banana plant may by the first method be regarded as hundreds or thousands of years old, since it is propagated entirely by vegetative means, or its age may, by the second method, be measured in days or months. The concept of physiological age which depends on the condition of the plant rather than on the time it has existed has proved to be of some value. Although 'a plant may be as old as it feels, the difficulty is to determine how it feels' (Robbins, *loc. cit.*). Change in leaf shape is of limited application, as in some plants leaf shape is markedly affected by the environment and is not determined primarily by the internal condition of the plant.

The ageing, senescence and death of annual plants are associated in part with the production of flowers, fruits and seeds. Loss of magnesium by the chlorophyll, and a decrease in ability to retain water with consequent wilting and withering are factors suggested as causing the death of annuals. Robbins considers these to be results of senility rather than causes, and attaches more importance to the transfer of food reserves, especially nitrogenous substances, to the flowers, fruits and seeds, with a resulting starvation of the vegetative parts; the movement of hormone-like accessory foods to the floral parts may also be involved. Physiological changes associated with ageing may occur in an annual plant even before flowering, and may perhaps be correlated with the formation of flowers, e.g. loss of effectivity of root system in the latter part of the growth period, or a loss of nitrogen in older plants.

The plastochrone index proposed by Erickson and Michelini (see Michelini, 1958) may have some value; this index is a mathematical representation of the morphological age of a plant. In the shoot of a higher plant, leaves appear periodically and the period between the initiation of successive leaves has been termed the plastochrone. When successive plastochrones are equal in duration, the plastochrone may be made to serve as the unit of a developmental scale. The index in terms of plastochrones and fractional parts of the plastochrone may be determined by the formula:

$$\mathrm{PI} = n + \frac{\log L_n - \log 10}{\log L_n - \log L_{n+1}}$$

where n is the serial number of the leaf just longer than an arbitrary reference length, 10 mm, and $\log L_n$ is the logarithm of the length of leaf n. The leaves are counted in their order of appearance on the apex, e.g. the oldest leaves are leaves number 1 and 2, etc., until the leaf on the apex exceeding 10 mm is reached. This leaf and the succeeding leaf on the apex, L_{n+1}, i.e., the leaves which lie on either side of the arbitrary leaf length of 10 mm, are then measured with vernier calipers to the nearest 0·1 mm and the calculation of the index is easily performed.

It would be interesting to establish whether this morphological index is also expressive of physiological development. Michelini collected leaves of *Xanthium italicum* in various stages of development, analyzed them for fresh weight, chlorophyll content and oxygen consumption, and found no consistent relationship between the developing leaf and these physiological characteristics on the basis of the selecting criteria of chronological age. Using the plastochrone index for expressing development in terms of leaf morphology, it was found that these same characteristics in individually developing leaves follow a straight line relationship to their particular stage of growth.

Many plants go through more or less well-defined juvenile and adult stages as a part of their normal ontogeny, e.g. English ivy (*Hedera helix*) and the creeping fig, *Ficus repens*. Juvenile and adult stages have also been distinguished in apples, apricots, pecans, beech, oak, rubber and citrus. A seed-grown tree may be juvenile for some years but eventually the new peripheral growth is adult—the tree is then made up of a cone in the juvenile condition enclosed by a zone in the adult condition. The juvenile portion of some trees retains its dead leaves in winter, but the adult parts drop them; beech and oak may retain their leaves in the interior juvenile portion of the tree, but lose them from the peripheral twigs. Seedlings of most types of citrus are thorny, but the tendency again declines in the peripheral portions; plants grown from buds taken from the base and inner portions are thorny, plants from peripheral buds are likely to be nearly thornless. Budwood from commercial varieties which have been propagated vegetatively for considerable periods yields trees which are virtually thornless.

Various criteria have been used to distinguish between the juvenile and adult stages, e.g. leaf shape, production of pigment (usually antho-cyanin), phyllotaxy, shedding of leaves, ease of rooting of cuttings, thorniness, growth habit and flowering. The most striking feature is that both the juvenile and adult states are transmitted by vegetative propaga-tion. Plants produced vegetatively from adult shoots continue to grow as adult unless sexual reproduction is permitted.

Robbins states that the origin of the juvenile and adult stages must be sought in the activity of the apical meristem, which changes or is changed with age. Two explanations have been put forward for these changes. The differentiation of a meristem may be determined by substances which come to it from other parts of the plant, but the meristem itself does not change or age. Alternatively, meristems may themselves age, and although their activity is affected by the materials they receive, the response differs as between a juvenile and an adult meristem. Juvenility may be an unstable metabolic state which proceeds by a series of steps to a relatively stable metabolic state characteristic of the adult meristem.

The adult forms of ivy may be induced to revert to the juvenile form by treatment with gibberellic acid (Robbins, 1957 b; see Plate 12). This may be a primary or a secondary effect, resulting from the increased growth induced by the acid. This raises the question: what causes the change from a juvenile metabolism to that of the adult and vice versa? Can it be the 'Jugendsubstanz' of Frank and Renner (1956), who report that a juvenile shoot, cultivated in the same vessel of mineral nutrient solution with an adult shoot, induces a considerable proportion of the adult shoots to revert to a juvenile state? They suggest that roots and leaves of the juvenile synthesize a substance which causes the meristem of the adult to produce juvenile structures and physiology, while the leaves of the adult produce an inhibitory substance. The balance between these in the meristem determines the ultimate growth form.

Working with the rubber tree, *Hevea brasiliensis*, which is notoriously difficult to propagate from cuttings, Muzik and Cruzado (1958), at the Federal Experimental Station in Puerto Rico, find further evidence that the juvenile form may transmit a substance to the adult which induces the adult to assume juvenile characteristics. If a substance is actually transferred from stock to scion, this material may not be readily soluble in ordinary solvents, but may be slowly absorbed and accumulated by the scion in sufficient amounts to induce a change in rooting ability.

Annual and Perennial Habit

To what extent can a grass plant with its agglomeration of tillers be regarded as perennial or annual? Experimental evidence on the perennial habit of grasses has so far been lacking; in general, the mechanism of survival has been oversimplified by leaving the continuous nature of tiller production and decay out of account, and by laying too much emphasis on flowering as the natural termination of life. Langer (1956) has now examined the problem in greater detail. In *Phleum pratense*, only part of the tillers complies with the typical growth pattern of monocarpic organs, in the sense that they produce inflorescences and subsequently die. Many tillers which are in existence during the period favourable for flowering remain vegetative until they die. The continued presence of vegetative shoots thus raises the question whether survival of tillers might not be prolonged for several years. This was not found to be so for timothy, although greater longevity might be induced in a different environment. Though failure to flower prolonged life, not a single tiller survived two complete growing seasons.

Langer describes the general pattern of survival as follows: Tillers arising sufficiently early before the flowering season may, unless they die prematurely, produce an inflorescence or only a flag leaf and thereby terminate their existence. Such tillers could be called annual in the strict sense. If the only response to long-day conditions is stem elongation, death may be deferred for some time but not beyond the following spring. On the other hand, a tiller may remain in the rosette stage and survive to the following flowering season. If an ear is produced, then the tiller will have behaved as a biennial. Tillers which do not flower at any time fall between these two extreme categories according to their longevity. The maximum length of life recorded in this experiment was not much more than a year. A possible exception to this rule might come from those tillers which were still alive at the end of the experimental period but, since they were nearly all in an elongated condition, their early death was probable. The mechanism of survival in grasses is thus quite different from that of other plants, for it is based neither on an annual leaf fall nor on the death of all aerial parts. Survival is ensured by continuous production of new tillers and by their ability to retain vitality for some time. The grass plant is never static but displays an always changing pattern of integrated tiller life histories. Successive new formation and decay of tillers maintain a dynamic state of continuous change.

Langer (1957) continued this work in studies on growth and nutrition designed to measure the progress of internal change and the morphological and nutritional differences among the separate parts of the plant, as tillers are formed and decay.

Physiology of Sexuality

It is not possible to formulate a general hypothesis with regard to the control of sexuality in flowers without making reference to the control of the flowering process itself. The hypothesis of Heslop-Harrison (1957), based upon a review of the extent to which sex expression may be modified by environmental factors, such as variations in mineral nutrition, in the light and temperature regime, the effects of mutilation, grafting and the application of chemicals and hormones, is as follows:

'Flowering is a process initiated by the accumulation at apical meristems of an agent generated elsewhere in the plant; this agent may be nucleoprotein in nature and possess limited powers of self-duplication giving it plasmagene-like properties. The formation of effective quantities of this agent depends upon the conditions prevailing for its self-duplication; of these auxin balance is most critical. It is largely, although probably not exclusively, through the agency of auxin metabolism of the plant that reduplication is governed in those plants in which flowering is profoundly affected by environmental influences. Reduplication depends initially upon a depression of the local auxin level; after it has begun, auxin levels become less critical. The course of floral morphogenesis, once initiated, is established by genetic factors at the reacting apex, and the activity of these is to some extent regulated by auxin levels there. The growth of stamen and pistil primordia is governed by auxin in the characteristic manner, the response following the optimum curve. The concentration promoting maximal stamen growth is lower than that promoting maximal pistil growth, so that auxin level at the differentiating apex determines the sex balance of the flowers produced. In some plants this level is susceptible to local control in the apex by such influences as temperature, and through the auxin economy of the whole plant, by such factors as nutrition and photoperiodism. Through these agencies the sex balance of the flowers may be modified.'

To the environmental factors reviewed by Heslop-Harrison, Baker (1957) would wish to add the effect of parasites. Both sexes in the dioecious species of *Melandrium* produce androecial and gynoecial primordia, but usually only one of these develops to maturity. The fact that the staminal rudiments of a pistillate plant may be caused to develop, while the ovary is aborted, as a result of infection by *Ustilago violacea*, is probably the result of hormone production or destruction by the fungus. This is not incompatible with the hypothesis developed by Heslop-Harrison that the control of sex expression depends basically upon local concentrations of auxin. Pistillate plants of *Melandrium* which are not systematically infected develop smutted staminate flowers where the fungus is present, pistillate flowers where it is absent, and staminate flowers with small ovaries and fairly well-developed ovules where the infection is light.

Sex-linked characters in *Melandrium* may be distinguished from secondary sexual characters by their behaviour following the infection of a pistillate plant. The latter quantitative characters tend to be replaced by their counterparts of a staminate flower, whereas the former, which are unaffected, are usually qualitative (and therefore unlikely to be determined by simple hormonal means). The single factor of infection may cause both the abortion of the gynoecium and the development of the androecium in a pistillate plant; this is regarded as contradicting the qualitative difference between 'female-suppressors' and 'male promoters' postulated by Westergaard. If, as Heslop-Harrison suggests, pistil development depends upon a high level of auxin and stamen development on a lower one, both 'female-suppressors' and 'male promoters' may prove to be inhibitory of auxin production or action. It may be profitable to investigate the auxin levels of infected and uninfected pistillate plants or parts of plants.

Having indicated that there is as yet no reliable evidence for a feminizing influence of a fungus on a staminate plant, Baker concludes: 'There are at least sixteen families of flowering plants where functionally pistillate flowers are known to occur in species which are usually hermaphrodite. Whether they occur in a gynodioecious or gynomonoecious manner, these pistillate flowers are regularly smaller than the hermaphrodite ones. By contrast, where androdioecism or andromonoecism occurs, the staminate flowers are generally as large as hermaphrodites. In at least six families which show what appears to be evolutionarily recent dioecism, there is a similar contrast between pistillate and staminate flower-sizes. This suggests that, although the separation of the sexes has undoubtedly evolved many times in the phylogeny of the flowering plants, the hormonal control of sex-expression is likely to be a relatively simple and general one and may well be connected with the level of auxin-activity in the developing flower-bud. In at least some gynodioecious members of the Labiatae, the abortion of the anthers is associated with a dwarfing of the plant in all its aerial parts.'

Genetically monoecious plants can be induced to flower as males (Thomas, 1956). Plants grown in continuous light at a low temperature (15°C) form inflorescences of the normal regular monoecious type at each node, whereas at a constant temperature of 24°C with continuous illumination, the production of female flowers is delayed until at least the fifth node in most plants. In one experiment, no female flowers had developed by the time the treatment was discontinued, when the thirteenth internode was elongating. On being placed in short days at a low temperature, these plants developed normal monoecious inflorescences. Using

63

the knowledge gained on *Mercurialis ambigua* and *Cannabis sativa*, an alternative hypothesis can be built up with regard to the possible mechanism by which sex is determined. A plant in the flowering condition will form female flowers as long as it can produce the morphogenetic factors necessary for the formation of female flowers; when the concentration of these factors is too low, the plant will produce male flowers only. Thus in male plants a gene on the Y chromosome must continually inhibit production or action of these factors, so that only male flowers are produced. Diploid female plants produce many female flowers, but towards the end of the growing season the concentration of female-determining factors falls and a few male flowers develop. Monoecious plants possibly produce only enough of these factors to form one female flower in each leaf axil and the remainder of the flowers at each node are consequently male (Thomas, 1958).

The more recent work of Heslop-Harrison is concerned with the morphogenetic effects of 2,3,5-triiodobenzoic acid on sex expression in *Cannabis sativa*, a dioecious species in which there is evidence that sexuality may be regulated by auxin levels in the neighbourhood of developing primordia; 2,3,5-triiodobenzoic acid does increase the total production of flowers in both sexes (Heslop-Harrison and Heslop-Harrison, Part I, 1957 a). Brief exposure to carbon monoxide in the young stages, before the floral primordia are 'sexually committed', induces the formation of intersexual or even functionally female flowers (Heslop-Harrison and Heslop-Harrison, Part II, 1957 a). Similar treatment applied to *Mercurialis ambigua* (male or monoecious) reduces pollen output very substantially, leading to 'female sexualization' in a species in which no pure-sexed female plants normally exist. It is thought possible that CO may act through modifying the natural auxin metabolism in a manner leading to the building up of a high level of 'free' auxin (Heslop-Harrison and Heslop-Harrison, 1957 b).

While *Silene pendula* reacts as a long-day plant in that flowering is hastened by exposure from germination onwards to days of 16 hours or more illumination, a high proportion of the flowers formed under such treatment is male-sterile (Heslop-Harrison and Heslop-Harrison, 1958 a and b). Full pollen fertility is obtained only when the plants are exposed to 40 to 50 short days in early life. Associated with the suppression of the androecium under long days is a diminution in size of the corolla, and an excessive enlargement of the gynoecium. Comparable effects can be induced by auxin treatment in plants exposed to a sufficient number of short days to ensure full androecial development. The aberrations of

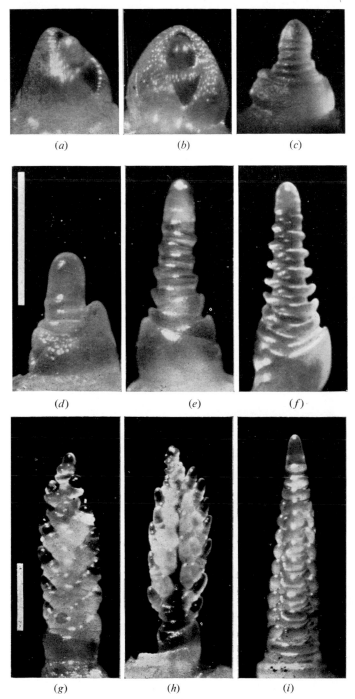

3. Apices dissected from grasses and cereals (see p. 48). Photo: B. C. Sharman. The scale in (d) represents 0·5 mm. (1/50 inch) and applies to a–f. That in g also represents 0·5 mm. and applies to g–i

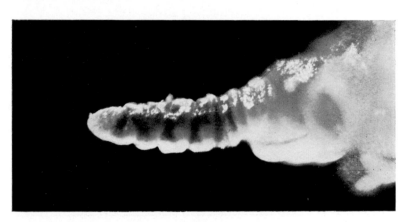

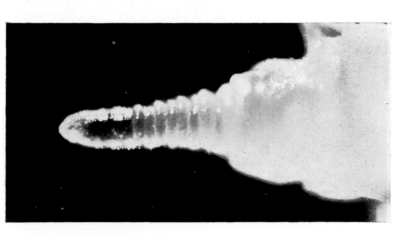

(a)   (b)   (c)

4. Primordial development in perennial ryegrass (*Lolium perenne*) (Jeater, 1956). (a) Vegetative primordia. Apex elongating prior to start of reproductive phase (×65). (b) Double ridges. Apex in transitional phase (×60). (c) Spear-shaped spikelet primordia with rachis. Apex in

(d)   (e)   (f)

5. Primordial development in perennial ryegrass (*Lolium* perenne)—continued. (*d*) Glume ridges. Glume ridges visible along practically whole length of apex (×40). (*e*) Lemma ridges. Lemma ridges visible on all prmordiia (×25). (*f*) Anthers budded off. All glumes and lemmas elongating and covering basal florets in each spikelet where anthers are being budded off (×3)

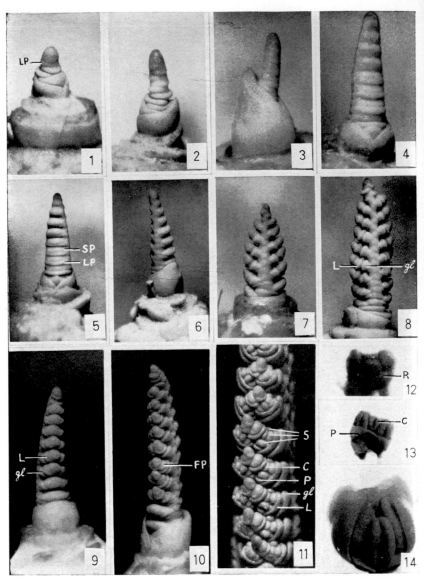

6. Morphology of a wheat spike (Barnard, 1955). *lp*, leaf primordium; *sp*, spikelet primordium; *gl*, glume; *fp*, flower primordium; *s*, stamen; *c*, carpel; *p*, palea; *r*, lodicule ridge; *l*, lemma. (1) Apex of vegetative axis commencing to elongate prior to spike formation. Fourteenth leaf primordium at *lp*. × 35. (2) Apex further elongated with younger leaf primordia as crescentic ridges only. × 35. (3) Apex much elongated and leaf primordia showing as ridges. Spikelet primordia almost distinguishable. × 35. (4) Spikelet primordia in the axils of the leaf primordia give a 'double ridge or ring' appearance. × 35. (5) Young spike showing double ridges of spikelet primordia and subtending leaf primordia at base. Towards apex spikelet primordia occur as rounded protuberances. × 24. (6) Young spike with spikelet primordia developing in acropetal succession. The leaf primordia subtending basal spikelets are still discernible. × 24. (7) Spikelet primordia with two empty glumes and first lemma developed as ridges; note apical spikelet. × 24. (8) Spikelet primordia showing two empty gumes and first and second lemmas. × 24. (9) Spikelet primordia about same stage as in (7) viewed directly. × 26. (10) Direct view on to spike with spikelets in which first flower primordium is developed. In the most advanced spikelet the flower primordium in the axil of the first lemma is a well-developed rounded structure and is just appearing in the axil of the second lemma. × 26. (11) Portion of a spike 3·5 mm. long showing spikelets in which fifth lemma is just arising; flower primordia in axils of first and second lemma have differentiated a palea, three stamens, and carpel, whilst those in axil of third lemma have not yet differentiated any parts. × 30. (12) Anterior view of young flower primordium showing three young stamens and carpel. Lodicules represented by ridge along anterior surface of primordium. × 65. (13) Posterior view of young flower primordium showing palea, two lateral stamens, and carpel in centre. View of anterior stamen is obscured. × 32. (14) Anterior view of older flower primordium in which palea extends above stamens and lodicules are well developed. × 32

microsporogenesis resulting from protracted exposure to long days appear to arise from an early degeneration of the tapetum, and again the effects may be simulated by auxin treatment. These facts appear to lend support to the view that the influence of photoperiod on sex expression is exerted through the native auxin metabolism of the plant.

Type of Fertilization

In his review of self-fertilization and population variability in plants, Stebbins (1957) refers to self-fertilization as a derived condition from cross-fertilizing ancestors, an outcome of pioneering in new and difficult environments. Self-fertilizing species generally appear to be more specialized in morphological characteristics than many of their cross-fertilizing relatives. In many instances they possess highly specialized mechanisms for seed dispersal (*Bromus, Hordeum, Medicago, Trifolium*); a very high proportion have annual life cycles (Stebbins, 1950), a condition generally regarded by morphologists as being derived from the perennial growth habit. Annual members of the genera mentioned can nearly always be associated in the sum total of their morphological characteristics with perennial species of the same genus.

One of the reasons which Stebbins gives to explain why some species should have given up cross-fertilization, 'with its attendant advantages of population variability and genetic heterozygosity,' is that self-fertilization is a means of fertility insurance in plants which are subject to periodic drought. Chase (1908) recorded the formation of axillary cleistogamous flowers at the base of plants of species of *Stipa* and *Danthonia* which inhabit dry places, and in which the usual culm inflorescences may set little seed under conditions of extreme heat or drought. Self-fertilization is also an advantage in the annual species of regions with a Mediterranean climate, where in dry years conditions favourable for cross-fertilization may be absent altogether. Indirect supporting evidence is provided by the occurrence under usually favourable conditions of cross pollination in normally self-pollinated species, e.g. the chasmogamous flowers of *Bromus* with large exserted anthers which are formed during the height of the spring blooming season and are completely absent when plants are forced to bloom in autumn or under low light intensities (Harlan, 1945).

Long distance dispersal is another factor in the origin of self-fertilization. In the centres of distribution, where the greatest morphological diversity occurs, self-incompatible, cross-fertilizing species of *Bromus*, *Hordeum* and *Secale* are found, while the geographically isolated species or ecotypes are generally or frequently self-compatible. This correlation 'occurs so widely and has such great significance for studies of the origin and migration of genera of flowering plants (Baker, 1955) that is deserves recognition as Baker's law. It was logically and reasonably explained by its author on the assumption that accidental long distance dispersal of a single propagule can lead to establishment of a colony only in a species capable of self-fertilization. If the type thus established is well adapted to its newly found ecological niche, it can spread throughout the area where these conditions are found, even though its capacity for genetic variation is much reduced. . . . Plant populations adapted to certain types of temporary habitats, particularly annual weeds and other colonizers of newly available situations, possess a considerable selective advantage if they remain constant genetically for periods of many generations, but still can produce occasional bursts of genetic variability. The commonest genetic system which brings about such cycles of alternating variability and constancy is that of predominant self-fertilization, with the capacity for occasional outcrossing being nevertheless retained' (Stebbins, *loc. cit.*).

Relation between Reproductive Development and Growth

The effect of developing flowers and fruit on vegetative increase has been demonstrated by Murneek (1926). There is no doubt that these organs exert a conspicuous physiological control on the metabolism of the plant, although this has been noted more particularly when reproduction is almost completed, i.e. at the stage of fruit and seed formation. At this time the influence is exhibited by various degrees of inhibition in the subsequent growth of the plant. Work has been done, however, on some of the earlier significant though less evident stages of reproduction which reveals quite a different phenomenon in operation with respect to their effect on plant metabolism. Instead of the inhibitory or retarding influence, as is exhibited during the formation of fruits and seeds, there are to be noted more or less specific stimulations of vegetative growth coincident with flowering and fruit setting (Murneek, 1939). Wittwer (see Missouri, 1943) has studied these stimulating effects of reproduction on vegetative growth and extension, with particular reference to two 'crucial' stages of sexual reproduction, namely, synapsis (chromosome conjugation in meiosis within the immature flower bud during gametophyte maturation),

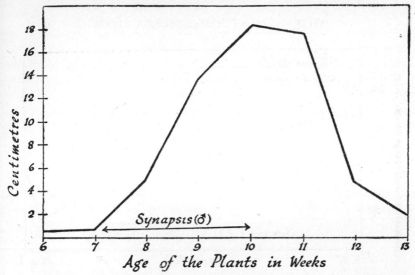

Fig. 8. Weekly elongation increments in flower stalks of male spinach plants. No appreciable extension is evident in the flower stems prior to synapsis (chromosome conjugation in meiosis within the immature flower bud), noticeable growth occurring only after the initiation of this phase of sexual reproduction (Missouri, 1943).

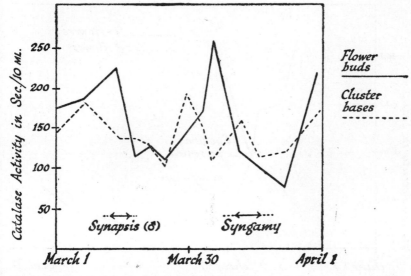

Fig. 9. Catalase activity in flower buds of Kieffer pear during development. Two maxima and two minima are evident. Catalase activity is relatively low just before and at the time of synapsis in microspore (pollen) mother cells. A second minimum is reached with full bloom, at the time of or just after fertilization. There is a remarkable increase in enzyme activity following the two minima, and corresponding precisely with the post-synaptic and post-fertilization periods. Wittwer (see Missouri, 1943) states that the changes in catalase activity are due to internal factors related to reproductive development, rather than to external environment directly.

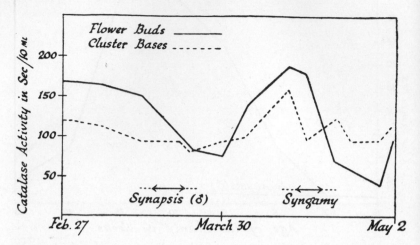

Fig. 10. Catalase activity in flower buds of Vermont Beauty pear during development (Missouri, 1943).

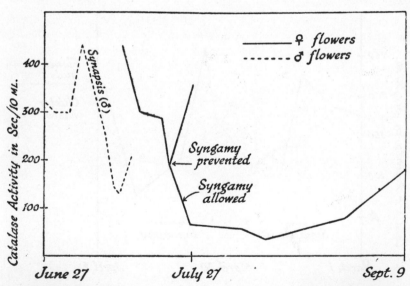

Fig. 11. Catalase activity in the reproductive organs of maize during their development; the staminate and pistillate flowers are treated separately. Tassels show an increase in catalase activity following chromosome conjugation in the anthers, while ovules depict a remarkable increase following fertilization (Missouri, 1943).

68

and syngamy (fertilization or gametic union in the embryo-sac). These stimulating phases were demonstrated in the cucumber, strawberry and

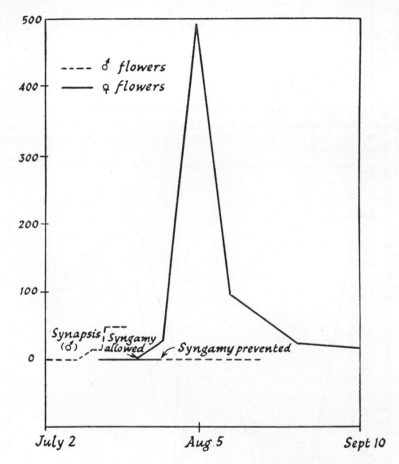

Fig. 12. Changes in growth hormone content of the reproductive organs of maize during their development. There is a complete absence of growth hormone in the male inflorescence prior to synapsis, and in the ovule before fertilization. A few days after chromosome conjugation in the tassel, and the union of gametes in the ear, growth hormones appear in considerable quantities in these structures (Missouri, 1943).

sour cherry by the treatments of disbudding, deflowering, and defruiting. The results are shown in Figs. 8 to 15.

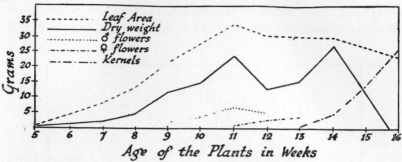

Fig. 13. Weekly increment in dry weight of maize during its growth period. Interpretation by Wittwer (see Missouri, 1943) of earlier figure by Kreusler, Prehn and Hornberger.

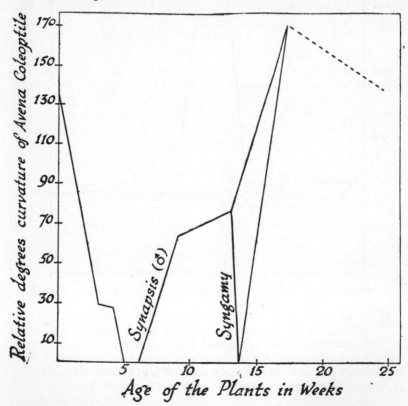

Fig. 14. Changes in auxin content during the growth period of maize. Interpretation by Wittwer (see Missouri, 1943) of earlier figures by Laibach and Meyer, again indicating the effects of synapsis and syngamy.

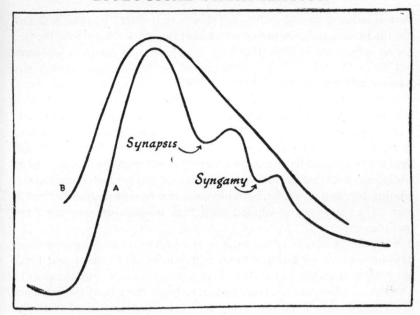

Fig. 15. Weekly percentage increase in dry weight of maize during its growth period. A, dry weight; B, leaf area. Interpretation by Wittwer (see Missouri, 1943) of earlier figure by Briggs, Kidd and West.

Nodulation of Legumes

In his review of the influence of the legume in root-nodule symbiosis, Nutman (1956) considered the effect of the environment, namely, the nutritional factors and the physical factors—light and temperature. In the following extract from the section on physical factors, it is assumed that reference will be made to the extensive bibliography in this review, and names only are quoted.

Light intensity, day length and temperature have been shown to influence nodulation. In the dark, nodules form on some species and not on others. On lucerne and vetch seedlings, only a very few nodules are formed in the complete absence of light, and, if nodulating plants are placed in the dark, nodule formation ceases and those already formed degenerate (Wilson, Thornton). *Leucaena glauca*, red clover and soybean are quite resistant to infection in the dark unless provided with sugar (Schweizer), whereas the number of nodules formed on peas in the

71

dark is reduced by sugar although their size is increased (McGonagle). On the other hand, Diener reported that nodule formation on the pea grown in light ceases altogether even if the light is reduced to a low level, but that reduction to 50 per cent normal intensity reduced nodule size without affecting number. Fred and Wilson, Orcutt and Fred, Fred, Wilson and Wyss, and Raju, found an optimal light intensity for maximal nodulation and nitrogen fixation. At very high light intensity, fixation was completely inhibited in the young seedlings which remained in the seedling nitrogen hunger phase. This depressing influence of high light intensity could be overcome either by a short period of shading or by adding nitrate. Observations on subterranean clover have confirmed this relationship, and it has also been observed that the few nodules formed at high light intensities combined with high temperature are large but ineffective.

With the exception of an incidental comparison of long and short days on soybean by Eaton, Orcutt and Wilson, and Orcutt and Fred, in which no effect was noted on yield or nitrogen content, and the work of Moškov and Borodulina, there appear to be no records of the influence of daylength, on nodulation. Long- and short-day varieties of *Phaseolus* responded more effectively when grown in their appropriate length of day. In view of the photoperiodic control of morphogenesis in many plants, a close study of the effect of length of day is overdue, in particular with regard to nodule number and size.

Information on the effect of temperature on nodulation is similarly sparse; little has been done since the early research of Jones and Tisdale, who applied a range of temperatures to the roots of lucerne, red clover, peas and soybeans grown in soil, maintaining the air temperature fairly uniform at between 14° and 20°C. For all species an optimal temperature of 24°C was found for nodule size and number. Plant growth was adversely affected at the higher temperatures, presumably through the effect of symbiosis; this occurred at lower temperature for peas and red clover than for lucerne and soybean. Stalder has shown that the optimal temperature for growth of *Pisum sativum* and for its nodule bacteria are the same, and that over a wide range, the infection of the root is unaffected by temperature (between 6·5° and 27°C). With red clover, on the other hand, it has been found that nodules form less readily during the winter, and this has been largely attributed to lower temperatures (Nutman).

Bach, Magee and Burris (1958) exposed the tops of Lincoln soybeans to $C^{14}O_2$, and then examined the root and nodule tissues for the distribution of C^{14} among their organic acids, amino-acids and carbohydrates, and for the changes occurring in this distribution when the plants were allowed to metabolize the radioactive material during a dark period following the initial light period. During the day, the organic acids of the roots have a higher percentage of total C^{14} than the amino-acids; the reverse is true of the nodules. At night, the percentage of total C^{14} in the organic acids of the roots decreases, but increases markedly in the nodules. The addition of sugar to sliced, excised nodules increases their fixation of N_2^{15}, due not to a prolongation of the period of N_2 fixation but rather to a continuous enhancement of fixation throughout the exposure to N_2^{15}.

It has been shown that daylength regulates both the number of the root nodules and the chlorophyll content of the leaves in the soybean (Bonnier and Sironval, 1956). An experiment has been made to discover whether the leaves are receptive organs for the control of nodule formation by daylength, and whether the action of daylength on chlorophyll content is related to its action on the formation of functional nodules (Plate 19). Transfer from long to short day or vice versa has an effect on nodulation which Sironval (1958) can explain only if the (second) leaf acts as the receptive organ for the control of nodulation by daylength. The action of daylength on chlorophyll content is found to be related in some way to its action on the formation of root nodules.

Chapter III

COMPETITION FOR LIGHT

The most important physical factors of the environment for the growth and economic production of sown crops and pastures are water, nutrients, light and temperature. In this context these are regarded as the secondary factors in crop and pasture production, since they do not necessarily govern the balance between growth and reproductive development, unless two of them, light and temperature, are operating in strictly specified intensities, degrees, qualities, sequences and alternations.

In a normal field stand of a crop or a sown or natural pasture, and certainly in the establishment of legumes and grasses under a nurse crop (Bula, Smith and Miller, 1954; Smith, Lowe, Strommen and Brooks, 1954), competition for light is a major factor in controlling the composition of the stand and so its ultimate productivity. The importance of the relationship of total leaf surface to light supply was stated by Boysen-Jensen (1943): 'in dense stands, where the total leaf surface is many times that of the surface of the soil covered, the self-shading may often result in sunlight becoming an important limiting factor' (quoted by Julén, 1952). Watson (1947) provided a quantitative basis for the relationship of leaf surface to soil surface: 'A comparison of the leaf area per plant of different species is of little interest, for these must be highly dependent on the spacing of the plants, which varies in accordance with normal agricultural practice. The measure of leaf area which is relevant to the comparison of agricultural yields, that is, of the weights of different crops produced per unit of land, is the leaf area per unit-area of land, which it is proposed to call the Leaf Area Index (L.A.I.)'.

Leaf Area Index

Watson postulated that the greatest dry matter production would occur when the maximum leaf area coincided with conditions most favourable for photosynthesis. In a later review of the physiological basis for variation in crop yields, he stated that the low efficiency of the overall utilization of incoming solar radiation by crop plants resulted in part from the long period following planting in which the L.A.I. was below 1 and much of the light penetrated to the soil surface; thus factors such as seed size, seed number per unit area and time of sowing, by influencing the early values of L.A.I., considerably affect the course of dry-matter production and yield. If L.A.I. were increased indefinitely, a stage would be reached at which the net assimilation rate would decline as a result of mutual shading of the leaves or possibly through a decrease of CO_2 concentration among the lower leaves. When values of L.A.I. are below the optimal for full utilization of incoming light energy, maximum growth cannot be achieved; at values of L.A.I. above the optimal, a reduction in growth rate may again arise due to mutual shading of leaves.

In his introduction to the volume containing the proceedings of the Third Easter School in Agricultural Science in the University of Nottingham, Milthorpe (1956 a) states: 'all aspects of agricultural production are intimately associated with the growth of leaves. Whilst this is immediately obvious with such crops as grass, cabbage or kale, it is perhaps less so with those crops, such as sugar beet or corn, of which the harvested product forms but part of the plant. But, even with these crops, the yield ultimately depends on the rate of addition of dry matter per unit area of land, i.e. on the efficiency of the photosynthetic processes and on the extent of the photosynthetic surface. Even a casual examination of agricultural writings reveals much confusion as to the relative importance of these two components of energy production with consequently much misdirected effort in plant breeding, fertilizer and other agronomic programmes. Thought still seems to be dominated largely by the rate and mechanism of the photosynthetic reactions. Yet these are relatively unimportant in determining yield compared with the effect of variations in the extent of the surface in which these reactions proceed. Further, over a fairly wide range of the environments normally experienced in agriculture, leaf growth is itself largely independent of the rate of assimilation.'

The paper to this symposium of greatest interest to agronomists relates to the studies at Rothamsted on leaf growth in relation to crop production; Watson (1956) discusses this under four heads: relative importance of leaf area as a determinant of yield; growth curve of L.A.I. and its relation to yield; effect of increasing L.A.I. on net assimilation rate, and the optimal L.A.I. for dry matter production; dependence of cereal grain yield on leaf area. Watson states: 'The material that a farmer harvests is the product of photosynthesis throughout the life of the crop; it does not represent the whole of the photosynthetic product because part is lost in respiration, and part, notably the roots, is not recovered by the harvest operations. Moreover, the economic yield may represent only a particular morphological or chemical fraction of the harvested produce, the remainder having much less or no value. Nevertheless, the problem of increasing agricultural yield is fundamentally the problem of how to increase the total annual photosynthesis per unit area of crop, so it is obvious that the size of the photosynthetic system must be one of the determinants of crop yield.'

The area of a leaf is usually assumed to be the best measure of its capacity for photosynthesis, more appropriate than leaf weight. The sum of the areas of all the leaf laminae per unit area of land, both areas being expressed in the same units—the leaf area index—is a measure of the size of the photosynthetic system. In adopting this measure, it is recognized that other parts of the plant are also capable of photosynthesis and may account for an appreciable fraction of the total production of dry matter.

Although leaf area throughout the growth period is the main determinant of the total yield of dry matter, it does not necessarily follow that the same is true of the yield of a particular organ or chemical constituent, for example, the grain yield of a cereal (Watson, *loc. cit.*). When nitrogenous fertilizer is applied to autumn-sown wheat in April, it greatly increases the leaf area index in May and June, nearly doubling it at the maximum. When the same amount of nitrogen is applied in a series of sprayings, near the time of ear emergence, in late May and early June, it causes a smaller increase in L.A.I. than the early application, and the effect does not appear until mid-June, by which time the index is rapidly decreasing. The increase in grain yield is, however, nearly equal for the two times of application (Thorne and Watson, 1955). The explanation given is that the dry matter that enters the grain is produced by photosynthesis after ear emergence; this was shown for barley by Archbold and Mukerjee and is presumed to be true also for wheat. 'The leaf area present before ear emergence makes no direct contribution to grain yield' (Watson, 1956).

After discussing these relationships further, Watson states that the conditions favouring a high yield of grain, insofar as this depends upon leaf area, appear to be: 'a high leaf area index at the time of ear emergence, slow senescence of the leaves then surviving, which implies a long interval between emergence of the ears and maturation of the crop, and the interval between ear emergence and harvest should occur in June and July. The fulfilment of these conditions probably depends particularly on the size and longevity of the flag leaf.' In these studies, senescence may play an important part. Net assimilation rate is dependent on L.A.I. in field crops of kale and sugar-beet (Watson, 1958). The index was varied experimentally by removing different fractions of the population distributed uniformly through the crop; the net assimilation rate was determined in subsequent periods of 10 to 14 days. The optimal L.A.I. for dry-matter production by sugar-beet crops probably lies near the upper limit of the current agricultural range; there is, therefore, little if any scope for increasing the dry-matter yield by further increase in the L.A.I. For heavy kale crops, the L.A.I. is already far in excess of the optimum, and it may be possible to increase the total dry-matter yield by repeated thinning or defoliation to hold the index near the optimum.

Evidence that mutual shading of leaves can account for a decrease in net assimilation rate with increase of the L.A.I. is given by changes induced in other growth attributes by the thinning treatments. Blackman and Wilson (1954) found on shading sunflowers that plants transferred from a lower to a higher light intensity have a smaller leaf area ratio after 4 or 8 days than plants held throughout in the low light intensity. The ratio of leaf area to leaf weight is also reduced by increase in light intensity. In two experiments, the relative leaf growth rate was little affected by transfer from low to high light intensity, and in a third experiment it was increased.

Light, Temperature and Leaf Production

As far as the effect of daylength on leaves is concerned, short days accelerate leaf production by long-day plants and retard it in short-day plants, but leaves of both types age more rapidly in long days. Although the total growth made during the light and dark period differs little, there are marked fluctuations in the rate of growth during these periods, the time when the maxima occur depending on the species (Bünning, 1956 a).

Although low temperatures retard all processes, differentiation of primordia appears to continue at a higher rate than does the rate of division and expansion of cells leading to growth of a leaf. After a check caused by temperature, a higher relative growth rate of leaves occurs if some leaves have expanded than if no leaves are present. The effect of conditions during germination persists long into the growing period (Milthorpe, 1956 b). The effects of light and temperature vary with species. A reduction of light intensity below full spring and summer daylight may have little effect on one group; in another, there may be a large increase in leaf surface with reduced light almost to compensation point; in a third, the effect may be intermediate. There is in general a direct curvilinear relation of net assimilation rate and an inverse relation to leaf area ratio with light intensity. A retarding effect of increasing light on leaf expansion occurs with intensities above 300 to 600 foot-candles; at lower intensities there is a positive effect. Leaf area increases with temperature up to about 25°C, but interactions occur between different levels of temperature and light (Blackman, 1956). The growth of grass is closely proportional to the total energy supplied at the surface, and also to the potential transpiration. Water becomes limiting at small values of moisture deficit; these values are smaller with low than with high nitrogen supply. The slope of the curve relating growth to incoming radiation is also influenced by the nitrogen level (Penman, 1956).

In grasses all new leaf and bud tissue arises from the apical growing point which is situated within the encircling leaf sheaths at the base of the shoot. During vegetative growth, the growing point gives rise to leaf primordia in a regular alternate sequence, and these later elongate through the action of a basal meristem to form the typical leaf sheath and blade. Once the leaf blade and sheath have fully expanded, the leaf stops growing and the next one continues to elongate. There are usually three or four expanding leaves between the growing point and the youngest fully expanded leaf.

During early germination, new leaf primordia are produced from the growing point on the main shoot only, but in the young seedling stage buds in the axils of the older leaves usually grow out to form new vegetative tillers. The number and position of these tillers vary with species and strain, and are also affected by light, temperature and nutrition. In rye-grass, for instance, tillering can begin as soon as there are three to four expanded leaves on the main shoot and a tiller can grow out as soon as the leaf above it has finished expanding. In timothy, however, tillering usually begins only at the fifth leaf stage and a tiller does not appear until the two leaves above it have expanded (Langer, 1956). The rate of leaf production, and hence of potential tiller production on the main shoot is regular and increases with temperature up to the optimum. Consequently, during early seedling growth until competition for light, water or nutrients occurs, the *total* number of leaves and the *total* number of tillers increase geometrically. A small difference in the initial rate of leaf appearance, or in the position at which the first tiller is formed can make a great difference to the total tissue production of the plant during early establishment, and hence to its competitive ability. Once a sward is established, tiller number remains fairly constant, and rate of leaf production per tiller and size of leaf are most important.

The productivity of a herbage plant or sward is greatly influenced by mineral nutrition, particularly nitrogen, but little information is available about the detailed effects of nutrition on the pattern of vegetative growth in herbage species. In the cereals, wheat and barley, Watson (1956) states that nitrogen increases both the number of tillers and the leaf area per tiller, but does not greatly influence the number of leaves per shoot; phosphorus increases both tiller number and leaf area in the early stages of growth, but hastens senescence of leaves and eventually reduces leaf area; potassium has little effect on tiller number but consistently increases leaf area and delays the senescence of leaves. These effects may also apply to the herbage grasses, since in *Lolium perenne* the addition of nitrogen increases the number of axillary buds which form tillers and also increases leaf size, but does not appear to affect the rate of leaf production per tiller (Cooper, 1951).

The influence of temperature, light intensity and defoliation on the pattern of leaf and bud development under controlled conditions has been studied by Mitchell (1953 a and b, and 1954), using short-rotation and perennial ryegrass grown under two light intensities (700 and 2,000 foot-candles) combined with two temperature regimes (55° to 45°F and 70° to 60°F). The rate of leaf appearance is similar for all the tillers on a plant and is increased at the higher light intensity or the higher temperature. In all treatments, short-rotation ryegrass produces leaves faster than S.23 perennial ryegrass, the difference being greatest when light intensity and temperature are low. The number of axillary buds which actually grow out to form tillers differ with strain and environment. Raising the light intensity or lowering the temperature, or both, increases the proportion of buds which produce tillers, especially at the basal nodes. The short-rotation ryegrass tillers more freely than the perennial under all treatments. These results from controlled conditions throw light on the difference in field behaviour between the two strains, short-rotation ryegrass being much more competitive in the first year and more quickly established than is perennial.

In later studies, Mitchell (1956) compares the vegetative growth of five temperate species, *Agrostis tenuis, Dactylis glomerata, Holcus lanatus,*

Lolium perenne and *L. perenne × multiflorum*, with that of the subtropical *Paspalum dilatatum* at a range of constant temperatures from 45° to 95°F. The optimum temperature range for the European species is 65° to 70°F, but for *Paspalum* it is much higher, 85°F. At this latter temperature *Paspalum* forms more than 25 mg of dry matter per day on the main tiller as compared to 5 to 6 mg in *Dactylis* or *Lolium*. For all species except *Paspalum* there is a wide range of temperature over which little change in rate of growth occurs.

Leaf Area Index in Pastures

Natural and sown pastures represent a type of ground cover to which the concept of leaf area index may be applied most profitably, and in which the density of stand may be controllable by appropriate agronomic measures or by grazing and cutting management. Unfortunately, Donald and Black (1958) find that few determinations are available on the L.A.I. of pastures, apart from studies made in the Grasslands Division, D.S.I.R., Palmerston North, New Zealand, and the Waite Agricultural Research Institute, Adelaide. Since it is clear that, where water and nutrient supplies are adequate, light may become the dominant factor governing the productivity of a pasture, the application of the concept of leaf area index to problems of pasture growth is of great potential value. It appears that the L.A.I. of pastures may considerably exceed that of crops, the L.A.I. of crops being in the range of 2·4 to 5·0, that of pasture mixtures or pure subterranean clover being 6·2 to 8·9.

Donald and Black explain this as follows: 'the types of plants which have been selected by man and his grazing animals for use in sown pastures are those with heavy leaf production. Successful pasture grasses, for example, are those which tiller abundantly and produce new leaf quickly after grazing. In contrast the grasses developed for grain production (the cereals) are relatively sparsely tillered and of upright habit. A second major aspect affecting maximum L.A.I. is the greater density (plants per unit area) of pastures than of crops.

'The few available measurements give but a limited account of the L.A.I. of pastures. It is likely to differ according to the species and the environment, particularly the light intensity, and hence both with locality and seasonal conditions; determinations in other centres will do much to clarify the importance of light as a factor governing production in various parts of the world. . . . There are many regions of the world in which competition for light is of little significance, more especially in the arid regions. But wherever a pasture forms a continuous canopy of foliage the study of light as a limiting factor in production and of L.A.I. as a criterion of light interception is deserving of study.'

In his earlier work in New Zealand, Brougham (1956 b) showed that the rate of growth of a pasture is related to the percentage of light intercepted by the herbage, and to leaf area, In the regrowth of a pasture composed of short-rotation ryegrass/red clover/white clover, a leaf area index (L.A.I.) of about 5 is necessary to intercept 95 per cent of the incident light; thereafter, growth is at a maximum rate, due to maximum photosynthetic activity. Since these individual species have very different growth habits, they should, when grown in pure stands, show different relationships between light perception and leaf area, and these relationships should vary with season.

Later, Brougham (1958) determined these relationships for four stands of four pasture species (short-rotation ryegrass, perennial ryegrass, timothy and white clover) and a mixed stand of short-rotation ryegrass and white clover. Two experiments were made: (a) to examine the relationship between leaf area and light interception in the regrowth of the different stands, and (b) to determine the relationship between light penetration and the angle of elevation of the sun at different stages of regrowth (to show whether critical L.A.I., or the amount of leaf required to intercept 95 per cent of the incident light at local noon, varied with season). The leaf area indices for the four species and the mixture at which 95 per cent of the incident light is intercepted about midday in midsummer are 7·1, 7·1, 6·5, 3·5 and 4·5 respectively. As the percentage of incident light penetrating through the foliage on cloudless days in summer changes considerably with time of day, due to the angle of incidence of the light, the leaf area required to intercept 95 per cent of the light shows marked seasonal differences. Midwinter values may be about one-half of midsummer values.

The importance of light as a major controlling factor in the growth of pasture species in the field has been fully recognized for some time. Brougham's results show that for maximum production per unit area it is essential that all light is utilized by photosynthetic tissue. They also illustrate that a continually changing relationship exists between light interception by the foliage of pasture and growth, being affected by stage of growth, species, and season of the year. Thus, for maximum pasture production the defoliation height and the height of herbage remaining after grazing will vary, depending on the botanical composition of the pasture and on the season.

Complete utilization of available light, and hence maximum rate of regrowth, will be obtained by a smaller amount of foliage in winter than in summer. For this reason, maximum growth during the winter will result from a management procedure where the herbage height at grazing and the amount of herbage remaining after grazing are appreciably lower than required in summer. Such a grazing procedure during the winter has the added advantage of preventing excessive herbage losses through decomposition of plant tissue under long spelling or resting (Brougham, 1956 a). Similarly, at all seasons, white clover will produce at its maximum rate under closer grazing than grass because of the higher light -intercepting capacity of white clover leaves. In mixed stands, particularly those containing species with contrasting forms of growth, the grazing procedure at different seasons of the year should be modified with changes in botanical composition. However, provided a satisfactory balance of the desired species is maintained, grazing height should be determined by reference to the light-intercepting capacity of the dominant species.

Similar studies have been made in the Waite Agricultural Research Institute, Adelaide, on the most important clover of Australia, *Trifolium subterraneum*. In earlier work on intraspecific competition, Donald (1951) showed that swards of this clover sown at a wide range of densities tend to achieve a common maximum yield, and stated that given adequate water and nutrients, pasture yields will be determined by the capacity of the sward to exploit the available light energy. Davidson (1954) later showed that with increasing density the morphology of the individual plants alters considerably. The prostrate growth habit is lost, stem development is suppressed, petioles become etiolated and elongated, and the number of leaves per plant is greatly reduced. In spite of these gross changes in the form of the individual plant, swards of different densities achieve similar leaf areas and total yields per unit area.

Davidson and Donald (1958) have examined growth and leaf area in terms of Watson's (1947) leaf area index and have also observed the effect on growth and total production of abrupt changes in leaf area brought about by defoliation (Plate 16). The design of the experiment may be summarized as follows:

Density	×	defoliation	×	replication	= 80 plots
4 levels (1, 4, 14 and 50 plants per sq. link)		4 (Aug., Sept., Oct.) and non-defoliated		4 of defoliation treatments, 8 of controls	

The results have important practical implications. 'While many aspects of sward development need to be examined or confirmed, it is clear that an understanding of the significance of leaf area and of leaf removal will enable a new approach to be made to many aspects of pasture management. The substantial reduction in total yield that may result from even light grazing when the L.A.I. is low, the potential benefits to be gained by heavy grazing when the L.A.I. is high, and the desirability of holding the L.A.I. at the optimum value for dry matter production are among the aspects which present themselves for examination in pasture management studies. Though the optimum and ceiling L.A.I. may vary greatly in different environments and with different species, and though defoliation is only one of the many components of grazing, an understanding of the significance of leaf production and removal should contribute much to effective pasture management' (Davidson and Donald, loc. cit.).

The following are some of the detailed observations made on sub-terranean clover. During the final months of the trials, the rate of dry matter production (tops) increases to a maximum when the L.A.I. is about 4 to 5, falling by about 30 per cent as the L.A.I. increases to 8·7. The rate of leaf production is greatest at L.A.I. 4 to 5, zero at L.A.I. 8·7. As climatic conditions during the growing season become more favourable, the values of the optimal L.A.I. for growth and of the ceiling L.A.I. progressively rise. Irrespective of density, all swards tend towards a common ceiling L.A.I. and yield by the end of the season.

The effect of defoliation depends on the L.A.I. at which defoliation occurs, on the value to which the L.A.I. is reduced and on current climatic conditions. If swards near the ceiling L.A.I. are defoliated, total production of dry matter is slightly increased and there is a great increase in leaf production. On the other hand, defoliation of swards from about the optimum L.A.I. to very low L.A.I. values leads to a substantial reduction in both dry matter and leaf production. Davidson and Donald suggest that all these effects depend upon the light relationships within the sward and their influence on the balance between photosynthesis and respiration.

Langer's work on the growth of the timothy plant in relation to tiller development (1957) is also relevant. It is noted that leaf area per plant rises to a maximum soon after ear emergence and then declines, largely because the loss in leaf surface sustained by the flowering tillers is not offset by a corresponding increase in the vegetative tillers. Leaf area ratio decreases at first rapidly but later more gradually, while net assimilation rate is relatively high until maximum leaf area is almost attained, but then falls continuously to negligible values by October. Relative growth rate decreased throughout the experiment. Initially the growth of the plant is largely determined by the flowering tillers in which, in close resemblance to the cereal plant, leaf area ratio and relative growth rate decline continuously. Tillers which do not flower are successively smaller in size and, because of their later origin, are exposed to less favourable environmental conditions by the time they have increased sufficiently in number to affect the growth of the plant.

Chapter IV

THE BIOCHEMISTRY OF REPRODUCTION

Promotion and Inhibition of Growth

Whereas knowledge about the initial light and dark reactions is limited to some physical aspects, 'even less is known about the subsequent reactions in plants which are physiologically and morphologically expressed as flowering, bulb and tuber formation, stem elongation, and abscission. Since the effective materials are formed in the leaves and bring about changes elsewhere in plants, they well might be hormones' (Borthwick, Hendricks and Parker, 1956).

The facts and speculations which arise in connection with the promotion and inhibition of plant growth, 'the twin themes of physiology', are reviewed by Thimann (1956). Inhibition is a universal phenomenon throughout the biological world, and inhibition and stimulation are often caused by the same substance. If a substance promotes or stimulates a process, it commonly inhibits it in higher concentrations, and generally, but not always, vice versa. Auxins promote shoot growth, but inhibit the growth of roots; at the lowest level of concentration, however, root growth is usually somewhat promoted. Lateral buds are inhibited by the concentration of auxin which stimulates the growth of their own axis. They remain inhibited while the terminal bud continues to produce auxin. As the terminal buds grow away from them, the auxin concentration becomes weakened by distance, and eventually lateral buds far down the stem begin to grow out. 'The principle that inhibition is often or usually accompanied by a change in the balance between opposing reactions seems to emerge with clarity; promotion of one reaction can be due to inhibition of another and vice versa, through the resulting removal of limiting factors, or the accumulation of reagents which previously were rate-limiting' (Thimann, *loc. cit.*).

There are several principal types of hormones in plants: (*a*) hormones controlling flowering; (*b*) the substances belonging to the vitamin B group that are necessary for root elongation; (*c*) the auxins, a group of organic acids which exert their action on many phases of growth and reproductive development; and (*d*) the wound hormones or traumatic acid, and others. The state of knowledge with regard to the first group is of primary interest in this connection.

In his review of the effect of auxin on growth, as expressed by elongation of stem and root, degree of tillering, bud development and similar reactions, Thimann (1941) states that the control of shoot growth by auxins is much more immediate than the stimulation of root elongation by the hormones of group (*b*) (see also de Ropp and Markley, 1955). The local application of auxin to almost any growing shoot causes a rapid local acceleration of growth, that is, growth is directly and immediately dependent on the available auxin; tropisms are the most striking example of this phenomenon. On a given tissue a given amount of applied auxin produces less growth in light than in the dark, an indication of the mechanism of the extreme elongation of etiolated plants; light in some way alters the sensitivity of the plant tissue.

It is possible to make the generalization that variations in shoot growth are directly and immediately referable to variations either in the rate of auxin supply or in the responsiveness to auxin. Variations in supply may have internal or external causes; as an example of the former is quoted van Overbeek's experiment on a dwarf variety of maize which differed genetically from the normal by a single gene, and which had an almost normal rate of auxin production but an increased rate of destruction. Zinc deficiency is quoted as an external cause, since the absence of this element in the nutrient solution causes a marked decrease in auxin content. Nitrogen deficiency greatly reduces growth and auxin content; reduced growth is often associated with tendency to flowering and raises the question whether 'flowering is in some way opposed by auxin supply'. Dostal and Hošek (1937) have shown that application of synthetic auxin to the stems causes flower buds to revert to vegetative shoot buds. Again Thimann raises a question: 'Perhaps the old association of flowering with high carbon/nitrogen ratios may receive its explanation along these lines.'

The response to auxin differs for different organs and different tissues within the same plant. While the elongation of shoots is in general promoted through cell enlargement, under certain conditions auxin may stimulate the cambium to divide and thus produce extra xylem; it may induce the cells of the cortical parenchyma, the cambium or the pericycle to undergo rapid division and form root initials, a procedure which is the basis of the hormonal treatment of cuttings. The formation of buds, and especially lateral buds, is powerfully inhibited by auxin. Dwarf plants become bushes or supertillering when the terminal bud is defective in supplying auxin, and thus loses its power of inhibiting lateral bud formation and growth. Thimann discusses the evidence brought forward by Snow and others to explain this phenomenon, but concludes that none of it is so far decisive. It is suggested that it is possible that the optimal concentration of auxin in buds may be very low, and that even physiological concentrations of auxin (those normally present in the plant) may be within the inhibiting range. Very low concentrations may conceivably promote bud growth, and Thimann states that there is good evidence that they do.

Response to Temperature

In their work at the Research Institute of Plant Physiology, London, on the reversibility of vernalization, Purvis and Gregory (1937) postulated the existence of a flower-forming substance, the effect of which on the labile primordia varies according to the factors to which the plant is exposed. At that time they considered the following facts to be established: (a) the hypothetical substance is not preformed in the endosperm and transferred to the embryo, as the embryo isolated from the seed behaves similarly; (b) the change can be reversed by high temperature; (c) an oxidative reaction is involved in the formation of the substance, as anaerobic conditions completely inhibit its production during vernalization of winter rye and partially so in spring rye. It appears possible that during vernalization some precursor of a 'flower-forming' substance accumulates in the embryo. This substance may be supposed to be translocated to and accumulated in all growing points of the shoot, and when a critical concentration is reached induces flower initiation. The increasing rate of formation of primordia indicates that the substance increases autocatalytically. In spring rye about 2 weeks at normal summer temperatures after germination suffice to reach the critical level, while in unvernalized winter rye somewhat less than 6 weeks are required.

During vernalization the 'flower-forming' substance or its precursor is assumed to increase in concentration so that the critical level is reached earlier; thus spikelet initiation sets in earlier in the sequence of labile primordia, and a progressive reduction in leaf number occurs, finally reaching the minimum of seven characteristic of spring rye. The progressive effect of longer duration of low-temperature vernalization can formally be accounted for on these lines.

'The relations to daylength are more difficult to formulate. The outstanding problem here is related to the fact that in both spring and winter rye in continuous short days a maximum leaf number is found, which is approximately constant and independent of temperature of germination. In spring rye the flower-forming substance is already present in high concentration, but only in long days do the early members of the series of labile primordia form spikelets. It appears, therefore, that two stages are involved in the process. A precursor depends for its formation on a genetic factor in spring rye and on low temperature of germination in winter rye. This precursor accumulates in all the growing points, increasing autocatalytically. A second stage in the process involves reactions depending on daylength.'

The highly complex nature of this research and the hypotheses based thereon may be seen from Melchers' (1954 b) review of the mechanics of vernalization presented to the 8th International Botanical Congress in Paris. It was recalled that the existence of the requirement for low temperature (vernalization), its nature (facultative in winter annuals, obligate in biennial herbs), and the optimal temperature of vernalization are determined by the genotype of the plant in question. It is necessary to appreciate the following facts to understand the mechanics of vernalization.

(1) It is sufficient to vernalize the apical meristem from which the flower primordium will develop later, after a longer or shorter period of production of vegetative organs.

(2) A certain amount of cell activity is necessary at the time of the temperature treatment; vernalization of inactive tissue (dry or inadequately soaked seed) is not possible.

(3) If treatment extends over a long period, the optimal vernalization temperature becomes lower.

(4) High temperatures following immediately upon low temperature treatment cancel the effect of vernalization (= devernalization).

(5) Low temperature treatment after devernalization restores vernalization (revernalization).

The apparently paradoxical fact that the processes leading to flower initiation can be accelerated by low temperatures might best be explained by a combination of several processes with different temperature coefficients:

$$\text{preliminary stage} \xrightarrow{\text{I}} \text{intermediate product} \xrightarrow{\text{II}} \text{final product}$$
$$\downarrow \text{III}$$

If the temperature coefficients of processes I, II and III have the following relative values: Q_{10} III > Q_{10} II $\geqq$ Q_{10} I, the final product of the overall process can be obtained only slowly, and at relatively low temperatures. At higher temperatures the speed of processes I and II is greater than at lower temperatures, but the rate of process III increases to such an extent that less and less 'final product' is obtained, and none at all as from a certain temperature. This is because the intermediate product, the basis for process II, is eliminated immediately, i.e. it is thermolabile.

Purvis and Gregory (1952) have given a similar interpretation: (see however page 91)

$$A \rightleftarrows A' \rightarrow B$$

calling the preliminary stage A, the intermediate product A', and the final product B. Experiments by Friend on winter rye and Napp-Zinn (1953) on a winter annual strain of *Arabidopsis thaliana* seem to contradict the more specific assumption made by Purvis and Gregory (as compared with Lang and Melchers, 1947) that the intermediate product A' reverts to the preliminary stage A with higher temperature; high temperature treatment prior to vernalization slows down flower formation. The experiments of Napp-Zinn make it necessary to assume the existence of further partial processes:

(1) the effect of vernalization increases with increasing duration of treatment (in accordance with findings on other plants);

(2) devernalization effected by exposure to 30°C for 5 days is complete, whatever the length of the vernalization immediately preceding;

(3) the effect of uniform revernalization treatment (30 days at $+2$°C) after complete devernalization is influenced by the length of the original vernalization; and

(4) high temperature prior to vernalization retards flower initiation.

These results are expressed in the following formula:

$$A \rightarrow A_1 \rightarrow A_2 \rightarrow A' \rightarrow B$$
$$\downarrow \qquad\quad \downarrow$$
$$X \qquad\quad Y$$

One may assume that the formation of a labile intermediate product (A_1) from a preliminary stage A is not reversible at higher temperatures, but leads to the destruction of A_1 in a process $A_1 \rightarrow X$. However, the actual devernalization (following vernalization) involves a second labile intermediate product A', the same as that suggested by Lang and Melchers and Purvis and Gregory. Process $A' \rightarrow Y$ has much higher temperature coefficients than processes $A_2 \rightarrow A'$ and $A' \rightarrow B$. The stable intermediate product A_2 is postulated because it provides the simplest explanation for certain experimental results: the longer vernalization lasts, the more A_2 can be formed. The fact that this store of A_2 has an effect only after revernalization, but not yet after devernalization, can, according to Melchers, be explained by the higher temperature coefficient of process $A' \rightarrow Y$ compared with that of process $A_2 \rightarrow A'$. This would mean that a possible surplus of A_2 can have no effect at medium temperatures (20°C). Napp-Zinn explains his results by assuming a different process from A or A_1 to B at higher temperatures, which would by-pass A_2. Melchers believes that it is not necessary to postulate an exception, and that all results can be explained by different temperature coefficients of the processes concerned, taking into account that the coefficient itself may vary in different temperature ranges.

Although our knowledge of the physiological and chemical nature of these hypothetical processes is not by any means complete, there is direct (Gregory and Purvis) and indirect (Chouard and Poignant) evidence that the vernalization processes require oxygen. High temperatures have a devernalizing effect, even under anaerobic conditions (Gregory and Purvis). A comparison of the absorption of O_2 and the release of CO_2 by summer and winter strains under vernalizing and non-vernalizing conditions in experiments with rye and *Arabidopsis* (Napp-Zinn, 1954) has not shown any clear correlation between vernalization and gaseous exchange; however, an interesting parallelism between gaseous exchange and the 'lag period' discovered by Purvis in the vernalization of excised embryos was detected. Although the experiments on gaseous exchange do not yet permit of a physiologico-chemical explanation, they do, according to Melchers, encourage a search for processes with different temperature coefficients, especially in the field of enzyme chemistry. An important method of shedding light on the mechanics of vernalization is the substitution of other external influences for the low temperatures. Treatment with enzyme toxins, mainly designed to inhibit the processes with high temperature coefficients, has not yet given any positive results.

The biennial strain of *Hyoscyamus*, which generally requires low temperatures, can be 'vernalized' without cold treatment: the growing points of the biennial strain can be induced by grafting with the annual strain, which does not require low temperatures, or with vernalized plants of the biennial strain. The final product of vernalization, or even one following the final product, is probably transmitted from the cutting to the root-stock. Purvis and Gregory (1953) produced a positive, although slight, effect on unvernalized rye embryos by means of a chloroform extract of vernalized rye embryos, but do not specify which product of the chain was contained in the active extract.

Finally, Melchers (1954 a) draws attention to an aspect of the research on the processes of vernalization. Both the biennial and annual strains of *Hyscyamus niger* are long-day plants. If completely vernalized plants are maintained under short days they will not flower, but at about 20°C the growing point continuously produces leaves. If the plants are transferred to long days after 100 days, flower initiation is not retarded as compared with controls coming direct from vernalization (Lang and Melchers, 1947). Since, on the other hand, it is known that vernalization occurs in the growing point, it may be thought that the final condition of vernalization, once it has been created in the growing point, is constantly multiplied there. Friend and Gregory (1953) also conclude that the final product of vernalization *B*, once it exists, is multiplied by autocatalysis. If incompletely vernalized winter rye grains are kept at 20° to 25°C for a short time, flowering is retarded; if they are maintained for a longer period at this temperature, which in itself should be devernalizing, flower initiation is accelerated. The best explanation seems to be a multiplication of *B* by autocatalysis, favoured by higher temperatures. These are indications but not conclusive evidence for the assumption that the final product of the vernalization processes is a substance which increases by autocatalysis. Current attempts made by H. G. Aach to detect such a substance among the cytoplasma-proteids by serological and electro-chemical methods have so far been unsuccessful.

Gregory and Purvis have produced an extension of their formal scheme noted above to account for the relation between the vernalization and photoperiodic reactions in the development of the rye plant:

$$A \rightleftarrows A' \rightarrow B \rightleftarrows C \rightarrow D \rightarrow$$
$$\downarrow$$
$$E$$

The interpretation of this formula is given in Gott, Gregory and Purvis (1955). The reactions *A* to *B* are related to temperature effects during the vernalization treatment; *A* is the precursor of the vernalization 'substance'; *A'* is a thermolabile intermediate which as vernalization progresses is converted to a thermostable product *B*. In the embryo of spring rye B is already present; its formation is determined by a genetic factor and is independent of the action of low temperature. In both spring and winter rye B is already present. In both spring and winter rye B is assumed to increase autocatalytically. All development beyond B is mediated by photoperiodic reactions.

Reaction $B \rightleftarrows C$. This leads to the production of the precursor of a flower-initiating substance. This reaction is assumed to progress more rapidly in short than in long days. By an alternative path B can be diverted to the formation of E, which is not concerned in flower initiation but may be a leaf-promoting substance. The reason for assuming that the reaction $B \rightleftarrows C$ is reversible derives from the inductive effect of short days given during the first 6 to 8 weeks' growth of unvernalized winter rye. This reaction $B \rightarrow C$ progresses most rapidly in darkness and is partially inhibited by light. Owing to the reversible nature of the reaction, B and C tend to reach an equilibrium. If therefore the further reaction $C \rightarrow D$ is prevented, both C and B are depleted by the reaction $B \rightarrow E$. That the reaction $B \rightleftarrows C$ is not completely arrested by light is deduced from the fact that even when grown in continuous light unvernalized winter rye proceeds to flower initiation. Nevertheless, that photo-induction of unvernalized winter rye is possible indicates that in the stage preceding flower initiation unvernalized winter rye behaves like a short-day plant. This is confirmed by the effect of interrupting the dark period at its mid-point by exposure to light which prevents photoperiodic induction. Unvernalized winter rye thus behaves like a facultative short-day plant.

Reaction $C \rightarrow D$. The stage C is the substrate for a further reaction $C \rightarrow D$ which proceeds only in light and is irreversible. C is responsible for early stages in flower initiation. The reaction $C \rightarrow D$ may be assumed to take place in the 'labile primordia' and as D accumulates to a threshold value the process of flower initiation becomes manifest by the production of 'double ridges' and the development of the spikelet primordium in the axil of the bract. For a time, therefore, both C and D must be present, but the faster the reaction $C \rightarrow D$ proceeds the higher the relative amount of D will become. As the development of the spikelet primordium advances the bract primordium is gradually obliterated (Fig. 16) and in the mature ear is found only as a mere vestige in the basal regions. In the labile or 'physiologically double' primordia both C and D are present and if the accumulation of D fails to reach the threshold value the primordium remains a 'simple ridge'. Owing to the reversible reaction $B \rightleftarrows C$ and the side reaction $B \rightarrow E$, short-day conditions, which

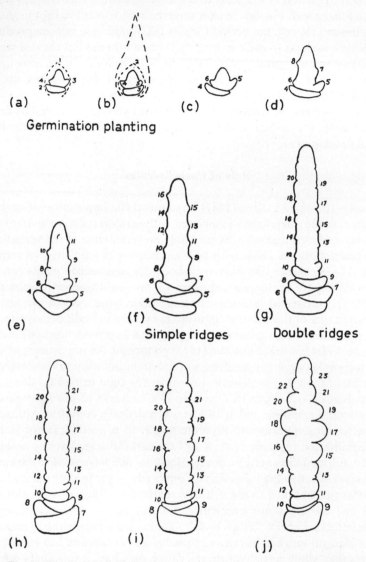

Germination planting

Simple ridges   Double ridges

Fig. 16. Flower primordia in winter rye. Semidiagrammatic representation of apex of main shoot before and after flower initiation. Primordia are numbered in serial order (Gott, Gregory and Purvis, 1955).

hinder the reaction $C \rightarrow D$, lead to the development of the 'simple ridge' into a foliage leaf. For this reason unvernalized winter rye kept in short days beyond the optimal period for short-day induction goes on producing leaves, whereas transfer to long days or continuous light at this stage results in spikelet production. The reactions beyond D are also light dependent and result in further development of floral organs up to complete spikelet formation.

The photoperiodic reactions thus comprise two stages; the first leading to initiation, the second to the production of double ridges and further floral development.

Role of Carbohydrates

Purvis (1947) and Claes (1947) have noted the importance of carbohydrates in the phenomena associated with vernalization; in winter rye, Purvis concluded that sugar is probably an accelerator of the vernalization reaction, but is unlikely to be the precursor of the active substance itself. Having shown that fully vernalized *Chrysanthemum* plants can be devernalized by prolonged exposure to low light intensity, Schwabe (1955) was interested in discovering the underlying mechanism; either of two results of the reduced light intensity were thought perhaps to be involved: carbohydrate starvation, or changes in growth hormone metabolism. In later work, Schwabe (1957) confirmed the importance of the interaction between temperature and low light intensity in the devernalization of the *Chrysanthemum*. Low-intensity light caused no devernalization at or just above 18°C, but at 23°C 4 weeks of low light gave a considerable response, and at 28°C it was practically complete. Although these results implicate carbohydrate supply as a possible factor in the devernalization reaction, lowering of the carbohydrate level by defoliation in full light did not cause devernalization, nor was complete darkness any more effective than dim light. Conversely, sugar feeding during low-light treatment failed to prevent devernalization. Rates of stem elongation and leaf expansion confirmed that substantial amounts of sugar were in fact taken up. Return to full light caused a rapid drop in rates of stem elongation while increasing those of leaf expansion. Schwabe concludes that, while carbohydrate starvation may have a subsidiary effect, it does not appear to be the main factor involved in low-light intensity devernalization. The vernalization of etiolated plants and the revernalization of devernalized plants also suggest that carbohydrate status is not the dominant factor in the vernalization reaction itself.

BIOCHEMISTRY OF REPRODUCTION

Metabolic Activity and Vernalization

It has been shown that the changes which are directly caused by chilling and which are decisive for vernalization are localized in the activated meristematic cells of the embryo or the growing point; for example, Purvis (1940) succeeded in vernalizing fragments of embryos of Petkus winter rye which consisted essentially only of the growing points. It has also been shown that the exchanges between the aleurone layer, the endosperm and the embryo which occur during swelling enhance the effect of vernalization or compensate for the delays observed in embryos which had been isolated in the dry state and then vernalized (Purvis, 1948). Augsten (1956) has been particularly interested in the distribution of enzymes within whole caryopsides.

Richter, Rankan and Pekker (1933, ref. in Borriss, 1952) found that amylase activity in the caryopsides of winter wheat increases with longer treatment without any striking extremes, while two characteristic peaks of catalase activity occur, on the 20th and 25th day of cold treatment respectively. Demkowskii (1932, ref. in Borriss, 1952) found the maximum effect of amylase activity in winter wheat on the 25th day of the cold treatment and Augsten (*loc. cit.*) obtained similar results with vernalized spring barley. The latter concludes, largely on the basis of the literature, that cold treatment is associated with greater intensity of numerous metabolic processes, leading to the activation of enzymes and of respiration rate. Some physiological processes become intensified increasingly throughout the cold treatment (activity of catalase and phosphatase and respiration) while others decline or remain stationary after the 15th day (activity of amylase and dehydrase). The sugar level of the caryopsides was also found to increase as treatment progresses.

Treated grain subsequently stored or dried under various conditions showed a continued increase in metabolic processes, in spite of the fall in moisture content. These processes decline again later, but their values remain higher than in cold-treated grain tested immediately, even when the caryopsides have again achieved the moisture content of normal seed. During the growth of the seedlings, the activity of the enzymes being studied follows the time pattern of the controls, but in general greater enzymatic activity is always found in the treated plants in the early stages. While this ratio persists in the later stages for amylase, phosphatase and dehydrase, the activity curves for catalase are higher in the controls.

Enzymatic activity in older plants is largely dependent upon stage of development and environmental conditions. Generally the enzyme ratio found in coleoptiles and primary leaves is also found in the leaves and stems of treated and untreated specimens up to the time of heading. Later there are considerable fluctuations in enzymatic activity, with at times marked shifts in ratios as between vernalized plants and controls. The processes in maturing caryopsides are greatly reduced with increasing maturity in both vernalized and control plants. In the mature grains of the treated specimens, respiration is lower, sugar content and activity of amylase, catalase and phosphatase higher than in the controls, while the activity ratio for dehydrase shifts in favour of the controls. In Augsten's work on the possible connections between metabolic processes and vernalization, a distinction is made between primary effects caused by low temperatures, which are possibly connected with the vernalization process, and those phenomena which are caused mainly by changes in the timing of development.

Evidence of Existence of Active Substance

Progress in the isolation of the active compounds concerned in the transition from a vegetative to a reproductive condition and on to flowering is so far blocked by the complete absence of adequate methods of assay. Since transfer of the stimuli has so far required contact of living tissue, as in grafting, the effective materials might not be very simple, and could be protein (Borthwick, Hendricks and Parker, 1956). Hypothetical substances which have been suggested as being concerned in the control of flowering include florigen (Čaǐlahjan, 1937), vernalin (Melchers, 1939; Melchers and Lang, 1941), metaplasm (Harder and Bode, 1943) and the 'flowering substance' of Struckmeyer (1950) which it was said can be extracted from leaves of *Xanthium* and applied as a spray to induce flower formation.

In his discussion of the concept of a rigid sequence of phases in the progress of a plant towards reproduction, Melchers (1954 b) states that it is necessary to acquire a thorough knowledge of the 'inneren Bedingungen' of Klebs, which have come to be regarded as the sequence of biochemical reactions leading from the gene to the character. It should be asked whether the same internal processes do not perhaps occur without chilling in annuals with low-temperature requirements as are induced by chilling of the low-temperature biennials. Plants having low-temperature requirements or those with photoperiodic reactions with regard to flowering are of special interest because they represent

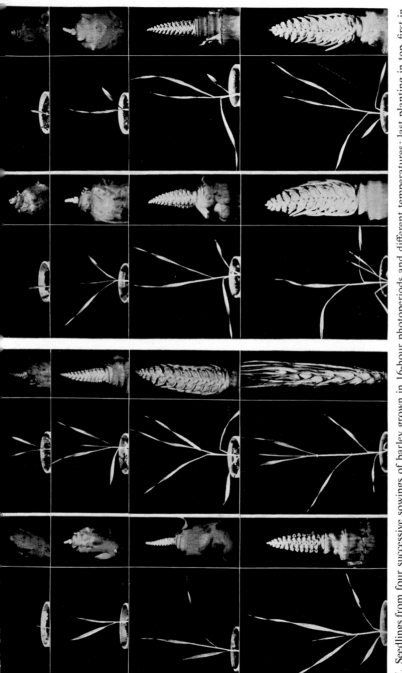

7. Seedlings from four successive sowings of barley grown in 16-hour photoperiods and different temperatures; last planting in top, first in bottom row. Enlargement of terminals shown at right of seedlings from which dissected. Photo: U.S. Department of Agriculture

8. The effects of photoperiod may be localized. The half of each plant which is blooming received a relatively long photoperiod each day, the other a short one of but 10 hours. Photo: Bureau of Plant Industry, Soils and Agricultural Engineering, U.S. Department of Agriculture

genotypes which need specific external factors to free blockages in the chain of processes leading to the determination of flower primordia. Their analysis will probably make it easier to recognize the 'normal' development of these internal processes than an attempt at a 'direct'

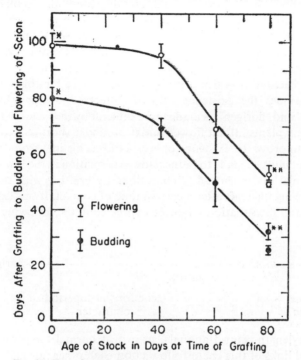

Fig. 17. Transfer of flowering stimulus from stock to scion in grafted sunflower plants. Times to budding and flowering of scions as a function of age of stocks at time of grafting. Means ± standard deviations of means are indicated. *Days to budding and flowering of normal green plants growing in greenhouse. **Green grafts. Data from albino grafts used for all other points (Haberman and Wallace, 1958).

discovery of this development. A change of certain 'block' mutants in the analysis of different biosyntheses has been successful in *Neurospora* and bacteria.

It has been possible to induce rapid flower initiation without chilling in low-temperature plants by grafting with strains not requiring such temperatures. On the other hand, it is also possible to induce flower formation in apical meristems of short-day plants under long-day conditions by grafting leaves of long-day plants. Melchers states that it is very likely that the 'hormones', the existence of which these experiments would seem to indicate, are not identical, since it is possible to induce flowering under both short-day and long-day conditions in plants of the biennial *Hyoscyamus niger* which does require low temperatures, by grafting with the short-day plant, *Nicotiana tabacum* 'Maryland Mammoth', which does not require low temperatures. Conversely, leaves of unvernalized biennial *Hyoscyamus* cannot be used as donors of photoperiodic reaction in grafting trials. The cross test for this hypothesis, which assumes the existence of two different flowering hormones, 'vernalin' and 'florigen', is made more difficult by the fact that the leaves of long-day plants inhibit flower initiation under short-day conditions. In order to prove the existence of 'vernalin' as distinct from 'florigen', an attempt must be made to induce flower formation in the low-temperature biennial under short-day conditions by grafting with the annual and removing the graft after a certain time of contact. If this experiment is successful, the situation might be expressed in the following diagram (Melchers, 1954 b).

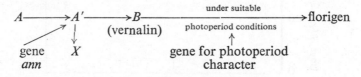

For daylength-neutral annuals, grown at normal temperatures, the individual links of this chain follow upon each other normally. In low-temperature plants, i.e. those which have gene *ann* + instead of *ann*, the intermediate product A' decomposes into X at normal temperatures which are optimal for growth; the 'protective' effect of gene *ann* is lacking; B (vernalin) cannot be produced, which also precludes the formation of 'florigen'. According to the presence of different genes for photoperiodic behaviour, florigen is formed from available vernalin, either only under short-day, or only under long-day conditions, or independent of daylength. Processes determined by other genes can of course intervene in this sequence or can add further links to the chain. After all, there are not only annuals and biennials, but also perennials and plants flowering in very particular rhythms (Melchers, 1954 b).

The grafting of scions of the genetically early Massey pea on stocks of the genetically late Telephone variety leads to flowering at a higher node

(Paton and Barber,1955). In reciprocal grafts, the scions of the late variety flower at an earlier (lower) node. Grafting of scions to stocks of the same variety has no effect with Massey scions, but leads to flowering at a lower node in the Telephone scions. Removal of cotyledons 3 to 7 days after germination has no effect on Massey, but leads to earlier flowering in Telephone. Paton and Barber assume that the genetically later variety produces a flower inhibitor or delaying substance which can pass a graft union and alter the flowering behaviour of genetically earlier scions.

Lang (1956 a), however, suggests a different interpretation on the basis of work by Haupt (1955, ref. in Lang, 1956 a) on *Pisum*. Haupt showed that all treatments which have an adverse and temporary effect on vegetative growth, such as the repeated taking of cuttings or grafting on soybean, after which growth is not resumed for some considerable time, lead to the appearance of the first flower on an earlier node. This is apparently not genuine promotion of flowering but rather a shift in balance between the processes responsible for growth and the initiation of flowering. Lang considers that the results of Paton and Barber might just as well be explained by the existence of a flower-promoting substance.

Oehlkers (1955, ref. in Lang, 1956 a) found that the flower-promoting substance is distributed unevenly over the leaf in unifoliate species and inter-specific hybrids of *Streptocarpus*, which form flowers after exposure to low temperature. When parts of the leaves of cold-treated plants are cultivated as cuttings, those taken from the outer parts produce vegetative plants which do not flower without further cold-treatment, those from intermediate parts generally give plants which flower without further cold-treatment, and those from the base, closest to the inflorescence axis of the mother plant, form inflorescences directly. There is thus a positive gradient of flowering substance from the peripheral regions towards the base of the inflorescence axis.

Movement of Hormones within Plants

Čaïlahjan (1940) investigated the way in which his hypothetical flower-promoting hormones move along the leaves, stems and roots of *Perilla* (see also Zeevart, 1958). Hormones which are formed in leaves exposed to a reduced period of daylight are able to pass from them to the flowering shoots not only along the veins but by way of the leaf parenchyma. When a main vein of a leaf is cut, only the nutrients which are required for the vegetative growth of shoots and the formation of dry matter are hindered in their passage from the leaves where they are formed.

In the experiments with stems, the top 10 cm was cut off and a strip from the remaining lower part of the stem was split downwards to the base. The shoots on the main part of the split stem were cut off, while the leaves were retained, those on some plants being exposed during the whole experiment to a full, those on others to a reduced, period of daylight. From the strip of stem split away, retaining some of the cortical and woody tissues, all but a few small leaves were cut off, only the shoots being left intact. Some of the strips were bent over and rooted in a separate pot, but the connection with the parent plant was maintained. Whether the shoots had been rooted or not, it was observed that they were able to form flowers, instead of vegetative growth, only when the leaves on the main part of the stem had been exposed to a reduced period of daylight.

The tops of some plants were not cut off, but a strip was split downwards, a large leaf left intact near the top of it, and all other leaves and shoots lower down the strip removed. As before, some of the leaves were exposed to long, others to short, periods of daylight, while the main part of the stem, all but the smallest leaves on which were removed and only the shoots retained, was always exposed to a full period of daylight. Some of the strips were rooted in separate pots.

It was observed that a flowering shoot was produced from the bud nearest to the leaf exposed to short periods of daylight, and others followed in succession down the strip and up the main part of the stem. When one of two shoots lying nearer to the leaf was cut off, the onset of flowering in the shoot next to it further away was hastened. The quantity of hormones required to induce flowering in a given number of shoots was determined by the leaf area and the amount of exposure to daylight. A lack of the hormone resulted in a part or all of the shoots being vegetative.

The purpose of the experiment with roots was to discover whether the hormones produced in the leaves could pass by way only of the roots to the axillary shoots and induce them to flower. The top of each plant was cut off and the stems split longitudinally downwards until the only connection between the two halves of the plant was the unsplit lower portion of its main root. The root systems of some of the plants were immersed in a nutrient solution; those of others were left suspended in somewhat damp air inside empty flasks. Three large leaves were retained and the shoots cut off on one half of each plant, while the shoots were retained and all but a few small leaves cut off on the other. With the exception of the control plants which were exposed to a full period of daylight, the three large leaves on one half of each split stem were exposed only for a short period of daylight. The hormones formed by the leaves on one half of the stem were able after some delay to pass down that half stem, by way of the main root and up the other half stem where they induced flowering. The rate of passage was the same whether the roots were in solution or in the air.

Lang (1956 a) comments on the results of experiments by Imamura and Takimoto (1955, ref. in Lang, 1956 a) on the determination of the speed of translocation of the flowering impulse (flowering hormone). By decapitating the epicotyl of *Pharbitis nil*, plants with two shoots are obtained. In the experimental plants (EP), all leaves and buds were removed except the second leaf on one shoot and the corresponding axillary bud on the other. The leaf serves as donor, the bud develops into the recipient shoot. The experimental plants are given 5 short days immediately after preparation. In several other groups of plants, the 'time-recording plants' (TRP), one leaf with its own axillary bud is left, corresponding to the donor leaf on the experimental plants. Some of the time-recording plants are placed under short-day conditions immediately after preparation (TRP-0), others only after one, two or more days (TRP-1, TRP-2, etc.). Records were made of the node of the recipient shoot on which the first flower appears. One experiment gave the following results:

Group	First flower after . . . nodes (average)
EP	4·23
TRP-0	2·53
TRP-1	3·73
TRP-2	5·14

In the experimental plants, the flowering impulse reached the recipient shoot later than in TRP-0 and TRP-1, but earlier than in TRP-2. It is possible to determine by interpolation when induction of the time-recording plants would have had to begin in order to induce them to form flower primordia at exactly the same time as the experimental plants; this time was found to be 32·5 hours. The additional distance to the recipient shoot which the impulse had to cover in the experimental plants, as compared with the time-recording plants, being 121·9 mm, the speed of translocation is 121·9 divided by 32·5, i.e. 3·8 mm/hour. The figures obtained in several experiments lie between 2·6 and 3·8 mm/hour, or about 6 to 9 cm in 24 hours. Čaĭlahjan (1940) obtained figures for the shoot of *Perilla* of about 2 cm in 24 hours. The coincidence between these figures is remarkable. The same values (2·4 to 2·8 mm/hour) were found in grafted plants after union (Imamura and Takimoto, 1956, ref. in Lang, 1956 a). The graft, therefore, apparently, does not impede translocation. All these calculations must, of course, be based on the assumption that the speed of translocation is the same in the shoot and the petiole, and also in both the acropetal and basipetal directions.

Crafts (1951) has reviewed the literature on the movement of hormones, viruses, indicators and assimilates in plants. There appears to be doubt whether the hormone itself, its degradation products, or its stimulus is actually translocated, since most reports of hormone movement are based on plant response.

Extraction of Florigen

Roberts (1951) has reported that the first successful extraction and subsequent flower induction of the short-day plant, *Xanthium echinatum*, was achieved in December 1946, and that by varying the conditions of extraction six crystalline substances have since been obtained. Partial characterization indicates that they are mineral salts of fatty acids. Poor solubility makes identification and the determination of physiological activity slow.

The following procedure is used to obtain the small, colourless, isotropic, granular particles of florigen. Soak a small sample of fresh or frozen leaves taken from plants in flower in the least practicable amount of a highly refined, odorless insecticide base such as Shell Dispersol, for an hour or longer. This solvent is a non-aromatic oil fraction recovered from kerosene and having an IBP of 387°F and an FBP of 485°F. Squeeze out the solvent, remove and discard the aqueous phase, if any is present, and filter. A yellowish pigment which seems not to interfere with florigen extraction or activity is present in the extract from most species. Deep freezing at 0°F or below is used to initiate separation of the particles. This progresses slowly for several hours or even days. The particles in extracts from some plants, for example, white sweet clover or sweet corn, dissolve at room temperatures. The florigen particles are recovered by filtering or decanting, and evaporating the remaining solvent at a temperature below 60°C.

The particles are highly insoluble in such solvents as water, alcohol, acetone, xylol, benzol, ether, ethylacetate, petroleum ether, ethanolamine, polyethylene, glycol and dioxane. Roberts states that this may explain why attempts by numerous workers to obtain florigen have been unsuccessful. The particles are poorly soluble in Dispersol. Consequently, repeated extractions of the leaves yield added amounts of particles.

Inhibitors of Flowering

Schwabe (1956) has produced evidence for a flowering inhibitor which arises in *Kalanchoë blossfeldiana* when grown in long days. In reviewing the literature, he states that nearly all theories on the mechanism of photoperiodic reactions are concerned with the effects of light and dark treatments during a single photoperiodic cycle (Gregory, 1948; Hamner, 1940; Harder and Bode, 1943; Bünning, 1950) and it is only a stable end product or flower hormone which is considered to accumulate. The unfavourable effect of non-inductive cycles has been envisaged as due to the destruction during each cycle of some intermediate substance which in short-day plants is usually postulated as being photolabile. Lang has, however, suggested the existence of inhibitory effects for the long-day plant, *Hyoscyamus niger*, kept in short-day, the annual variety of which can be made to flower under these conditions by defoliation. Wareing (1954) has interpreted the effect of light breaks in long dark periods by suggesting that an inhibitor is formed. Wareing and Carr (1951–4) modify Gregory's hypothetical scheme by postulating the interaction of two substances under unfavourable conditions. Hypotheses of flowering based on auxin have generally regarded growth substances as inhibitors of flowering (Bonner and Bandurski, 1952).

In Schwabe's experiments, periods of short-day treatment were interrupted by intercalated long days or light breaks during long dark periods. The effects of 24-hour dark periods preceding and following such intercalated long days were also investigated. The experiments supply positive evidence of the inhibitory effect of long days extending well outside the cycle in which such conditions are given, affecting the product either of preceding or succeeding inductive cycles.

Single long days intercalated between numbers of short days have a positive inhibitory effect on flower initiation and are not merely ineffective. The inhibitory effect expressed as the number of inductive cycles annulled is approximately additive, provided the long days are interspersed with short days, but not if several long days are given consecutively. On the average 1 long day is capable of annulling the flower-promoting effect of about 1·5 to 2 short days. In a first approximation, flower numbers in *Kalanchoë* increase exponentially with the number of inductive cycles given—up to at least 12 short days; the inhibitory effect of long days interspersed with short days also fits an exponential curve; i.e. the inhibition is roughly proportional to the amount of previous photoperiodic induction. A light break of as little as 30 seconds' duration given in the middle of a long dark period is as inhibitory as a long day. If followed by a long dark period the inhibition of an intercalated long day is almost completely neutralized; a long dark period preceding it has no such effect. Schwabe interprets these results as being due to the interaction of a flowering inhibitor with a reaction leading to flowering, and describes a mechanism involving competitive inhibition of an adaptively formed enzyme as a possible example of the kind of reaction which could account for the results obtained.

In their experiments on grafting between genetically early and late varieties of garden peas, Paton and Barber (1955) concluded that the dominant *Sn* gene causing late flowering is responsible for the production of a substance delaying flowering. This inhibitor passes into the plumule from the cotyledons over a period from 10 to 14 days after germination. Cuttings taken soon after germination usually flower at a lower node than those taken later, or than whole plants. This effect is most marked in short days, since the delay in flowering produced by the *Sn* gene is the greater the shorter the photoperiod.

Numerous attempts using cuttings have been made by Sprent and Barber (1957) to isolate the inhibitor hormone; when young cuttings were soaked in weak solutions of a variety of chemical substances, it was noted that controls soaked in water flower at a lower node than those planted directly in the soil. This effect was investigated further in a factorial experiment combining cuttings of the late variety, Greenfeast, taken 6, 11, 15 and 20 days after germination and soaked in water for 0, 4, 8, 12 or 16 days before planting into the soil. The experiment was carried out in summer under the natural photoperiod of Hobart, Tasmania (about 16 hours). The leaching of young cuttings leads to flowering at a lower node, and the effect is greatest if the cutting are taken 6 to 11 days after germination, when two to four internodes are fully expanded. Sprent and Barber state that these results are best explained by the leaching out of a flower-inhibitor which is still in a labile phase following transport from the cotyledons. After 15 to 20 days from germination, the inhibitor becomes incorporated into the cytoplasm and can no longer be removed. At this stage soaking in water has no

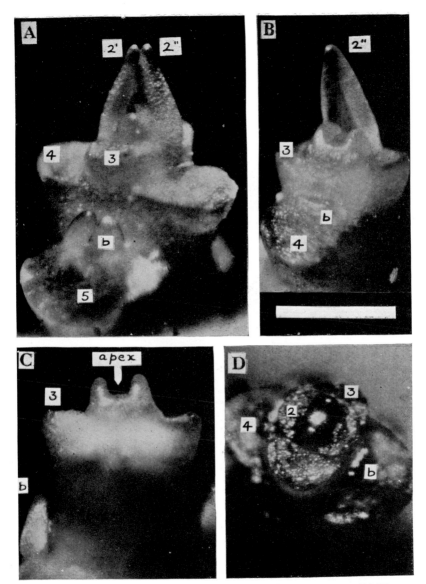

9. Dissection of vegetative shoot of a dicotyledon (privet). (See p. 49.) Photo: B. C. Sharman. The scale below B represents 0·5 mm. (1/50 inch approx.)

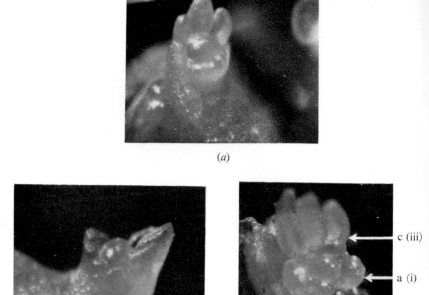

10. Flower initiation in subterranean clover (Aitken, 1955). (*a*, *b*) Vegetative shoot ape:
Two angles showing domed-shaped growing point and the two youngest leaf primordi:
(*c*) Shoot apex in flowering state: (i) growing point; (ii) youngest flower cluster prin
ordium; (iii) flower cluster primordium with floret primordium

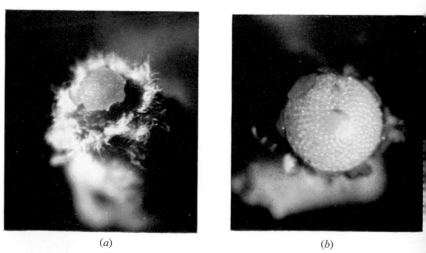

11. Primordia in the chrysanthemum. Inflorescence bud apices dissected when they
are macroscopically visible (Schwabe, 1951). (*a*) From vernalized plants in long day,
showing bare receptacle. (*b*) From vernalized plants in short day, showing floret initiation
nearing completion

effect on flowering of cuttings. Analyses are being made to identify the substances leached out of the young cuttings.

In American experiments, plants of *Xanthium pennsylvanicum* were treated with a series of growth regulators just before being induced to flower by a single 16-hour dark period (Salisbury, 1957). After 9 days notes were taken on the macroscopic condition of the plants, and apical buds were classified according to a series of stages of floral bud development described in an earlier paper. The growth regulators used inhibit flowering by blocking or otherwise influencing the steps of photoperiodic induction, as follows: maleic hydrazide, dalapon and 2,4-D inhibit development of floral buds; IAA, NAA and low concentrations of 2,4-D

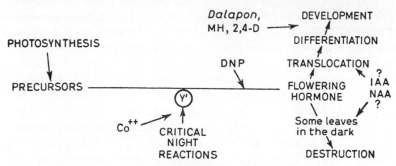

Fig. 18. The effect of seven growth regulators at various stages of reproductive development. The two phases of the critical night reaction are combined (Salisbury, 1957).

probably cause a destruction of flowering hormone in the leaf in either light or darkness; DNP inhibits synthesis of flowering hormone; cobaltous ion interferes with the mechanism which controls the critical night length (see Fig. 18).

(See Chapter VII for practical application.)

Conclusion

We might again, as in the first edition, quote Cholodny (1939): 'The very diversity of the possible suppositions in this field suggests how far we are from any satisfactory decision as to the nature of the biochemical and physiological reactions connected with the effect of photoperiods on plants. No matter how this question will be solved in the future, it is necessary to remember that at the basis of the different photoperiodic response of different plants there lies their hereditary constitution, particularly their genotype, formed in the evolution of the species in question in relation to the natural-historical conditions of its existence.'

Recent work on the gibberellins (see Chapter VI) and gibberellin-like hormones in the regulation of plant growth and flowering may, according to a recent article by Brian (1958), clear up much of the confusion which exists and begin to show the relationship between many of the physiological responses of plants to environmental factors.

Brian states that, although the effects of gibberellin on shoot growth, through cell extension, are similar to those induced by auxins, gibberellin is not an auxin, but depends for its activity on the presence of auxins. Gibberellic acid does, however, induce other physiological responses, such as: (a) breaking of dormancy of light-sensitive seeds; (b) prevention of arrested fruit growth of some varieties of tomato; (c) induction of flowering of long-day plants grown in short day; (d) inhibition of flowering of short-day plants grown in inductive short days; (e) inhibition of tuber-formation of potatoes despite increased top growth; (f) reduced tillering of cereals; (g) breaking of epicotyl dormancy of tree paeonies; (h) reversal of physiological dwarfing of *Malus* spp. associated with the use of non-after-ripened seed; and (i) induction of stem formation in biennials kept in temperatures above the threshold for vernalization. In effects (a) to (f) gibberellic acid simulates light; effects (c) to (f) are typical responses to long days. In effects (g) to (i) gibberellic acid simulates exposure to low temperatures. Brian sees an underlying physiological unity in these responses, strengthened by a similarity in action spectrum in the light-induced responses, red light usually being most effective. A further common characteristic is the reversibility of the photoreaction, a response to red light being reversed by subsequent exposure to far red, and repromoted on return to red light (see page 273).

The significance of these observations is increased by the discovery that substances similar to gibberellic acid have been found in extracts from all parts of seedlings of tall and dwarf peas, and in mature seeds of wheat, French bean and tall and dwarf peas (Radley, 1958); also in wheat seedlings, the younger inflorescences of *Brassica napus*, and the seeds of several genera of flowering plants. Gibberellin A_1, a dihydro-derivative of gibberellic acid, has been isolated from seed of runner bean. Brian believes it is virtually certain that these natural gibberellin-like hormones are involved in light-induced physiological responses.

The photoperiodic responses of plants are explained by the following scheme: 'In response to light, gibberellin-like hormones are formed in leaves, a physiologically inactive (or less active) precursor (P) being an intermediary:

$$CO_2 \rightarrow P \rightarrow \text{gibberellin-like hormone}$$

The hormone is converted slowly back to P in darkness, and, more rapidly, if the leaf is exposed to far-red light. If the leaf is then exposed to red light once more, the hormone is again formed from P. Thus in long-day conditions increasing concentrations of the hormone will be built up, but in short days concentrations will be much lower. Thus, if it is supposed that high levels of gibberellin-like hormone induce flowering in long-day plants, but that flowering takes place in short-day plants only when levels of the hormone are low, the response of these plants to light and to exogenous gibberellic acid is explained.

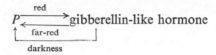

'The scheme has the further advantage that it accounts for the general association of shoot extension with flowering in long-day plants, and for the dwarfed appearance of many short-day plants in inductive short days and their far greater vegetative development in long days (shown particularly well in *Kalanchoë* and soybean. Day-neutral plants can be regarded as plants independent of light for biosynthesis of gibberellin-like hormones, a view supported by the detection of such hormones in etiolated pea tissues.

'The effects of gibberellic acid and light on germination of light-sensitive seeds can similarly be understood if we assume that, during maturation of the seed, gibberellin-like hormones are converted to the precursor P; treatment with red light after imbibition leads to reconstitution of the hormone and germination can proceed, as is also possible in darkness if gibberellic acid is supplied exogenously. The other light-induced responses mentioned earlier can be simply explained by the same general hypothesis, and also the effects of vernalization if it is assumed that low-temperature treatments are also concerned with building up suitable concentrations of gibberellin-like hormone.' (Brian, *loc. cit.*)

Brian states that his scheme, which owes much to those of Borthwick, Hendricks and Parker (1952) and Liverman and Bonner (1953), proposed before the significance of the gibberellins was appreciated, accounts for most of the observed facts. The proposed relationship between light and biosynthesis of gibberellin-like hormones is admitted to be purely speculative, and the evidence that the effects of exogenous gibberellic acid should be reversed by far-red light is conflicting.

What of the ultimate flower-forming substance or flowering hormone, generally supposed to be identical in long-day and short-day plants? If florigen is in fact produced, then Brian believes that it must be formed at a later stage in the series of reactions initiated by exposure to light than the gibberellin-like hormone. It is necessary to assume that florigen is elaborated in long-day and short-day plants in different circumstances, namely, in long-day plants only when levels of the gibberellin-like hormone are high, in short-day plants only at some lower critical level.

Chapter V

SYNTHETIC REGULATORY
SUBSTANCES

Auxins in Agriculture and Horticulture

In his review of our present knowledge of the action of auxins and of their utilization in agriculture and horticulture, Leopold (1955) states that, since the original reference to the subject by Charles Darwin in 'The power of movement in plants', the role of growth hormones in plants has been clarified 'to an almost startling degree. The revealed capacity of many chemical compounds to exploit the same mechanisms in plants has led to a situation nearly approaching an agricultural revolution. Auxins and growth regulators promise to have an impact on agriculture as great as the advent of the windmill or perhaps even of the mechanical harvester. At the same time the impact on the science of plant physiology is as great as that of any other single development since the turn of the century.' The literature is already voluminous and complex in character; it will be possible to deal only briefly with some of the interrelationships between hormones and growth and reproductive development, and to refer the reader to the comprehensive reviews listed in the bibliography.

The terminology applied to auxins and growth hormones has been somewhat confused. Leopold quotes the definition of a hormone proposed by Went and Thimann (1937): 'a substance which, produced in any one part of an organism, is transferred to another part and there influences a specific physiological process'. It is important to emphasize that hormones are produced in the organism and that they have the property of serving as 'chemical messengers' (Leopold), transported from a site of formation to a site of action. The term cannot therefore be used for chemicals produced in a laboratory, nor for sugars, amino-acids or other substrates for growth.

It therefore becomes obvious that a phytohormone is a hormone produced specifically in plants, and includes the growth hormone, the hypothetical flowering hormone not yet fully identified, and possibly some vitamins. A phytohormone is 'an organic substance produced naturally in higher plants, controlling growth or other physiological functions at a site remote from its place of production, and active in minute amounts' (Thimann, 1948). Auxin is defined as 'an organic substance which promotes growth (i.e. irreversible increase in volume) along the longitudinal axis when applied in low concentrations to shoots of plants freed as far as practicable from their own inherent growth-promoting substances' (Thimann, *loc. cit.*). Leopold notes that there has been an unfortunate tendency, largely for commercial reasons, to apply the term hormone to synthetic substances used both experimentally and in crop production as growth regulators. 'Such a misuse of terms is definitely confusing and has no place in scientific writing'.

The concept of hormonal regulation of growth dates back nearly a century to Julius Sachs, who deduced that special substances are responsible for the formation and growth of different organs in plants. Proof of this action was not obtained until 1926–28, when Went demonstrated a growth substance in the tip of the oat seedling. Twenty-five years ago only a few botanists worked on plant growth substances in European laboratories, and a laboratory for this type of research was under construction in Pasadena by Herman Dolk (Skoog, 1951). From this slow beginning, work has developed with great rapidity, and now affects all branches of botany, as well as having far-reaching application in agriculture and horticulture.

Today several thousand persons are engaged in investigation, manufacture and applied work on growth-regulating compounds. In the United States, synthetic plant growth regulators have become one of two main groups of organic chemicals for agricultural use as weedkillers on more than 20 million acres of cropland (1951). Leopold (1955) agrees that the trend of research in auxin physiology is increasingly of a technological type, and less and less of the nature of fundamental research. A report published in 1950 showed that 81 per cent of the plant physiologists in the United States are in the applied fields, and many of the remainder are probably doing some practical research in experiment stations and other centres. Because of the greater availability of funds for applied research, more technological studies are in progress in University departments of botany or biological sciences. If the technological science of auxin physiology is to continue to progress, it is essential that it must be supported and nourished by the results obtained in research on the fundamental aspects of this large and promising field of work.

Murneek (1951) expresses himself in similar terms, in a review of the function of hormones in sexual reproduction of horticultural plants, with special reference to the use of synthetic growth regulators in certain cultural practices. These regulators effectively control the development of certain tissues and organs from flower initiation to delay of fruit abscission during the preharvest period. Their practical application has outrun our present scientific knowledge. As a result of further experimental work, more uses will be found for these substances, and progress would certainly be more rapid if more information on the physiology of reproduction were available, particularly with regard to the crucial phases (Murneek, *loc. cit.*).

Methods of Application and Testing

The research worker needs to have a working knowledge of the precautions to be observed in making up solutions or other preparations based on auxin, as well as an appreciation of the degree of persistence of auxins in plants, in soils, and in the greenhouse. Auxins are usually applied in aqueous solution, by (*a*) spraying solutions on the foliage, (*b*) infiltration into leaves, (*c*) injection into fleshy parts, and (*d*) immersion of plant parts in auxin solutions. As some salts of the acids are more soluble in water than the free acids themselves, the salts are generally used when high concentrations are required. The acidity of a solution of auxin greatly influences its effectiveness as well as its solubility, in two ways: by affecting the entry of the auxin into the cells, and the action of the auxin within the cells themselves.

The persistence of auxins in soils is of great practical importance, particularly in connection with the application of herbicides to the soil or before emergence of the seedlings. Persistence in soils appears to be dependent upon three factors: adsorption, leaching and destruction by micro-organisms.

The persistence of auxin effects in plants varies with the type of auxin and the plant which has been treated. Naphthaleneacetic acid prevents pre-harvest drop of apples up to 14 days; 2,4-D and 2,4,5-TP are effective for 30 to 50 days in apples but for up to 7 months in citrus. It is not known whether it is the auxins themselves or the effects which they generate which persist for this length of time. Pineapple growers use sprays of naphthaleneacetic acid or sometimes 2,4-D to force flower initiation, even though the bulk of the growth hormone in the pineapple plant is indoleacetic acid, which is markedly ineffective. Auxins which have been applied to foliage generally remain active in the plant for only a limited time (Leopold, 1955).

The U.S. Department of Agriculture has produced a fully illustrated Agricultural Handbook describing in what the authors call a cookery book layout the methods which have been devised by American workers for studying the plant-regulating properties of compounds. The compilation is divided into three parts. The first section includes methods designed to detect regulating properties of organic compounds and measure the response of plants to these compounds. The second section includes methods designed to detect and, in some instances, to measure the amounts of regulating compounds present in plants, in water, and to some extent in animals. The third section describes pictorially some techniques that are of general use in experimenting with plant-regulating compounds.

The authors (Mitchell, Livingston and Marth, 1958) hope that the publication will be useful in several ways: First, by affording those experienced in this field of research an opportunity to compare the ways in which scientists have tested chemicals for plant-regulating properties, and how they have recorded and evaluated responses obtained with these compounds. This information should lead to the development of even more suitable methods. Second, the compilation will afford the experienced worker and the novice ready access to many current methods. Third, it may aid in the teaching of college courses where laboratory exercises are used to demonstrate the effects of regulating chemicals. Some of the methods described may also be useful as laboratory exercises in the teaching of high school courses in biology and plant science.

Chemical Control of Growth

The outstanding examples of the use of chemicals to control growth in a desirable or undesirable direction (from the point of view of the grower or the plant) are in the stimulation of rooting and the control of weeds or unwanted plant growth generally. Since the original discovery of the high degree of effectiveness of auxins in promoting the rooting of cuttings (Went, 1934), and the discovery immediately following by Thimann and Went (1934) that auxin exerts a primary control over root formation in general, it at once became clear that this had a wide practical application in horticulture. Over 300 reports have now appeared in the literature on a subject which has become an important branch of plant physiology (Leopold, 1955; Nickell, 1952).

Almost any plant organ (not only stems, but leaves, stolons, roots, and even flowers and fruits) can be induced to form roots. Stems are usually chosen because they have sufficient undifferentiated tissues to permit early differentiation of root primordia and buds are already formed. The ability of cuttings to root is influenced by environmental factors, such as the season of the year at which cuttings are taken, the photoperiod, and conditions of light, temperature, aeration and humidity. The physiological condition of the cuttings is also important; as auxins move in the stem from apex to base, root formation takes place preferentially at the base of a cutting where the auxins accumulate. The presence of leaves ensures the availability of nutrients for root formation, and the presence of buds has a strong promotive effect on rooting. Inorganic materials such as nitrogen and boron are influential in rooting.

Other uses of auxins in the control of vegetative plants include the elimination of undesirable plants by the use of synthetic growth hormones as selective weedkillers, the control of abscission (Avery et al., 1947), the control of bud growth in stored onions, potatoes and carrots, the prevention of sprouting in stored rose-bushes in nursery stock, and the control of wound healing in trees (so far only of limited application).

Chemical Control of Reproduction

Until success has been achieved in the recognition and extraction of a flower-promoting hormone (Ullrich, 1939; Bonner and Bonner, 1948; Roberts, 1951), the chemical control of flowering in practice must be limited to the use of certain synthetic substances on relatively few crop plants. The best known example is the chemical control of flowering of pineapple practised on a wide scale in Hawaii and Puerto Rico. After an initial use of acetylene and ethylene, it has been found that naphthaleneacetic and 2,4-dichlorophenoxyacetic acids are more satisfactory for controlling the time of flower initiation. Complete control is now possible, since a single application of 25 g/acre will cause flower initiation, while high concentrations are said to inhibit. Spraying the foliage of litchi trees with 50 p.p.m. naphthaleneacetic acid causes vegetative growth to cease and 88 per cent of the trees to flower.

Although auxins can induce flower initiation only in the pineapple and possibly in the litchi, they can cause a quantitative modification in many plants if applied to the growing plant or if seeds are soaked in auxin solutions. Although the inhibitory effects on flower initiation may be pronounced, especially at relatively high concentrations, auxin may also promote initiation in species in which flower initiation has been induced by low temperatures or long days. The properties of auxins and the auxin antagonists in modifying floral initiation in one direction or the other are now fairly clear, but their practical application has been limited (control of celery flowering with maleic hydrazide, inhibition of bolting of sugar-beets). Experiments on short-term treatment of seeds to increase earliness and vigour of grains in a manner similar to vernalization have not been promising (Leopold, 1955).

The other major applications of synthetic growth substances are in thinning of flowers and fruits, the prevention of pre-harvest fruit drop, and in inducing fruit-set parthenocarpically, i.e. without pollination, by applications of synthetic auxins on the pistil. Gustafson (1936) established that auxins could induce parthenocarpy in many species of plants, and later that parthenocarpy and fruit-set are brought about in nature by the growth hormone; natural parthenocarpy occurs in ovaries which have naturally high auxin contents (Gustafson, 1939). Most of the information on the induction of parthenocarpy is concerned with the tomato, since fruit is set most readily by auxin in this plant. The choice of the concentration to be used in practice must be related to the injurious effects which the spray may have on the plant, and the undesirable effects which the auxin may have on the fruit. Although auxins in general can be used to set parthenocarpic fruit in the fig, the customer's preference for a seeded fig may necessitate the use of a special auxin in weak solution which can set fruit and stimulate the development of the seed coat at the same time. A simple aqueous spray applied to the flower is effective, but it is not essential for the auxin spray to reach the stigma, the ovary, or even the face of the tomato flower; growth regulators may also be applied to the soil beneath the plant.

Leopold's (1955) summary of the practical application of these techniques states that auxin will not increase fruit-set unless a limitation of fruit-set exists at the time of use. Recognized limitations which may make the use of auxins feasible are weak light, excessively high or low temperatures, high nitrogen content, low leaf areas, and conditions of excessive flower abscission. Auxins will increase early yields in tomatoes by overcoming those limitations of fruit-set which commonly exist in winter greenhouse conditions and in field plantings in the early spring.

Hastening of maturity of the fruits will also contribute to the production of early yields.

It is clear from the studies of fruit-set which have been carried out that not only is auxin essential to fruit-set, but nutrient substrates for growth are needed as well. Normally auxin is supplied by the pollen plus some auxin-forming mechanism activated by the pollen; the substrates for growth are apparently supplied by mature leaves. The application of auxin can replace the former requirement, and in some cases at least alleviate the latter. The interesting fact that auxins can alleviate what appear to be limitations in nutrients suggests that auxins may exert their effect in part by bringing about a mobilization of nutrient materials in the flower. Although many species have been caused to set fruit partheno-carpically by auxin sprays, the practice appears to be commercially feasible only in tomatoes and figs at the present time (Leopold, 1955).

Interaction of Auxins and Primary Factors

Treatment of the growing points of *Trigonella foenum-graecum* and *Brassica chinensis* with ascorbic acid for a few hours during early growth results in enhanced growth and acceleration of flowering at a much later period, an inductive effect analogous to that of vernalization by temperature (Chinoy, Nanda and Garg, 1957). The work of Leopold and Guernsey (1953 a and b, 1954) may be regarded as an example of chemical vernalization, the combined action or interaction of auxin (naphthaleneacetic acid) and temperature in floral initiation which they find exists in all types of floral initiation known, namely, photoperiodic initiation, vernalization, and indeterminate initiation. A similar example of combined action of gibberellin and temperature is given in Chapter VI. Leopold and Guernsey (1953 b) showed that the treatment of seeds with naphthaleneacetic acid followed by a short exposure to low temperature (3°C) promotes flowering in Wintex barley, teosinte, Biloxi soybean, Victory oats and Sun-up corn. The promotive effect is manifested by greater numbers of flower primordia, more advanced stages of flower development, and the appearance of flowers at lower nodes. Auxin treatment followed by exposure to room temperatures (18°C) either inhibited flowering or had no effect. The stimulative effect is altered by shading the plants. (See also De Zeeuw and Leopold, 1955, under Brussels sprouts, p. 222). Leopold and Guernsey (1954) later analysed the promotion of flowering in Alaska pea by auxin treatment of seeds followed by low temperature. Taking the node of the first flower after treatment as the criterion of earliness of flowering, the following conclusions are drawn:

Several materials are effective in chemical vernalization, including auxins (naphthaleneacetic acid, β-naphthoxyacetic acid) and auxin synergists (2,3,5-triiodobenzoic acid, thiamine). Varied day lengths applied after chemical vernalization do not alter the response, but varied light intensities show that the promotive effect is greatly reduced by high intensities of light (800 foot-candles). Chemical vernalization effects are nullified by heat (39°C for 18–24 hours), by nitrogen atmosphere (for 48–96 hours) or by CO_2-free air (for 12 hours) applied after the cold treatment. The requirement for CO_2 was not found to hold for the cold period, but only after it. Leopold and Guernsey suggest that chemical vernalization takes place in two steps, the first requiring auxin and low temperature, and the second requiring CO_2.

Purvis and Gregory (1937) first postulated that the cold temperature step in vernalization was reversible, on the basis of experiments on devernalization with heat and with N_2; they later (1952) stated that a first step in vernalization was reversible, but that a subsequent irreversible step could take place either at chilling temperatures or subsequent room temperature (17°C). Leopold and Guernsey state that the reversal of chemical vernalization of peas can be obtained by depriving the seedlings of CO_2 for very brief periods after the cold treatment. The reversals of chemical vernalization by heat and by N_2 may each be a function of the requirement for CO_2 for the completion of some reaction following the cold treatment. This requirement is strikingly parallel to the requirement for CO_2 for the effectiveness of the dark period in the photoperiodic response of the soybean (Langston and Leopold, 1954 b; see p. 30).

Hussey and Gregory (1954) injected plants of Petkus rye and Wintex barley with auxin according to the method of Leopold and Thimann (1949). The flowering behaviour of Petkus rye is not affected; auxin increases the number of primordia in low concentration, and reduces it in high, confirming the results of Leopold and Thimann, although the magnitude of the effects is much less. The results of Leopold and Thimann may be evidence for a post-initiation effect of auxin on the developing ear, which in this sense may be said to promote or inhibit flowering; Hussey and Gregory find no evidence that auxin has any determinable effect on flower initiation.

However, De Zeeuw and Leopold (1956) found later that a low auxin concentration (1 to 5 p.p.m.) applied to the short-day cocklebur and

Biloxi soybean before the induction period has a marked promotive effect on floral initiation; the effect is small when auxin is applied after the induction period. The response takes place in two phases, similar to other growth responses to auxin. Liverman and Lang (1956) showed that the long-day *Hyoscyamus niger* and *Silene armeria* can be induced to flower by the application of IAA to the leaves of plants grown under low intensity light, in which the non-auxin-treated controls remain vegetative. Hamner and Nanda (1956), studying a relationship between IAA and the high-intensity-light reaction of photoperiodism, found that IAA inhibits flowering in short-day plants through an interaction with some product of the photoperiod, since the concentration of applied IAA required to inhibit flowering is proportional to the length of the photoperiod of a photoinductive cycle.

Chapter VI

GIBBERELLIN

Origin and Effects

The latest addition to the class of growth-regulating (and perhaps flower-promoting) substances, joining those auxins and selective herbicides already in common use in practice, is gibberellin (Brian and Grove, 1957). In Japan in 1926, it was found that, if cell-free filtrates made from the soil-borne fungus, *Gibberella fujikuroi* (the sexual stage of *Fusarium moniliforme*), were sprayed in very low concentrations on rice seedlings, the characteristic symptoms of Bakanae or 'crazy seedling' already noted on infected paddy fields were produced. 'The first crystalline material separated from the crude culture medium in 1939 was given the name of Gibberellin A. During the war and immediately afterwards, investigations were continued in Japan, and it was found that Gibberellin A and another compound named Gibberellin B were both mixtures of active substances. Since the late 1940s research has been stimulated in Great Britain and the U.S.A., and in 1953— almost simultaneously in the two countries—a pure substance, known as gibberellic acid, was isolated and its chemical structure determined. Once this stage had been reached, the possibility of synthesizing any chemical substance would make likely the production of a reasonable quantity of material for investigation and practical tests, which if successful could probably lead to comparatively cheap production on a commercial scale' (Patterson, 1957). When the production of gibberellic acid (tetracyclic dihydroxylactonic acid, $C_{19}H_{22}O_6$) by the penicillin-like fermentation method was evolved, commercial production began; now one English and four American companies market the product at about £10 per gramme. Grove (1958) has provided a statement of the chemistry of the gibberellins, a subject which is undergoing rapid expansion and in which it is difficult to keep up to date.

'The known gibberellins are colourless crystalline solids which melt

118

with decomposition above 210°C. Four gibberellins have been described; gibberellic acid, $C_{19}H_{22}O_6$, $[\alpha]_D + 92°$, the known chemical reactions of

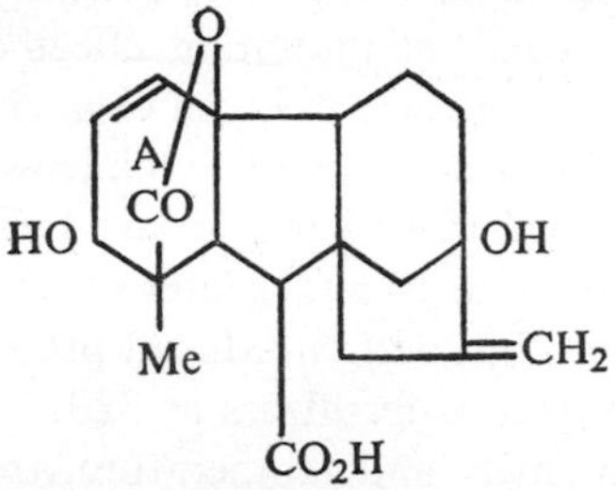

I 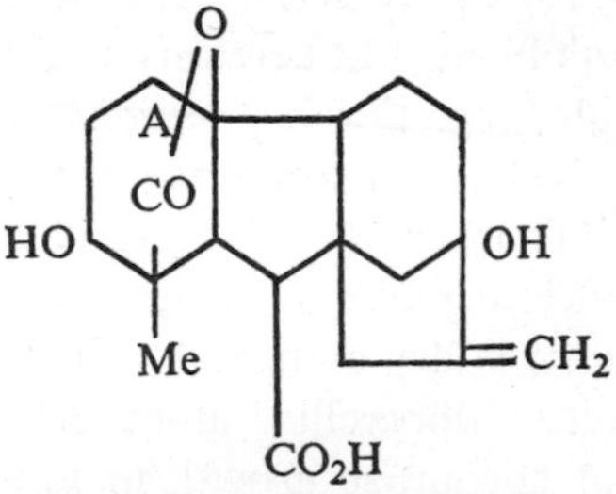   II

which are explained satisfactorily by structure I;

gibberellin A_1, $C_{19}H_{24}O_6$, $[\alpha]_D + 36°$, a dihydrogibberellic acid II in which the ethylenic double bond in ring A of gibberellic acid has been reduced;

gibberellin A_2, $C_{19}H_{26}O_6$, $[\alpha]_D + 12°$; and

gibberellin A_4, $C_{19}H_{24}O_5$, $[\alpha]_D - 20°$. Gibberellin A_2 and gibberellin A_4 are also tetracyclic lactonic carboxylic acids: gibberellin A_2 has two hydroxyl substituents but no ethylenic double bonds, whereas gibberellin A_4 has an ethylenic double bond, present in a terminal methylene group, and only one hydroxyl substituent; recent work strongly suggests that gibberellin A_4 has structure III and gibberellin A_2 structure IV.'

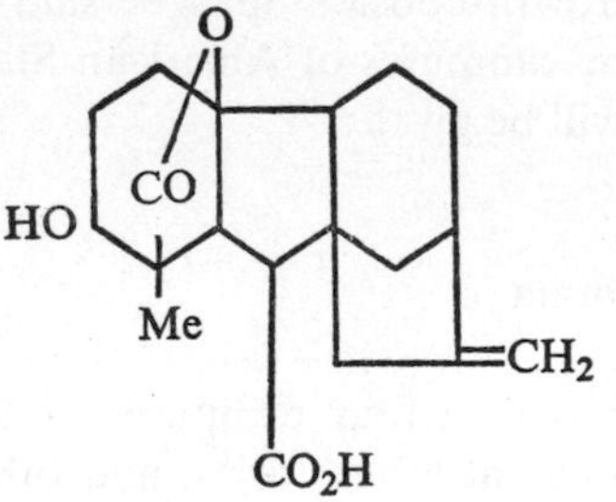

III 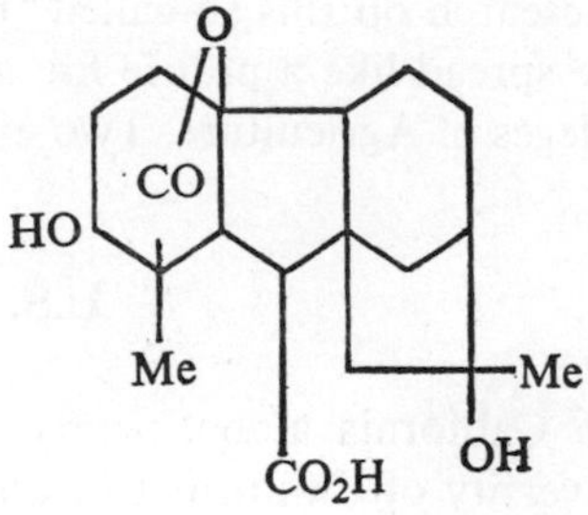   IV

    As distinct from the usual run of plant growth hormones, gibberellic acid stimulates extra growth which is normal and may produce giant plants. It may seem surprising that a material produced by a single species of fungus should induce changes in metabolism comparable to those which can be brought about by changes in the environment of light and temperature. Plants respond to gibberellic acid in different ways. Dwarf garden peas become tall, with the same number of internodes but large cells. Root growth is not stimulated and may at fairly high concentrations be inhibited. Gibberellins do, however, have an inhibiting effect on nodule formation in *Phaseolus vulgaris*; the mechanism is not clear, but it is obvious that applications to leguminous plants should be made with care (Thurber, Douglas and Galston, 1958). Grass swards sprayed with 2 ounces per acre of gibberellic acid and cut 4 to 10 weeks later show an increase in dry matter of 14 to 46 per cent, but with a reduced protein content. Gibberellins alone or with nitrogenous fertilizers at 320:1 or 640:1 encourage growth in low light intensity and temperature, thus having practical possibilities in the promotion of an early bite in northern latitudes or the extension of the growing season in the autumn or early winter. Gibberellins may also be useful to induce flowering and seeding, to increase the production of carbohydrate and cellulose, and to improve fibre length in such crops as flax, hemp, sisal and jute through the suppressive effect on branching. Increases in stem length of woody perennials have been reported by Marth, Audia and Mitchell (1956), quantitative effect on weights of leaves, stems and roots, and the number of leaves on the main stem of *Eucalyptus melliodora* by Scurfield and Moore (1958), and an effect on the photoperiod-controlled growth of *Camellia japonica*, in particular the initiation of vegetative growth in short days, as a result of the periodic application of gibberellic acid (Lockhart and Bonner, 1957).

Research on this so-called 'miracle-growth-booster' may be said to have spread like a prairie fire around the campuses of American State Colleges of Agriculture. Two examples will be given:

U.S.A.: California

In California alone, nearly 100 scientists on four campuses of the University of California, in State and Federal laboratories, and other research centres have been experimenting with the new chemical. Basic work was and is still being carried out on the Los Angeles campus. Phinney found that dwarf maize could be transformed into normal maize, and therefore assumed that the dwarf varieties lacked some type of gibberellin-like substance. Such a substance was isolated from normal maize grain in the milk stage, and produced the same kind of stimulation as gibberellic acid (GA). Attempts have been made to isolate pure forms

120

12. Effect of gibberellic acid on the ivy, Hedera canariensis variegata var. arborescens (Robbins, 1957b). *Left*: untreated; *right*: treated. *Note*: On treated plant one branch with juvenile leaves and aerial roots but orthotropic growth; the apical 45 cm. of the second branch have become completely juvenile. Both branches grew from apical buds

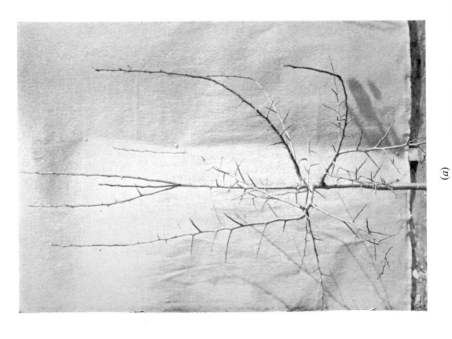

13. Growth habit in the pear tree (Blair, MacArthur and Nelson, 1956). *Left:* thorny, juvenile type of branch growth. *Right:*

of these 'natural gibberellins' from extracts of bean seed and wild cucumber fruit. An extract of recently fertilized bean seed applied to bean seedlings increases the growth of all internodes, causes earlier flowering, and reverses the light inhibition of growth. An active substance extracted from wild cucumber seed will promote growth of dwarf maize mutants. Paper chromatography has shown that beans produce a substance which behaves similarly to known gibberellins. Anton Lang and R. M. Sachs find that GA stimulates more rapid cell division, and also elongation of cells; an increase of 1,000 per cent in number of cells at a growing point treated with GA was observed. On the Davis campus, a radioactive tracer technique is being used to follow the absorption and translocation of GA through stems and roots.

Vegetables. Growers do not necessarily wish to have giant plants, but have a considerable interest in anything that will hasten germination, flowering and fruit setting. Research at Davis and Riverside is producing the following results. Dipping sections of potato in GA for 5 minutes accelerates sprouting; the chemical also breaks dormancy by systemic action. Rappaport reports systemic effect on tomatoes; if applied to new foliage of male-sterile plants, GA will travel through the plant and stimulate fruit production without normal pollination, but the resultant tomatoes are small. GA may eliminate the need for the chilling period (vernalization). Why do GA and a chilling period produce the same effects on some plants and not on others? If it were possible to produce earlier germination of lettuce in hot weather by GA treatment, the crop might be harvested more uniformly and cheaply. Certain varieties of lettuce, endive and celery can be induced to bolt. Tomato seeds soaked in GA germinate in cold soil much earlier than untreated seeds; the same result is noted in beans and celery but not in onions, asparagus, cabbage, broccoli and carrots. It is apparently expected that a systemic influence on germination of seeds from GA-treated plants will be found (peppers, cucumbers, muskmelons, lettuce and endive).

Florist crops. Tests are in progress on, among others, the big five of the florist crops of California, carnations, roses, stocks, chrysanthemums and asters. Cyclamens need autumn weather to develop flowers; with GA they will flower in mid-summer. Hydrangeas need a low temperature treatment for normal development of flower buds, but will flower without this treatment when GA is applied.

Vineyard and orchard crops. The questions are: Can GA lengthen grape clusters and branches? Can it increase the size of the grapes? What is the relation of GA to the carbohydrate nutrition of the vines? Can GA be used to break dormancy of cuttings? Can GA influence the rate of fruit maturity? GA treatment of figs produces fruit setting without pollination, with normal figs as the result. GA increases the early growth of apricot fruits, but there is then an abrupt retardation in development and an eventual delay in maturity. GA increases the production of xylem in apricot trees. Citrus seedlings grow very fast during the first 40 days after treatment, but fall back when the treatment ceases and the control seedlings catch up.

U.S.A.: Michigan

Wittwer and Bukovac (1958) of the Department of Horticulture of Michigan State University, East Lansing, have studied the effect of GA on the growth of vegetables. GA incorporated with a slurry seed protectant and applied to the seed-coat of peas and beans promotes earlier emergence in both greenhouse and field plantings. Height and length of hypocotyls and internodes are directly related to concentration of GA, appropriate concentrations in a slurry for promotion of earlier emergence and production of acceptable seedlings in peas and beans ranging from 500 to 1,000 p.p.m. Early emergence and rapid growth may help the young plants to escape some of the diseases and pests associated with germination and early growth. After studying GA effects on a wider range of vegetables (snap beans, celery, cucumbers, muskmelons, radish, rhubarb, sweet corn and tomatoes), Wittwer and Bukovac (ref. in Wittwer and Bukovac, 1958) concluded that it is impossible in 1 or 2 years to make an accurate evaluation for crop production of a chemical producing so many and diverse effects as gibberellin. Commercial application of foliar sprays to vegetable crops must be done cautiously, since favourable effects must be carefully weighed against deleterious ones, as shown in Table 1.

In the growing of celery, seed production in radish and perhaps certain long-day annuals, and for early fruiting and increased vigour of determinate tomato varieties such as Fireball, Wittwer and Bukovac conclude that important benefits are now apparent and the eventual use of GA can be seen. With beans, cucumbers, muskmelons, peas, rhubarb, and sweet corn, the potentially useful effects may not be realized until some control has been obtained over the accompanying unfavourable responses. The comparative effectiveness of gibberellins A_1, A_2, A_3, and A_4 and the methyl esters of A_1 and A_3 in promoting vegetative extension,

GIBBERELLIN

flowering of facultative long-day annuals and in fruit setting has been reported by Wittwer and Bukovac (1958).

Table 1

FAVOURABLE AND DELETERIOUS EFFECTS OF GIBBERELLIN ON VEGETABLES

Crop and varieties	Favourable effects	Deleterious effects
Bush snap beans (Contender Bountiful)	Flowering and edible pods 2 to 3 days earlier, plant height subject to control.	Internodes elongated; leaves often wilt and fire, and turn lighter green; vines may require support.
Celery (E. Fortune, Cornell 19, Utah 15, 10–B, 52–70, 52–70H, Gunson 6)	20 to 50 per cent increase in yield, maturity 5 to 7 days earlier, greater stalk weight and length, easier to blanch and trim.	Plants require more fertilizer and water, more susceptible to blackheart and bolting; time of acceptable harvest is reduced; greater pithiness in outer petioles may occur if overmature.
Tomatoes—Forcing (WR–7, Michigan–Ohio Hybrid)	Promotes greater fruit set, with no modification or injury of foliage.	Treated fruit more russeted, peduncles and pedicels longer; total yield of marketable fruit may be reduced.
Tomatoes—Field (Fireball)	Greater vegetative growth, flowering and fruiting; plants continued to grow and fruit, and foliage remained green weeks longer; less injury from early blight (*Alternaria solani*).	May result in excessive vegetative growth of indeterminate varieties; greater susceptibility to wilting under hot, dry conditions.

Effect on Metabolism

Gibberellic acid differs from other auxins in that the growth stimulation often results in substantial increases in height and in fresh and dry weights. In treated plants of wheat and peas, a net increase has been noted in the ash, nitrogen, phosphorus, potassium, total soluble carbohydrates, and carbon; these constituents increase in the shoots but decrease in the roots (Brian, Hemming and Radley, 1955). In rice no difference was found in treated plants by Yabuta et al. (1948) in ash, reducing sugar, total nitrogen or total weight, although the chlorophyll and total sugar is less. Kato (1956) has noted significant increases in oxygen and water uptake of pea stem sections treated with gibberellin. Weller *et al.* (1957) have studied certain enzyme systems and rates of oxygen uptake. Young intact bean plants 96 hours after the application of 10 micrograms of gibberellic acid to the apex of the epicotyl show on a fresh weight basis that phosphatase activity is increased in the leaves and stems of the treated plants. No differences could be detected for α-amylase and phosphorylase. Treatment with gibberellic acid results in a decrease in activity for β-amylase in the leaves and stems, for pectin methyl-esterase in the roots, for oxygen uptake in the first internode, and an increase for β-amylase in the roots. On a plant-part basis, however, the oxygen absorption is greater in the internodes of the treated plants.

Brian and Hemming of the Akers Research Laboratories, Imperial Chemical Industries, Welwyn, Herts., have also made a series of studies on the effects of gibberellic acid and other substances on plant cell expansion, the growth of pea stem sections, and the extension of pea internodes (most recent reference, Brian and Hemming, 1958).

Relation to Vernalization and Photoperiodism

In addition to overcoming undesirable characteristics such as dwarfism, both genetic (Brian and Hemming, 1955; Phinney, 1956) and physiological (Barton, 1956), gibberellin does now appear to be the first substance to be generally effective in promoting or at least in accelerating flowering. Lang (1956 b) has found that a mixture of gibberellin A and gibberellic acid greatly accelerates the initiation of flowers in unvernalized *Hyoscyamus niger*, a vernalizable long-day biennial plant. Bünsow and Harder (1956) used the same mixture to induce flower formation in short-day conditions in *Bryophyllum crenatum*, a plant which requires long day for internode elongation, short day for floral initiation, followed by long day for the development of functional flowers. Gibberellin accelerates flower formation in non-vernalizable 'races' of *Arabidopsis thaliana* grown under short day, and in non-vernalized, but vernalizable 'races' grown under long-day conditions (Gregory and Hussey, 1953). Carr, McComb and Osborne (1957) found that it is possible to replace the requirement for vernalization in certain forms of *Centaurium minus* by treatment of the rosettes with gibberellic acid.

Lona and Bocchi (1956) in the University of Parma were interested in discovering whether gibberellic acid can be used to initiate reproductive development, or whether some apparent manifestations of reproductive development provoked by this substance are due primarily to modifications of vegetative processes determined by it. GA accelerates flowering in *Papaver somniferum* in short-day conditions in plants already induced to flower, replacing the long-day factor insofar as this affects the lengthening of the floral axis. In *Oenothera acaulis*, a long-day plant only for the macroscopic development of the flower, but indeterminate for the formation of floral primordia, GA can eventually partially substitute for the long-day effect. GA can also substitute sooner or later for the long-day requirement for flowering of the long-day plant, *Myosurus minimus*. Lona (1956) has also studied the relationship between gibberellin, thermoperiodism and photoperiodism in a number of plants which do or do not form stems in their juvenile stage.

Langridge (1957 a) has studied the effect of daylength and gibberellic acid on the flowering of *Arabidopsis* in the Division of Plant Industry, C.S.I.R.O., Canberra, using the rapidly growing race, Estland, which does not respond to vernalization (Plate 21). A highly significant acceleration of flowering was obtained when plants were treated with GA and grown in an 8-hour day. It is suggested that a more complete replacement of daylength might be obtained by applying GA more frequently. The presence of an interaction between daylength and GA is confirmed by the ability of the compound significantly to reduce the time required for flowering under long day. This effect cannot be due to a partial replacement of a vernalization requirement as in *Hyoscyamus niger*.

Wittwer and Bukovac (1958) report on the degree of success they achieved in inducing flowering by gibberellin treatment of cold-requiring biennials and long-day annuals which had been grown under environmental conditions not conducive to flowering. 'Regardless of whether the effects of gibberellin on flower formation are direct or indirect, it has now been established that treatment with gibberellin has resulted in complete flowering responses. Often a single application is sufficient to induce flowering in a wide variety of economic crops grown under non-flowering conditions of temperature (the cold-requiring biennials) and photoperiod (long-day-requiring annuals). All cold-requiring biennials, when grown close to, but slightly higher than the known inductive temperatures have been induced to flower with gibberellin. Similarly, long-day plants, after treatment, have flowered under short photoperiods. Exceptions have not thus far been observed. Widespread usefulness of such findings will be realized in earlier flowering for seed production and in the commercial culture of many flowering annuals and biennials' (Wittwer and Bukovac, *loc. cit.*).

Grass Species and Pastures

Research at Jealott's Hill Research Station of Imperial Chemical Industries has been concerned with the effect of gibberellic acid on the yield and quality of grassland and on the behaviour of wheat, root crops, and certain market garden crops (Morgan and Mees, 1958). When 2 oz/ acre of gibberellic acid are sprayed at 100 gal/acre, the growth of all components of a sward is stimulated, particularly in spring and autumn when the natural growth rate is slow. The stimulation is accompanied by yellowing, but recovery to a normal green is speeded up if nitrogen is applied at the time of spraying. The dry-matter yields from the first cut are increased by 0·6 to 10·8 cwt/acre following treatment with gibberellic acid. Crude protein yields are increased to a lesser degree, while protein content is reduced by 0·5 to 2 per cent. The effects of gibberellic acid and fertilizer on yields of dry matter and crude protein are additive.

If after cutting, grass is not treated with gibberellic acid, yields at a second cut are reduced by about the amount of the increase at the first cut. At a third cut there are no significant differences between grass which has initially been treated and that which has not. In no case is there any net increase of yield over two or more cuts as a result of an initial treatment. A second application after the first cut prevents these decreases in yield. Third and fourth applications after the second and third cuts respectively give a net increase in yield over four cuts. Repeated applications lead to a progressive thinning of the sward.

The practical conclusion is that gibberellic acid has no advantage over a fertilizer application for increasing the growth of grass, except in spring or autumn when the action of fertilizers is slow. Gibberellic acid may therefore be of some value in producing an early or a late bite. 'The difficulty of using the grass at these times of the year, should the season be wet, and the reductions of yield which follow later are important objections to its use even in this way' (Morgan and Mees, *loc. cit.*).

At Michigan Agricultural Experiment Station, Wittwer and Bukovac (1958) studied the effect of gibberellin on growth of grass species at low temperatures, and found that growth of treated plots is promoted in early spring, when growth would not otherwise have occurred. The percentage dry matter or mineral composition of Kentucky bluegrass

(*Poa pratensis*) are not affected, although total sugars are significantly reduced (Wittwer, Bukovac and Grigsby, 1957). Quantities of the active chemical were about $\frac{1}{10}$, 1 and 10 oz/acre, and growth is roughly proportional to the amounts applied. Treated grass turns light green when fertility is low, but a bright green colour is retained if soil fertility is high or fertilizers are applied. The grass species show the following reactions:

very responsive: the bluegrasses (*Poa pratensis* and *P. trivialis*) and
Bermuda grass (*Cynodon dactylon*);
moderately responsive: species of *Agrostis* and *Festuca*;
slightly responsive: *Lolium perenne* and *L. multiflorum*;
no response: *Zoysia*.

Again a practical use is seen in the possibility of providing grass for early grazing in the Northern States of U.S.A., and of establishing winter cover crops when temperatures are low. The fact that green turf can be produced weeks earlier than normal may be of practical or novelty interest for nurserymen, seedsmen, organizers of spring flower shows and amateur gardeners.

Conclusions

We have quoted Brian's conclusions on the possible role of gibberellin in the physiological control of plant growth and reproduction (p. 106). Wittwer and Bukovac (1958) summarize American experience by stating that 'we may project that many of the agricultural uses of gibberellin will be unlike those of other chemicals. It is not likely to be used to correct disorders, serve as a defoliant or fruit thinner, prevent abscission or blossom drop, kill weeds, or control the spread of plant diseases although its potentiality in these areas should not be ignored. New possibilities for gibberellin probably lie in unexplored areas of chemical regulation. New uses will not be realized hastily, nor will they develop without disturbing accompanying side effects which may be decidedly deleterious unless certain cultural practices, fertility and moisture levels, and harvest and handling procedures are adjusted.

'A meaningful aspect of the present and future impact of gibberellin in the plant kingdom is that in several areas it has served as a major scientific break-through for physiologists. It offers a means of controlling important responses—elimination of dwarfism, elongation of stems, expansion of leaves, production of dry matter, flowering in biennials and long-day annuals, induction of normal growth rates at sub-optimal temperatures—heretofore not easily subject to chemical regulation, at least on intact plants. The fact that these responses can be initiated or modified by gibberellin may direct research toward biochemical mechanisms by which heritable and environmental factors exert their control. As a chemical approach in mediating the effects of temperature, light, photoperiod, and nutrition on plant behaviour, the versatility of gibberellin does not augur badly for its future in eliciting specialized responses and, in some crops, extending the boundaries and magnitude of production.'

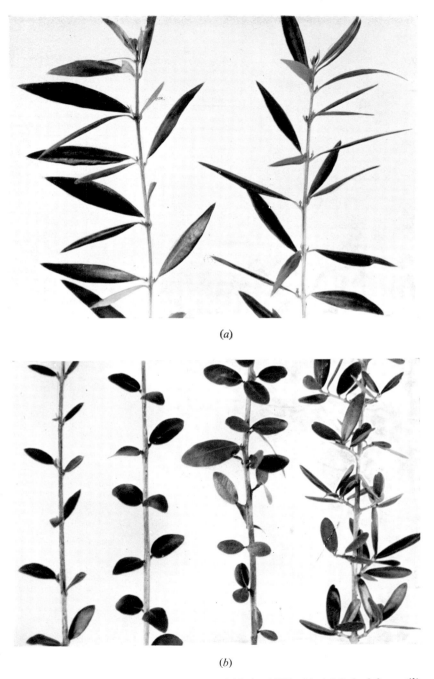

(a)

(b)

14. Growth habit in the olive (Vieira Natividade, 1957). (a) Adult leaf form. (b) Branches in the juvenile or transitional stage, produced at the base of the trunk of the same tree

(a)

(b)

15. Growth habit in the olive. Heavy grazing keeps plant in juvenile stage for: (*a*) 52 years; (*b*) 23 years (Vieira Natividade, 1957)

Chapter VII

CHEMICAL RETARDATION OF
GROWTH AND FLOWERING

Further progress towards the limitation or retardation of growth and reproductive development according to the will of the growers has been made by American scientists. In a screening operation initiated by the National Academy of Sciences, National Research Council, in cooperation with the Growth Regulator and Antibiotic Laboratory of the U.S. Department of Agriculture, Wirwillie and Mitchell (1950) found that certain quaternary ammonium compounds retard elongation without having any injurious effects. The chemicals were originally synthesized for testing as nerve gases; they have little effect on nerves, but retard growth of Black Valentine snap beans, sunflower and chrysanthemum. The most active quaternary ammonium compound was found to be 4-hydroxy-5-isopropyl-2-methyl-phenyl-trimethyl-ammonium chloride, 1-piperidine carboxylate, called Amo–1618. Elongation of snap beans is retarded when this chemical is applied to seeds, roots, soil, stems and leaves. This retardation is not associated with any development of dormancy. The chemical may be translocated into the seed and affect the subsequent generation of plants (Marth, Preston and Mitchell, 1953).

In a personal communication, Cathey (1958) of the U.S. Department of Agriculture, Beltsville, Maryland, has provided information on the use of Amo–1618 in changing the growth and flowering processes of chrysanthemum for commercial purposes (Plate 23). Amo–1618 is not at present available commercially, but several American firms are interested in its synthesis and potential use. A small supply has been made available by the Pesticides Synthesis Laboratory of the U.S. Department of Agriculture for experimental purposes, and samples have been released for trial to interested cooperators in various States. Cathey states the commercial potentiality of Amo–1618 in chrysanthemum culture as follows: 'Amo–1618 has immediate uses in the growing of chrysanthemums. First, many chrysanthemum varieties, regardless of their natural growth characteristics, may be used as pot plants. Few pot-plant varieties now in use would be considered if they were tall. Most varieties are too tall for the best ratio of pot to plant. Furthermore, tall plants require staking and a large amount of space for shipping. The fact that Amo–1618 reduces the height of many varieties means that the best varieties for form and colour may be used both for cut flowers and for dwarf potted plants. Secondly, chrysanthemums may be grown as compact pot plants for mass-market selling. The procedure is simple: Amo–1618 should be applied by soaking the rooted cuttings in a solution containing a specific concentration for a definite period and at a predetermined temperature. The cutting should be planted in a 3-inch pot, pinched, placed on short days immediately, and during growth pruned to three lateral branches. Thirdly, many chrysanthemum varieties produce peduncles too long for the most attractive flower spray. Application of Amo–1618 at the time when flower buds are visible retards the elongation of the peduncle but does not affect the time of flowering. Finally, garden varieties are often too tall, especially when they are used in small borders. Staking and repeated training are necessary to hold the plants off the ground. Mixing Amo–1618 in the soil at the time of planting would greatly reduce the care required for growing compact plants.'

There is a marked varietal response, since varieties with similar growth characteristics do not respond to a given concentration of Amo–1618 with similar retardation of growth. Many varieties can, however, be used as pot plants by appropriate adjustment of height with Amo–1618. Flowering is delayed in proportion to retardation of growth. Amo–1618 may be applied either before or after the rooting of cuttings of chrysanthemums. The basal ends of rooted and unrooted cuttings of the Shasta variety were treated for 24 hours at 50°F with solutions containing 0 and 250 p.p.m. of Amo–1618, planted in 3-in. pots, pinched and immediately placed in short days. During growth, the plants were pruned to three lateral branches.

	Stem length at flowering (inches)	Days to flowering (number)
Untreated cuttings	19·4	72
Cuttings treated before rooting	11·9	86
Cuttings treated after rooting	10·9	86

Treatment of unrooted cuttings with solutions containing more than 500 p.p.m. of Amo–1618 retards rooting and delays flowering by 4 to 5 weeks. Concentrations need to be adjusted to the temperature during the treatment. One-tenth as much solution (35 p.p.m.) is necessary to reduce the stem length 4 to 5 in. when unrooted cuttings are treated at 85°F as when they are treated at 50°F.

Yellow Lace chrysanthemums growing in long day were sprayed on three alternate days with aqueous solutions at various concentrations. The plants were not damaged, but retardation was obtained as follows:

p.p.m.	Average heights in inches 1 month after treatment
0	25·9
20	24·7
100	23·1
500	18·6
1000	14·1

When the same variety was grown in short days, growth of the stem was retarded less the later the chemical treatment was given after the start of the short days. Regardless of the amount of retardation caused by the treatment, the treated plants flowered 14 to 18 days later than untreated ones.

The present conclusion is, therefore, that Amo–1618 retards growth of chrysanthemums when applied by the techniques found to be effective on snap beans, namely, on roots, soil, stems and leaves. More Amo–1618 is required to suppress growth when it is applied to the soil than to the growing point. The most effective times to apply for growth retardation are during long days or during the first three weeks of short days. Delay of flowering by several days to 4 to 5 weeks as compared with flowering of untreated plants is always associated with retardation of elongation of the stem. Applications later than the third week of exposure to short days has little effect on stem length or on the time of flowering.

Maleic hydrazide is widely used as a growth inhibitor to arrest sprouting in stored root crops, for the temporary inhibition of growth of lawn grass and hedges, for the prevention of the formation of suckers in tobacco and for the control of flowering in celery. It may be translocated in plants and is toxic to meristematic tissues causing a loss of apical dominance. Its use has been suggested for checking the growth without killing the plants of perennial grasses on channel and ditch banks in irrigated districts (Levi, 1955).

Towers, Hutchinson and Andreae (1958) have noted the formation of a glycoside of maleic hydrazide in plants. They conclude that, if this glycoside is inactive on growth, the observed detoxication mechanism could explain the relatively high concentrations of maleic hydrazide which are needed to bring about a physiological response. Misra and Sahu (1958) soaked rice seeds in solutions of maleic hydrazide of 10,000, 1,000, 100 and 10 p.p.m. for 48 hours and later sprayed the resultant plants with the same solutions. All the plants receiving 10,000 p.p.m. and most of those receiving 1,000 p.p.m. died; the few plants surviving 1,000 p.p.m. flowered later than the controls. Plants receiving 10 p.p.m. showed greater vegetative growth, but not those receiving 100 p.p.m. The greatest increase in grain yield was obtained with 10 p.p.m., due to a promotive effect on number of panicles, length of panicle and number of spikelets per panicle.

Chapter VIII

DEVELOPMENT BEFORE SEED
DORMANCY

Seed obtained from an ear on a parent plant only 5 days after fertilization has been found to be capable of germinating and ultimately producing perfectly normal plants. It is to be expected that a plant may from this very early stage in its life history begin to respond to the environment in which it finds itself while ripening on the mother plant. It is now well established both by observations made under natural conditions under wide variations of latitude and by experiments that it is possible for a plant organism to receive part or all of its low temperature requirement or to be vernalized during the period between the formation of the zygote and the entry of the ripe seed into a state of dormancy.

The discovery that developing seeds respond to environmental conditions while still attached to the mother plant makes it essential to give careful consideration to the environment, and particularly to the temperatures experienced before harvest. For example, the recommendations made regarding the duration of temperature treatment required for the vernalization of many crop plants may have to be revised. But more important is the possibility that the anomalous behaviour of some varieties when imported from one environment (particularly latitude) to another may be explained; a late variety may become earlier and an early one later according to the degree to which the old or the new environment provides the low temperature quota for the particular variety before the seed becomes ripe on the mother plant.

Two Russian investigators, Kostjučenko and Zarubaïlo, reported natural vernalization in varieties of wheat, and Gregory and Purvis independently demonstrated the fact experimentally. Later, the same Russian workers, as well as others, described the phenomenon in a number of crop plants. Some Russian investigators have referred to a phase preceding the thermo-phase, when conditions other than low temperature are claimed to be decisive; if such a phase exists, its completion might also be expected to occur before the seed becomes dormant.

133

PRE-DORMANCY VERNALIZATION

Natural Vernalization of Grain during Ripening

In two Russian articles, and subsequently in an English translation, Kostjučenko and Zarubaïlo (1936) described the observations and experiments which led them to attach such importance to the possibility of vernalization during seed ripening. In the spring of 1935, a comparative trial of several varieties of winter wheat was laid down at the Polar Experimental Station of the All-Union Institute of Plant Industry (V.I.R.) located at Hibiny. The grain used for this trial had been grown in two localities which differ sharply in environmental conditions, namely, Hibiny itself, at 67° 44′ N. latitude, and Kirovobad, at 40° 41′ N. latitude. There was a slight but not significant difference in the actual time of sowing, the Hibiny grain being sown on 27 May and the Kirovobad grain on 31 May. In both sowings, vernalized and unvernalized grains were used.

In September of the same year, a marked difference could be seen in the development of each variety, when the plants grown from grains of different origin were compared. Plants from Kirovobad grain, artificially vernalized, were then at the milk-ripe stage, while their unvernalized counterparts were at the tillering stage. Plants from Hibiny grain, also artificially vernalized, were almost at the stage of wax ripeness, while plants from the same grain, not artificially vernalized, exhibited partial or complete flowering; some of them had set seed in the ears of the main stem, while other tillers were at various stages of maturity.

Thus, these varieties of Russian wheat, generally regarded as winter forms, behaved as spring forms when grown from grain which had been ripened in Hibiny, whereas they retained their winter habit when grown from Kirovobad grain. Kostjučenko and Zarubaïlo conclude that the Hibiny grains had passed their 'stage of vernalization' under the natural conditions of these northern latitudes, while the Kirovobad grains had not done so, and still required artificial vernalization before they could reach maturity in one season. It was assumed that the embryos of the Hibiny grain were vernalized by low temperature while still attached to the mother plant. An embryo which has not entered the dormant state may be as sensitive to vernalization as an embryo brought from the resting condition by soaking.

Dormancy, state Kostjučenko and Zarubaïlo, is merely an interruption in the development of the plant organism, which begins on the mother plant and recommences as soon as the seed begins to germinate. Dormancy is characterized by a fall in the vital activity of the embryo to a minimum, and by a maximum increase in its insensitivity to environmental conditions.

In order to confirm their first observations and assumptions, Kostjučenko and Zarubaĭlo conducted another series of experiments in 1936 at the Experimental Station of the Institute of Plant Industry, Pushkin, Leningrad. The first objective was to ascertain whether the difference in development between seeds of different geographical origin observed in 1935 was due to the difference in the conditions under which the grain had been grown, or to other causes. Results of a comparative trial in which grain of winter wheat varieties grown and ripened in Hibiny and Kirovobad respectively were sown together in the Leningrad latitude on 29 May 1936 fully confirmed the observations made at Hibiny in the previous year. Plants from Kirovobad grain, artificially vernalized for 20 days, did not ear, and passed the following winter at the tillering phase after having been in the field throughout the summer and the autumn. Plants from Hibiny grain, which had also received 20 days' artificial vernalization, eared in July of the same year.

In order to ascertain that this difference in development was actually caused by the effect of low temperature upon the ripening grain, and not by differences in other factors, such as the length of day (characteristic of the widely separated latitudes in which the grain had been reproduced), grains of winter wheat raised in Pushkin in 1935 and which had ripened at different times were also tested alongside the grains from Hibiny and Kirovobad. Early-season grains ripened in Pushkin in August, late-season grains in September. The 10-day mean temperatures recorded during these periods are shown in Fig. 19. The authors recognize that the length of day was also changed, but note that, in the Pushkin grains, lower temperatures were linked with the *shorter* days of September, whereas in the experiments with grain of different geographical origins lower temperatures were linked with the *longer* northern day earlier in the season.

Grain from these early and later ripenings were sown at Pushkin in the spring of 1936 at the same time and on the same land as the grain reproduced in different latitudes. The grains which had ripened in the previous autumn at the lower temperatures showed a much reduced requirement for vernalization, as compared with those which had ripened at the higher temperatures of the early part of the period indicated in Fig. 19. It is, therefore, concluded that temperature is the decisive factor.

An examination of the temperature curve given in Fig. 19 shows that the early-season grains ripened at mean temperatures above 14°C, while the late-season grains ripened at temperatures below that level. The authors conclude, therefore, that a vernalizing effect on ripening grain of winter wheat is produced by temperatures below 14°C. It should be noted, however, that this is a mean figure, and does not indicate the total number of hours during which the effective temperature for vernalization (probably lower than 14°C) would be operative. Early grains, ripened during August 1935, were left on the field and harvested at the same time as the late grain; they were thus subjected to the effect of low September temperatures, but were not affected owing to their fully ripe condition. Low temperatures act only on ripening grains, which are in the milk-ripe

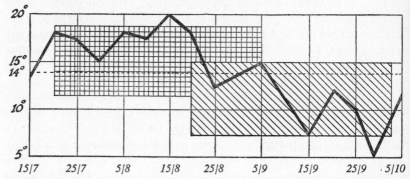

Fig. 19. Relation of temperature during the ripening of seed in the ear of the mother plant to the behaviour of the subsequent plants. The mean 10-day temperatures during August to September at Pushkin, near Leningrad (Kostjučenko and Zarubaïlo, 1937).

or wax-ripe state, and contain an active embryo. Capacity to react decreases as dormancy approaches.

The same investigators then proceeded to ascertain whether their results actually meant that vernalization was occurring, or whether it was a question of a shortening of the vegetative period in general. To decide this, spring varieties of wheat were tested alongside winter varieties, using grains raised at Hibiny and in the Crimea (Nikita Botanic Garden, Jalta, at 44° 31′ N. latitude). The temperature at which the Hibiny and Nikita grain had ripened are shown in Fig. 20.

The varieties chosen include those not normally responding to artificial pre-sowing vernalization, as well as others which show a varying response. It was assumed that, if the ripening of grain (on the mother plant) at low temperatures can shorten the vegetative period as a whole, irrespective of the 'stage of vernalization' (thermo-phase), this reduction must to a varying degree take place in the plants of all varieties grown from grain originating from Hibiny, irrespective of the length of the 'stage of vernalization'. If, on the other hand, vernalization has actually occurred, the vegetative period in plants from Hibiny grain should be curtailed only in those varieties with a relatively long stage of vernalization (that is, those requiring a large number of hours below the critical vernalizing

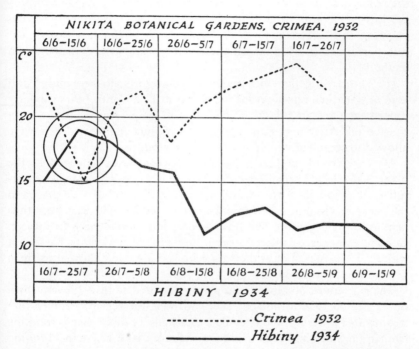

.... Crimea 1932
——————— Hibiny 1934

Fig. 20. The mean 5-day temperatures at which the seed of the Hibiny (Northern U.S.S.R.) and Crimean reproductions in the experiments of Kostjučenko and Zarubaïlo (1937) formed and ripened. Period of earing indicated by circles.

temperature for that variety), and the reduction should be in proportion to the length of this stage. Varieties which do not normally respond to artificial vernalization show no response to the difference in the conditions under which the grain ripened. Varieties which normally respond to artificial vernalization also showed a reaction to the lower temperatures under which their grain had ripened at Hibiny. The authors therefore conclude from this and the other experiments that the vernalization of grain during seed ripening has been established.

E*   137

Vernalization of Immature Ears and Excised Embryos

After their experiments on the vernalization of excised embryos, Gregory and Purvis (1936 and 1938) studied the effect of vernalization on developing embryos and immature ears (see also McKinney and Sando, 1935). Having shown that the vernalization process occurred in the embryo apart from the endosperm, it appeared possible to apply the low-temperature treatment after anthesis, while the embryo is developing, and before the onset of dormancy. A preliminary experiment was performed in 1935, when the ripening ears were chilled by two methods.

(1) The ears together with several nodes of the stem were cut off and kept in water in a refrigerator for 5 weeks at 1°C. Control ears similarly treated were kept in a dark room at normal temperature until the grain ripened off. After the low-temperature exposure the treated ears were allowed to complete ripening at room temperature.

(2) The second method consisted in treating ears attached to the plant. The selected ears after anthesis were inserted into wide glass test-tubes, plugged with cotton-wool. In one set these tubes were placed in the necks of vacuum flasks containing crushed ice. The ears were thus kept at low temperature but did not come into contact with free water. Control ears were similarly treated and placed in vacuum flasks but without ice. After 24 days the ears were removed and allowed to ripen normally in the open air.

The ripe grains obtained from plants thus treated in 1935 were sown on 17 March 1936 in pots of sand, without further low-temperature treatment. Flowering was irregular, especially in those plants resulting from grain which had been treated in vacuum flasks, where the duration of the treatment was less than that known to be optimal for vernalization; results were sufficiently encouraging to warrant repetition of the experiment in the following year, when longer periods of treatment were used. When a larger number of ears was treated in 1936, the ears were placed in a refrigerator while still attached to the stem, and in some cases whole plants were treated in this way. The period of chilling was increased to 45 days, and final ripening was carried out at medium temperatures. The ears were air-dried and the grain sown on 31 May 1937 without further treatment with low temperature. The results indicate clearly the marked effect of the low-temperature treatment during the previous season, although Gregory and Purvis note that not all the treated grains had attained the vernalized state. Only 38 per cent of the treated grains produced plants with fully emerged ears, although others were approaching that stage.

More recently, Weibel (1958) has succeeded in vernalizing winter wheat during the fruiting period, using the obligate winter variety, Comanche. Immature embryos were vernalized by harvesting spikes with attached culms from 8 to 12 days after anthesis, standing them in water, and storing them in a refrigerator at 32° to 40°F for 40 to 50 days. Plants grown from seeds from these experiments headed only when grown under long days. Weibel believes that this technique might be used for testing winter cereals for disease reactions in places suitable only for spring crops, or for the breeding and testing of winter cereals by growing two or three generations a year as is done with spring cereals.

The results obtained by Gregory and Purvis on this point lead to the same conclusion as that reached by Kostjučenko and Zarubaĭlo with regard to the sensitivity of an active embryo and insensitivity of a dormant one. Gregory and Purvis (1938) dated the ears at anthesis and thus determined the age of the treated embryos. The results of the experiment, presented graphically in their paper, were grouped into 10-day classes covering the period from 5 days to 35 days after anthesis. The treatment is effective from the earliest stage of the development of the embryo, decreasing in intensity as beginning of treatment is delayed. Low temperature is therefore effective only while the embryo is actively growing, and ceases to be operative when the embryo becomes dormant. Gregory and Purvis conclude that the effect is quantitative, depending on the duration of the exposure to low temperature, as had been shown to be the case in normal vernalization (Purvis and Gregory, 1937).

An important result which probably indicates how early a developing embryo is fully sensitive to environmental conditions is that obtained by Gregory and Purvis (1938), who showed that seed obtained from ears removed from the parent plant as early as 5 days after anthesis germinated after being sown in the following spring. Completely normal plants were produced, although the individual immature grains were very small (4 × 1 mm) and had apparently no reserves. When winter rye was used, the plants grown from seeds having a range of maturity of 5 to 50 days showed no difference in the stage of development reached after 17 weeks. As the plants had not been vernalized, no ears emerged. In spring rye, on the other hand, a variation was found in the days from germination to anthesis varying from $51·8 \pm 1·17$ days (mean of ten plants) in completely matured seeds, to $62·7 \pm 0·91$ days (mean of three plants) in grain from ears removed 11 days after anthesis, the earliest removed ears to give viable grain. A decrease in the time taken to flower is correlated with maturity of the ripening grain. Gregory and Purvis suggest the possibility of partial devernalization of the very immature grains of spring rye.

Later studies made at the Research Institute of Plant Physiology, London, were concerned with a more detailed investigation of the processes occurring in the embryo-sac of a cereal subsequent to fertilization, and of the conditions of formation and the subsequent growth of dwarf embryos of rye. Nutman's account of the former investigation is concerned with the anatomical and cytological evidence for the formation of growth-promoting substances in the developing grain of rye. Later Nutman (1941) describes the formation of the dwarf grain of rye in ears harvested at an immature stage, and compares the morphology and anatomy of dwarf and normal grains and embryos. He confirms observations made by Gregory and Purvis with rye, and earlier by Harlan and Pope with barley that ears removed from the plants as early as 5 days after fertilization produce viable grain.

Pre-Dormancy Vernalization and Varietal Behaviour

The facts so far established are considered by Kostjučenko and Zarubaïlo (1936) to be of great importance in the setting up and interpretation of varietal tests. It is obvious that, in such tests, only seeds which have been produced locally for at least one generation should be used, and even here, the conditions under which they were formed and ripened must be considered in order to avoid false conclusions. If the use of imported seeds in unavoidable, these same conditions should again be known fully. This is particularly important when dealing with plants from northern latitudes, where the period of seed setting and ripening frequently coincides with a season of low temperature. The same variety may in one year be early and in others very late, according to whether the conditions during ripening in the previous season were such as to vernalize the developing embryos, that is, to provide them with their requirement of low temperature.

Even in less extreme latitudes, this factor has to be taken into consideration. Varieties of, say, Welsh oats might receive quite a considerable proportion of their requirement of hours of temperatures below the critical maximum, particularly if they had been formed at higher elevations under the temperate and frequently quite cool autumn temperatures of their home country. If this hypothetical variety grown under such conditions is transferred in the form of grain to a different habitat, say, South Australia, it may appear in the first season to be a reasonably early variety, since the embryos are still in the partially vernalized (developmentally older) state produced by the environment while they were ripening in the Welsh hills. But when the next generation of grains is forming on the first generation plants grown from the imported grain, the conditions may be (theoretically) such as to preclude the possibility of natural vernalization of the developing embryo before dormancy. The variety which was generally regarded as early in Wales, and would have been recorded as early in the first generation in Australia, now acts as a later variety. If this example should be substantiated, and there is some evidence to this effect, it raises the whole question of locality for production of seed in relation to its place of cultivation, particularly with regard to wide changes in latitude or elevation between the two localities.

An important aspect to be considered is the effect of natural, and particularly pre-dormancy vernalization, on the degree of winter hardiness of a particular variety. Certain workers believe that plants show a reduction in winter hardiness according to the degree of their completion of the thermo-phase, or according to the degree to which they have been vernalized. If this evidence is substantiated, then it is clear that, again, the possibility of pre-dormancy vernalization must be considered in making field or plot observations upon this character. Otherwise, say Kostjučenko and Zarubaïlo, a variety may quite inexplicably be quite hardy over one winter, due to absence of vernalization in the pre-dormant stage of embryo development in the preceding late summer-autumn ripening period, and yet non-hardy or only slightly hardy in other years, as the embryos in the sown grain had already 'passed the thermo-phase' while still attached to the mother plant.

Chapter IX

EQUIPMENT FOR RESEARCH
AND PRODUCTION

The equipment used in experiments on the response of plants to the aerial environment, and in providing an optimal environment for economic production of crops varies widely in nature and complexity. It may be said that the simplest form of equipment is actually the observation plot laid down by agronomists and plant breeders to test the degree of adaptability to the environment of indigenous or exotic species, varieties and strains of economic plants. The Uniform Mediterranean Nurseries established under the aegis of the F.A.O. Working Party on Mediterranean Pasture and Fodder Development are an example. Some two hundred varieties and strains of herbage grasses and legumes have been tested under a wide range of conditions, varying in amount and seasonal distribution of rainfall, seasonal temperatures, latitude, altitude, exposure, proximity to the sea and similar factors. A co-operative varietal trial of this type represents the dispersion of the varieties in order to ensure that they shall be exposed to highly variable conditions. These trials are conducted for at least 3 years to allow for the high degree of irregularity, season by season, of a Mediterranean environment.

The opposite extreme to this dispersal method, with all the inaccuracies which are associated with it, is the concentration of varieties at one centre where facilities exist to give them all possible combinations and permutations of environmental factors under scientifically controlled conditions. In experimental physiology, these conditions are provided by the so-called phytotron (see p. 147). Between the two extremes of the varietal plot trial and the phytotron, there are a great many types of equipment which provide a greater or lesser control of the aerial environment, primarily for experimental purposes.

Types in Britain

A list of installations of this intermediate type at present in use for experimental work in Britain has been given by Hudson (1957 a), under the heads of growth cabinets with artificial light, growth cabinets using natural light, wind tunnels, temperature-controlled rooms, growth rooms and glasshouses for environmental work. The survey has shown that there are many different approaches to the problem of controlling the plant environment, some much more costly than others both in capital equipment and running expenses. A high degree of control is difficult and expensive to achieve where crop plants are to be grown to maturity to produce heavy acreage yields per plant and in replicated experiments. It is a question whether it is best for a country like Great Britain to have a few large expensive phytotrons, or many more simpler cheaper installations; the general opinion in Britain is quoted by Hudson: 'At the present state of knowledge, there is need for one installation, which need not be large but must be well instrumented, for the most precise work of setting standards. There is also a pressing need for a much larger number of simpler, cheaper installations, which seem likely to produce more results, more quickly, for a given total national expenditure on capital and running costs, than one or two phytotrons, which would necessarily only be accessible to a small number of workers and available for a strictly limited number of projects.'

In designing growth rooms and cabinets, more information is needed on the tolerances which can be accepted in time and space. Many installations are too elaborate, or do not provide the degree of control that is needed. There is a need for labour-saving devices to provide automatic control during 24-hour cycles and at weekends. In achieving a high degree of control of factors such as temperature, light and relative humidity in glasshouses, the efficiency of ventilation has to be considered, so as to reduce gradients of environmental factors in both space and time. The possibility of end-to-end ventilation instead of the traditional lateral method may be considered. At present, none of the light sources which are available give intensities approaching those which occur on bright summer days in Britain. Several lamps of new design enable higher light intensities to be provided, although with the associated difficulty of keeping temperatures down to reasonable levels.

The factors which it is necessary to control in environmental studies include:
air temperature,
light intensity, quality and duration of photoperiod,
relative humidity of the air,
composition of the atmosphere, including degree of pollution,
air speed, and
temperature of soil.

Hudson states that the approach to environmental control has been largely empirical, but that a number of basic principles seem to be emerging from work in Britain as follows.

Temperature regulation is most easily achieved in small well-insulated containers located in larger rooms which are themselves at fairly constant temperatures, e.g. cellars. A glasshouse is probably the most unsuitable closed structure because of its poor insulation and the ready admission of uncontrollable amounts of radiant energy during the daytime.

Light may be from natural or artificial sources. As natural light, although cheap, fluctuates unpredictably in intensity and in higher latitudes in daylength, it is fortunate that many plants are able to grow well in artificial light at intensities far below natural sunlight. The use in enclosed spaces of artificial light sufficiently intense to support good plant growth does introduce difficulties, particularly with regard to excessive heat. Hudson states that the usual compromise is either (*a*) in glasshouses, to use artificial light during the day to supplement daylight on dull days to ensure a minimum light intensity, and/or at night, to lengthen the photoperiod, or (*b*) in opaque structures, to use artificial light of considerably lower intensity than maximum natural daylight.

Relative humidity is one of the most difficult factors to control within close limits, although this may be done if temperature can also be closely controlled.

Composition of the air is not controllable in most experimental environments. It is generally assumed that carbon dioxide adequate for photosynthesis is evolved from the soil or compost, or is ensured by frequent air changes; in a few cases, CO_2 may be introduced into the air stream. Provision may also be made for removal of atmospheric pollution in a big city.

Air speed (rate of winds) may be controlled in wind tunnels.

Soil temperature is usually allowed to find equilibrium with the controlled air temperature, but soil may be heated or cooled electrically.

Regarding flexibility of control, Hudson draws the following conclusions from his review of British techniques: In planning a controlled environment it may be an advantage to make provision for varying the levels of each factor over a wide range, to meet the needs of future experiments and thus avoid the temptation to devise experiments to fit available environments rather than the reverse. This approach results in a flexible installation but is apt to be expensive, since heating and cooling equipment must be adequate to meet exceptional demands which may very rarely occur, and the equipment will be working for most of the time at much less than its full capacity. On the other hand, some research workers prefer to devise special equipment to meet the *ad hoc* needs of particular research and dismantle it afterwards, thus using the minimum of apparatus for each experiment. While this may save capital, it can be wasteful of time since it may take months to design, construct and learn to operate an installation.

Regarding control of temperature, there are advantages in allowing a cabinet or room to run for long periods at a constant temperature since it oftens takes some time to adjust controls to give accurate and specific responses. Once an environment has 'settled down', and is running well at the required levels, there is much to be said for leaving it alone. Rapid flexibility may, however, be called for in controlled environments of the future. In the past, much physiological work has been based on treatments using constant temperatures, stable humidities and fixed daylengths. In nature, conditions are rarely constant for any appreciable time but are marked by regular variations in daylength, and strong but irregular diurnal fluctuations in light intensity, temperature and humidity. Such changing conditions presumably influence growth, but little is known of such effects and few installations are at present capable of producing controlled hourly or daily changes in temperature, light intensity or humidity.

There is a growing interest in these effects and also in the response of plants to longer-term seasonal fluctuations in temperature, light intensity and daylength. Where the effects of diurnal temperature changes are being studied, it seems usual to have two environments, running at different constant temperatures, and to move plants from one to another night and morning, rather than to attempt to achieve different temperatures in the same chamber at different times each day. The latter approach is, however, being followed in some laboratories. Where rapid and frequent changes in environmental conditions are required, there seems to be some advantage in using an air-conditioning plant situated outside the controlled space and supplying it with large volumes of air at the required temperature and relative humidity.

Types in Canada

Commercial growth cabinets manufactured by the Fleming-Pedlar Company, Winnipeg, Manitoba, are used in the Cereal Laboratory of the Canadian Department of Agriculture at Winnipeg (Dr. C. H.

Goulden), at some other experimental stations in Canada, and at Universities and Experiment Stations in the United States. In general, these commercial pre-fabricated, self-contained units are of special value where an organization requires a built-up unit which does not need additional engineering service for design purposes. Originally, the design was developed to produce a cabinet suitable for cereal breeding and it is very satisfactory for this purpose. However, these cabinets are being used for forage work and other purposes. The general specifications of temperature indicate the utility of the unit. No special provision is made for humidity control, but moisture conditions can be partially regulated by watering the crop or by locating a spray nozzle in the machine.

The cabinet itself is entirely self-contained and measures approximately 10 ft long, 4 ft wide and 8 ft high. At one end in an area measuring 4 ft by 8 ft is located a plant growth section, while the other compartment measuring about 2 ft by 4 ft contains the refrigeration apparatus and circulating fan. In the growth compartment, light is supplied by thirty-two fluorescent tubes of the 96T-12 C.W. type with or without reflectors as required, with an additional light supplement consisting of eight 100-watt incandescent bulbs. The light panel or source in this compartment can be adjusted to any suitable height above the plants and the crop can be grown to full height of 3 ft if required. The refrigeration section contains a compressor with a capacity of 1·5 horse-power for nominal operating conditions or a compressor with 2 horse-power for special installations. Cooling for the compressor coil can be provided by a water cooling system from any suitable water source.

The nominal operating condition for the growth section is 48° to 90°F. The cabinet is usually kept at about 70°F during the day part of the cycle, while 48°F can be used at night, if required. In general, these temperatures can be obtained when the outside temperature is at approximately 90° to 95° depending on circumstances. Time clocks are provided for controlling temperature and lights. Depending on the number of units supplied, these cost $5,000 to 6,000 depending on requirements. In addition to the pre-fabricated type of commercial cabinets, some general-purpose growth rooms of various sizes are in use. The majority measure approximately 8 by 12 ft and are supplied with fluorescent light supplemented with incandescent light, while the refrigeration is nominally rated at roughly 3 horse-power.

Experiments are now being conducted on a study of light panel intensities. To date, it has been possible to obtain in engineering experiments intensities as high as 3,300 foot-candles under incandescent tubes at a distance of 24 in. However, this work is continuing in order to improve the distribution of light (Kalbfleisch, 1958).

Types in South Africa

Two temperature-controlled greenhouses with plate glass roofs are used at the Plant Physiological Research Institute, Pretoria. No water-spray is used on the roofs for technical and economic reasons, and to obtain as much light as possible. The day and night temperatures (°C) in the two greenhouses are respectively:

	day	*night*
A.	27	21
B.	18 or 21	15

Temperature changes are made at 8 a.m. and 5 p.m. Other night tempera-tures and photoperiods differing from normal daylength are obtained by using four constant temperature rooms, each with a bank of eighty-eight 3-ft, 30-watt, fluorescent lamps and nine 150-watt incandescent lamps above a perspex plate recessed into the ceiling. One cold room, two dark rooms with accurate temperature control, four temperature-controlled incubators with artificial illumination, and two rooting boxes with temperature control of the rooting medium are also available.

Plants on trucks are moved to the required night conditions at 4.30 p.m. and to the day conditions at 8.30 a.m. With a 12- or 16-hour photo-period, plants therefore receive 4 or 8 hours of artificial illumination in addition to 8 hours of sunlight. To compare the influence of normal growing conditions in the open during the day with those in the green-house, one set of night treatments is usually combined with a day treat-ment out-of-doors. The plants are therefore moved into the open at 8.30 a.m. and back into the constant temperature rooms at 4.30 p.m.

The Phytotron

The term 'phytotron' was coined by the physicist, Prof. R. A. Millikan, as analogous to the cyclotron, the prototype of most machines for the acceleration of nuclear particles to high energies. The phytotron is an instrument designed to provide at one spot all possible variations in the environment which affect the growth and reproductive development of plants, even to the extent of including conditions which have no counterpart in nature. Berrie (1957) has stated the word 'phytotron' has been accepted as describing a building used to grow plants under any desired climatic condition, at the press of a button; it is better to regard it as much as a system of management as a collection of growth rooms, since the flexibility is largely achieved by the management. When Berrie described the original phytotron, built by Prof. F. W. Went at the Earhart Plant Research Laboratory at Pasadena, California (see Went, 1957), to the Nottingham University Easter School in 1957, considerable doubt was expressed by participants in the degree of control claimed for this equipment.

Similar constructions of the phytotron type have since been built at the University of Liège (Prof. R. Bouillenne), the Institute of Horticultural Plant Breeding and the Institute for Biological and Chemical Research on Field Crops and Herbage at Wageningen; others are under construction by the Centre National de la Recherche Scientifique at Gif-sur-Yvette near Paris, and by the Institute of Plant Physiology near Moscow; similar equipment is planned by the Division of Plant Industry, C.S.I.R.O., Canberra, and by the Department of Scientific and Industrial Research in New Zealand.

It is claimed that a well-designed phytotron makes it feasible to have complete control of all the factors of the environment. For example, the phytotron building near Paris, which is being built at the instigation of Professor Pierre Chouard of the Sorbonne, and which will cost about £2 million to complete, is planned to have thirty-four chambers for plant experiments, in addition to biochemical and other laboratories. Thirteen out of the thirty-four chambers are of the type in which illumination is entirely artificial and in which temperature, humidity and other factors can be fully controlled. Artificial rain is also available in some. Air is replaced at a rate ten times that normal with air conditioning. There is provision for chemical control of the atmosphere, for the use of radio-isotopes in tracer experiments and for special forms of illumination. There are thirteen dark chambers and eight in which the main illumination is by sunlight, but in which other factors can be controlled. The construction of all the chambers of this phytotron is to be done progressively, so that modifications based on experience may be installed in the later chambers.

Equipment which may be regarded as a lesser phytotron has been installed at the John Innes Horticultural Institution, Bayfordbury, Hertfordshire, and came into full use in June 1958. It consists of three

identical rooms, independently controlled in all respects, planned specifically for the growing of small plants on benches 5 ft long, 4 ft wide,
and having a maximum vertical range of adjustment of 4 ft. Heating,
cooling, dehumidification and steam humidification are electronically
controlled from central panels. Light is supplied to each room by
thirty-two, 80-watt 'White' (3500°K) fluorescent lamps with internal
reflectors. The air circulation fans run continuously, control of temperature and humidity being achieved by relatively frequent cycling of
heaters and coolers. The rooms have been designed by members of the
Department of Physiology and Plant Culture to give (a) the highest
practicable uniformity of light intensity, air temperature, air velocity
and relative humidity in the whole of the space available for the plants,
(b) great flexibility and adaptability in operation commensurate with
low cost, and (c) comprehensive data on the influence of construction
and control on the climate and performance of the rooms. Many of the
data can be obtained only from long-term measurements to be made
concurrently with the use of the rooms for plant studies. Already,
however, it is possible to state the salient features of light and temperature control with some degree of accuracy, and this has been done in
the Annual Report for 1958.

The phytotron of the Institute of Horticultural Plant Breeding at
Wageningen, put into service in 1953, represents a compromise necessi-
tated by the funds available, the dimensions of the rooms required to
deal with crops, and the degree of perfection of the system of climatic
control (Braak and Smeets, 1956). The design of the experimental part
is based on the principle of maintaining constant temperature and air
humidity in each of the glasshouses and growth chambers, and on the
mobility of the plant material, achieved by placing potted plants on
specially designed trucks. The experimental section consists of the
central corridor, eight experimental rooms (A–H) of 3×5 metres, five
cold ($-15°C$ to $+20°C$) and three warm ($+18°C$ to $+30°C$), and six
glasshouses (G_3–G_8) of 6×10 metres with fixed side benches and a central
space for trucks (see Figs. 21, 22, and 23).

Braak and Smeets summarize the experience of 3 years of operation
in Table 2.

The Institute for Biological and Chemical Research on Field Crops and
Herbage, primarily intended for fundamental research in agriculture,
has the following facilities (Alberda, 1958):

(1) seven glasshouses in which temperature and relative humidity
can be controlled,

(2) six air-conditioned growth rooms with different sources of artificial light,

(3) cold storage rooms, and

(4) a phytotron consisting of three glasshouses and six growth rooms (see Figs. 24, 25 and 26).

Table 2

POSSIBILITIES AND LIMITATIONS OF A PHYTOTRON

(Institute of Horticultural Plant Breeding, Wageningen)

Room	Climatic factor	Range	Accuracy
Glasshouses	Temperatures winter season	+10°C to +25°C	2°C
	Temperatures summer season	+23°C to +35°C (+18°C to +35°C in cooled glasshouse)	3°C
	Humidity winter season	65 to 95 per cent	20 per cent
	Humidity summer season	85 to 95 per cent	20 per cent
Experimental rooms	Temperature	−15°C to +40°C	1°C
	Humidity	65 to 95 per cent	10 per cent

An alternative design has been developed by the Division of Plant Industry, C.S.I.R.O., Canberra (see Fig. 27). The classical phytotrons consist of a relatively small number of rooms (less than fifty at Pasadena) with which a large number of different climatic treatments (almost 500 at Pasadena) can be obtained by moving the plants daily from one room to another. In the Australian design, the controlled environment space will be provided in a large number (about 300) of small cabinets, each under separate control, and each capable of providing a very wide range of conditions (Evans, 1958 a). The plants are to remain in the cabinets throughout the experiment, except for measurement and manipulation, and the periods of loss of control at moving would be eliminated. There would be no restrictions on the type of temperature or daylength conditions that could be obtained, provided they fell within the operating range of the cabinets, and there would be no limitations to expansion of the amount of controlled space to meet future needs. Further advantages of the cabinet-type phytotron are that more uniform air-conditioning should be possible within the smaller cabinets than within rooms, and

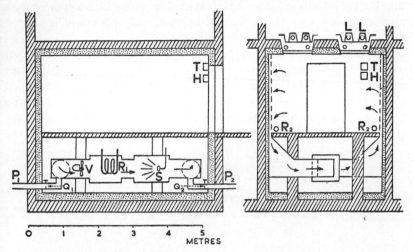

Fig. 21. Phytotron of the Institute of Horticultural Plant Breeding, Wageningen (Braak and Smeets, 1956).

    Longitudinal section and cross-section of a cold room: H, humidistat; L, lamp; P, pipe; Q, damper; R_1, heat exchanger; R_2, electric heater; S, spray chamber; T, thermostat; V, ventilator.

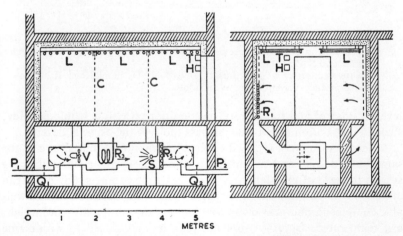

Fig. 22. Phytotron of the Institute of Horticultural Plant Breeding, Wageningen (Braak and Smeets, 1956).

    Longitudinal section and cross-section of a warm room: H, humidistat; L, lamp; P, pipe; Q, damper; R_1, cooler; R_3, heat exchanger; R_5, re-heating coil; S, spray chamber; T, thermostat; V, ventilator.

151

that the complexity of the whole installation would be no greater than that of one unit, since the entire machinery of each unit would be located within it and would be of a standard type.

The soundness of such a design depends upon the possibility of constructing a satisfactory and economical unit. Prototype units with an extremely high level of performance have now been successfully developed by the C.S.I.R.O. Engineering Section. The feasibility of a cabinet-type phytotron has thus been established, and plans have been drawn for the erection of such an installation in Canberra. In flexibility, and in the

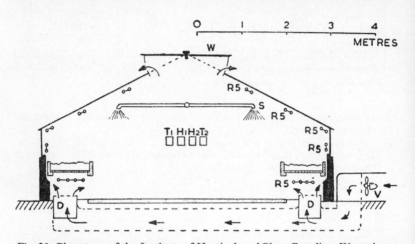

Fig. 23. Phytotron of the Institute of Horticultural Plant Breeding, Wageningen (Braak and Smeets, 1956).
Cross-section of a glasshouse: D, airduct; H, humidistat; R_5, pipes; T, thermostat; V, ventilator; W, windows.

level of control and uniformity of conditions which it would provide, such an installation might well surpass those of the original design.

At least six different types of cabinet are envisaged, but all are of the same basic design, and will utilize a standard type of air-conditioning system for ease of maintenance. The size of the cabinets, 6 ft by 3 ft in area, is the most economical for construction with commercially available equipment, and is also suitable biologically. In the present models, any temperature from 40° to 100°F can be maintained to within one degree, while daylength is controlled by automatic shutters and by the provision of supplementary artificial illumination.

Most of the cabinets will be naturally illuminated, and these will be enclosed within a long narrow glasshouse divided into fifteen sections.

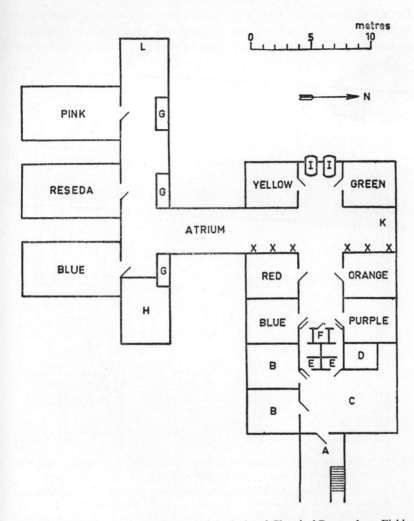

Fig. 24. Phytotron of the Institute of Biological and Chemical Research on Field Crops and Herbage, Wageningen (Alberda, 1958).

General layout: A, corridor with staircase to basement; B, sitting room; C, laboratory; D, weighing room; E, entrance to phytotron proper; F, lavatory; G, air conditioning duct for glasshouse; H, machine room for glasshouses; I, sterilizing unit; K, photography room; L, potting room; X, tap for nutrient solution.

153

Each section will contain eight cabinets with similar temperature regimes. In the four central sections the cabinets will also condition the space around them, and this will be occupied by plants on trolleys which can be

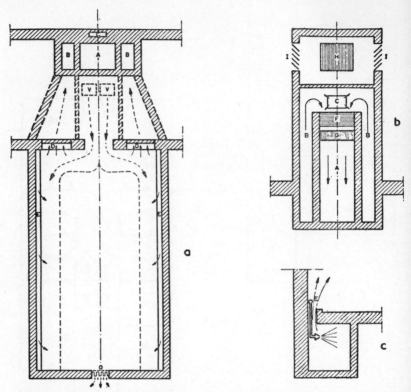

Fig. 25. Phytotron of the Institute of Biological and Chemical Research on Field Crops and Herbage, Wageningen (Alberda, 1958).

a, air-circulation system in glasshouse; *b*, cross-section through air-conditioning system; *c*, air-supply duct with water spray; A, air-supply duct with heater (F) and cooler (G); B, duct leading from glasshouse to conditioning apparatus; C, fresh air supply duct; D, opening for air leaving the glasshouse; E, longitudinal slit for air entering the glasshouse; H, cooler for the atrium; I, dampers to regulate the atrium cooling; V, fan.

wheeled to the other enclosures or to the dark rooms opposite. The remaining cabinets will be artificially illuminated and will be enclosed in rooms in the body of the building. There will also be special rooms for the control of atmospheric composition, frost and humidity, as well as a

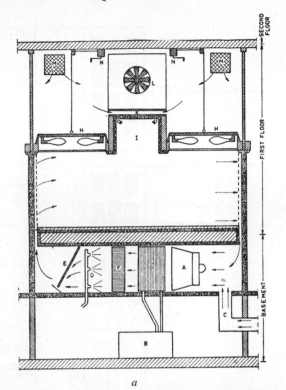

a

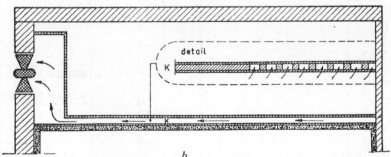

b

Fig. 26. Phytotron of the Institute of Biological and Chemical Research on Field Crops and Herbage, Wageningen (Alberda, 1958).

a, cross-section through a growth room; *b*, removal of the warm air from the lamp room. A, fan; B, freon compressor; C, fresh air supply duct; D, water spray; E, screen; F, heater; G, cooler; H, lamp frame; I, corridor; K, double-walled ceiling in the corridor; L, fan; M, opening through which fresh air enters the lamp room; N, winding drum for lamp frame.

155

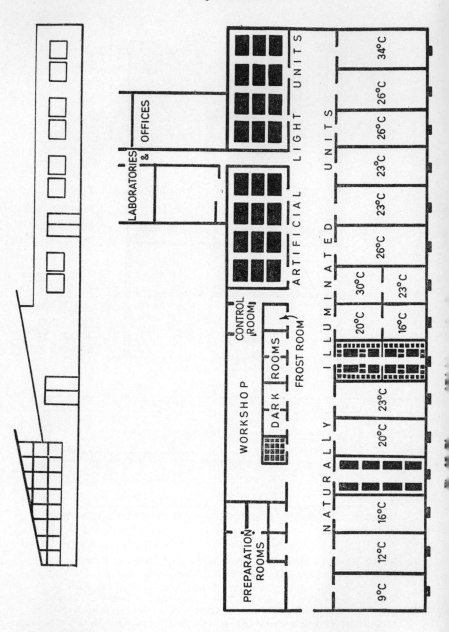

156

laboratory, preparation and instrument control rooms, and a workshop for mechanical maintenance.

About 200 cabinets are considered to be the minimal requirement for the installation of the Australian phytotron. This apparently large number is essential owing to the necessity for studying the interactions of the climatic factors. Consider, for instance, the investigation of winter growth of pastures. One might wish to test the effects of five different day temperatures, at four light intensities, and each of these at three day-lengths. For this alone each variety tested would require $5 \times 4 \times 3 = 60$ cabinets. Similar investigations of summer growth in *Phalaris*, of flowering in subterranean clover, of leaf quality in tobacco, or of fertilizer response in any crop, would require as many, if not more, cabinets. Others would be required for the screening of new plant introductions. The estimated capital cost of the 200 unit cabinets needed to provide the necessary amount and range of controlled conditions, and of the enclosing structure is approximately £A 500,000 (February, 1958). The operating expenses are expected to be comparatively modest, rather less than for a C.S.I.R.O. field station.

The design and equipment of a 'station of artificial climate' in the Soviet Union has been described by Tumanov (1957). In 1940, the first attempts to construct a physiological laboratory in which climate would be controlled was made at the Timirjazev Agricultural Academy; building began in 1941 but ceased because of the War. A few years ago a new plan was prepared and the erection began in Ostankino. In 1957, the Institute of Plant Physiology took over the first part of the 'Station of Artificial Climate', which represents in fact, a whole complex of separate laboratories and climatic control rooms, with a small but complicated plant for the treatment of air necessary for the creation of various weather conditions. The Soviet station is stated to differ from those in other countries in that it serves not only for experiments on growth and reproductive development, but also for thorough studies of the resistance of organisms to unfavourable environments, winter extremes, drought, saline soils, etc. These installations allow experimentation over a large range of temperatures and air humidity, the maintenance of different temperatures for various parts of a plant, etc.

The experimental rooms occupy a two-storey building. For work with low temperatures there are seven refrigerated cabinets each of 1 m^3 capacity in which it is possible to obtain temperatures down to $-70°C$. The temperature is measured by electric resistance thermometers and is automatically recorded. The task regime is maintained by automatic controls. Thawing is done in the same cabinets, by means of electric heaters. All refrigerators work with freon which, in contrast to ammonia, does not have an unfavourable influence on organisms. For studies on and storage of frozen plants, there are two rooms in which freezing temperatures of any degree may be created. These are also for research on winter resistance of fruit trees under shortened vegetative periods, which in natural conditions would happen with a late spring and/or early autumn frost, as well as by the extension of the cultivation of southern plants northwards. For studying vernalization and stratification of seeds and dormancy periods, and also to find optimal conditions for storage of fruits and vegetables, there are three more cold rooms in which it is possible to keep temperatures from $0°C$ upwards. Finally, there are rooms each measuring $4·5$ m^2, where with special installations it is possible not only to maintain any desired temperature but also any air humidity (see Plate 2).

In these installations the air, before it enters the experimental rooms, is washed, heated or cooled, dried or saturated with humidity, as the experiment may require. These chambers are intended for conditioning of winter cereals, for obtaining data on growth and development in cold weather, but are also suitable for experimentation on the cold resistance of warm-climate plants. A number of chambers have special electric lighting for changing the duration of day and night. There are also warm rooms for temperatures from $+10°C$ upwards, with variable humidities, for investigation of the influence of various types of weather on growth, development and productivity, and also of photoperiods at variable day and night temperatures.

The Soviet workers state that it is most difficult to create a desired light regime. Daylight generally fluctuates widely in intensity and quality, and is not easy to regulate. Electric lighting is provided as follows: thirty-six incandescent lamps of 500 watts each are situated above the glass ceiling of a room; for the absorption of heat they are submerged in water that flows over the ceiling in an 18-cm thick layer; an airing dome is installed above the water for the removal of heat emanating from the lamp parts which are above the water. The combination of the upper incandescent lamps with the fluorescent daylight lamps inside the chamber ensures not only a balanced constant, but also overall lighting of the plants (i.e. both from above and from the sides). The quality of light is improved and it is stated that its intensity can be brought up to 40,000 lux. Electric light cannot, of course, completely replace sunlight. Therefore, on the southern side on the second floor of the station is a

EQUIPMENT

greenhouse comprising four compartments of 25 m² each, in which temperatures of +10°C and above and various air humidities are obtainable. The glass roof of the greenhouse is shaded during hot sunny days. The rooms have fluorescent lights to provide additional light when necessary. Special elevators can be used to lower plants into separate conditioned rooms.

Special equipment is available to study the processes of growth and development of separate organs and parts of plants at various temperatures. It is possible to study the influence of various temperatures on the growth of a tomato fruit placed in a special receptacle with double walls between which flows a liquid at temperatures ranging from 0° to 40°C. There is equipment to maintain a temperature regime for root studies. Research on root activity at different temperatures is made possible by means of twenty-eight special thermostats, each with a capacity for twenty plant containers. The solution in the tanks can be cooled by a refrigerator or heated from 0° to 40°C, thereby maintaining the temperature in the containers at a desired level. Thermostats are fitted in conditioned chambers as well as in a specially equipped 'lighted yard', which is a room with a movable glass roof where the plants can be protected against wind and rain or can be kept in the open air in fair weather. In this 'yard' are installed sixteen thermostats for the study of the processes of absorption of nutrient solutions and water by roots at various temperatures, as well as for studying the synthesis of various substances in the underground parts. The glasshouse has special lysimeters for growing plants in inert media, through which nutrient solutions may be passed.

The station also has laboratories with special equipment, e.g. an operation room sterilized by bactericide lamps for experiments with excised organs and tissues; a special climatized room for growing tissues in nutrients under fixed external conditions; two equipped conditioned rooms with a laboratory for studying germination and the processes of growth; a special building with adequate laboratories for work on radio-isotopes; special rooms for studies of metabolism in an organism by means of chromatography; for experiments with Warburg's apparatus for gas exchange in photosynthesis and respiration at various temperatures and air humidities, including one special freezing laboratory for work with frozen objects, for instance, to ascertain their plasma viscosity, resistance to mechanical stresses, etc. The laboratories are fully equipped for physiological, microscopic and chemical experiments, possess electric current of different voltages, compressed air, etc. Electric recorders register temperature and humidity in the climatized rooms. Some laboratories are so equipped that experiments may be carried out in the open air. The total area of climatized rooms is 600 m², but special machinery and equipment have been provided to serve experimental installations on double that area.

The Glasshouse

The horticulturist is, of course, the producer most concerned with the possibilities of commercial plant production under controlled conditions. In this connection, Maatsch (1955) makes the point in his paper to the 14th International Horticultural Congress that the idea has spread in horticultural circles that the best results can be obtained when the cultural environment of the plant is exactly the same as the natural environment from which it came. Here one tends to overlook the fact that conditions for optimal growth seldom obtain in the natural habitat, and that the plant may have become established there because of its particular vitality or its degree of adaptability to unfavourable conditions. With the modern knowledge of physiological requirements and responses at his command, the horticulturist is able to provide artificial conditions much superior to any that may be found in the plant's natural environment.

Again, as in the experimental studies on the plant and its environment, the soil is only rarely an important factor in pot plant production, particularly since the special potting composts evolved by W. J. C. Lawrence and others became available. The producer must, therefore, concern himself primarily with temperature and light, which he must consider together since their influences are largely interrelated or complementary. Some knowledge of the temperature conditions of the natural habitat may be of value, but so much has now been discovered about the photoperiodic control of growth and reproduction that information regarding the photoperiodic characteristics of the natural habitat is not of great significance for market production.

The glasshouse, although inferior to the growth chamber for experimental studies, nevertheless represents the chief method of providing a controlled environment for commercial production. Important work on the design and operation of glasshouses has been done at the John Innes Horticultural Institution. After stating that 'the problem of the control of glasshouse environment has rarely been adequately considered and comprehended', Lawrence (1955; see also 1950) presented a general survey of the subject to the 14th International Horticultural Congress,

(a)

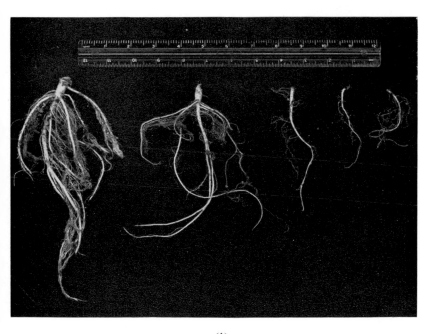

(b)

16. Influence of density of stand on the growth form of: (a) tops and (b) roots of subterranean clover (Davidson and Donald, 1958). *Left to right:* plants from swards initially
sown at 1, 4, 25, 100 and 250 plants per square link. Photographed 19 weeks after
sowing, when the densities were 1, 4, 25, 54 and 60 plants per square link

(*a*)

(*b*)

17. The effects of night temperature on seedstalk development in Great Lakes lettuce (Rappaport and Wittwer, 1956*a*). *Left to right:* Night temperatures of 70, 65, 60, 50° F. *Above:* Vernalized. *Below:* not vernalized

illustrated by examples from the John Innes experiments. Although these remarks were made with reference to the use of the glasshouse in plant research, they do, however, provide an excellent basis for considering commercial techniques as well.

Lawrence defines the ideal glasshouse environment as uniform in space, sensitively controlled in time, and adjusted to give the maximum rate of balanced growth and reproductive development; the average glasshouse falls far short of this ideal. 'A glasshouse may be bought and equipped without any knowledge of its characteristics; it is put in an odd spot, often adjoining a brick building because it is convenient, and with no better control than operation, by hand, of both ventilators and heating system' (Lawrence, *loc. cit.*). In considering the factors which must be measured and evaluated, the environment may be divided into two major components: air and soil. The components of air are: solar radiation, its subdivisions light, temperature, moisture and air change rate; of soil: moisture, temperature, mechanical condition, and nutrient content.

Light in glasshouses north of about latitude 48° is deficient for half the year. Maximum admission of light and reduction of light gradients to a minimum can be obtained by correct siting and design. Heat is supplied by solar radiation or heating systems; the former has to be utilized to the full to conserve the latter. Maximum use may be made of solar heat in winter by improving both the glasshouse design and the system of heating; artificial heat may be conserved by reducing air change to a minimum and by providing windbreaks.

Conclusions reached from studies of glasshouses at the Institute for Horticulture at Grossbeeren of the German Academy of Agricultural Science of Berlin are (Reinhold, 1955): The aim should be a multiple-purpose glasshouse for optimal plant growing. On large holdings, block construction is preferable to single construction as it promotes rational soil cultivation. For Central-German conditions the optimal direction of a layout is about north–south. The width of a unit should be adapted to all vegetable crops (about 4 m). To save cost and material, the construction should be as light as possible. The parts should be manufactured in series. It should be possible for growers to build their glasshouses (prefabrication). The constructional parts should be resistant to corrosion. The physiological disadvantages of the rain-gutter (shade, fall of drops) should be met. There should be good ventilation (shaft). The light conditions should be favourable (wide panes, narrow laths, continuous panes without overlapping, light colours inside the glasshouse). Shading is also

F

important. The construction should allow for additional lighting, and for sprinkling and underground irrigation, to serve also for drainage, soil heating and soil steaming. Warm water is not essential for watering. It will be worthwhile to give more attention to hot-air heating in future.

Under tropical conditions the objectives in using a glasshouse are different, the aim being to dissipate solar energy, not to accumulate it as in temperate regions, and to attempt to reduce the internal glasshouse temperature to the same value as it is outside (Bolle-Jones, 1956). The light which is available at certain seasons in temperate climates is frequently below the optimal for plant growth, but in a tropical environment more than enough light is available and some crops such as tea and cocoa will grow better if the light intensity is reduced by various types of shading. The avoidance of high humidity is perhaps not so essential as in temperate equipment, because the atmospheric humidity in the tropics is usually high and any excessive or prolonged accumulation of water vapour is prevented by the high atmospheric temperature. A high humidity may have a slight effect in reducing insolation, but efficient air movement is probably of greater importance in the reduction of atmospheric temperature.

It was to meet these factors that Bolle-Jones (*loc. cit.*) designed and constructed a glasshouse suitable for physiological experiments under tropical climatic conditions, in this case particularly on rubber. The glasshouse at the Rubber Research Institute of Malaya at Kuala Lumpur is partially open-sided, has a jack roof, and is supported by angle framework. All the metal parts employed, except for some iron-wire network, are of either aluminium or aluminium alloy. The glasshouse was easy to construct and requires the minimum of maintenance. The internal atmosphere of the glasshouse has lower maximum and higher minimum temperatures and a lower humidity than an adjacent area outside used for pot experiments.

The glasshouse proved to be satisfactory for experimentation with rubber seedlings, as indicated by their good growth and as judged by a study of the temperature and humidity of the internal atmosphere. Contamination of growing plants within the house by rust has been practically eliminated by the use of aluminium-alloy framework; consequently the glasshouse has proved most suitable for the production of symptoms of micronutrient-element deficiency in rubber seedlings grown in sand culture. The design of the house has proved satisfactory and there has been no evidence of any excessive strain or defect in its constructional design.

EQUIPMENT

In England, there are two tropical houses (6 + 12 ft) for experimental purposes at the Forest Products Research Laboratory, in which the daily cycles of temperature and humidity of the wet and dry tropics can be reproduced, though without high light intensities. Equipment has been installed to maintain specified cycles which involve successive heating, cooling, wetting and drying of the circulating air (Hudson, 1957 a).

Quality of light

Studies in the use of different types and sources of artificial light have been made at, among other places, the Department of Horticulture of Reading University. Stoughton and Vince (1957) have reviewed the present state of knowledge and experience. The commercial use of artificial light to supplement daylight involves a consideration of the kind or type of light source and the economics of its use. Photosynthesis can proceed in light of any wave-length within the visible region but the longer wave-lengths, the red or yellow region of the spectrum, are utilized most efficiently. The shorter wave-lengths of the blue end do, however, ensure a normal habit of growth in many species. In practice, the light sources currently available provide light through the visible spectrum but differ widely in the proportions emitted in each wave-length region. Irradiation should provide energy of the same order as the daylight it is to supplement. Midday winter sunlight in England in a glasshouse has an intensity of 500 to 700 lumens/sq. ft. In terms of luminous efficiency, availability and initial cost, the choice is very limited.

The use of the common incandescent tungsten-filament lamp entails some method of screening against heat radiation from the longer or thermal wave-lengths, and this is not commercially practicable. The neon discharge tube also has a very suitable emission spectrum but has a high initial cost. The fluorescent tube is more promising; the emission spectrum can be varied over a wide range, the luminous efficiency is high, and the lamp is practically free from thermal radiation. As the intrinsic brightness is low, a number of tubes must be used in efficient reflectors; some means of removing the lights when not in use is necessary to avoid shading. This type has been and is widely used. Until recently the readily available high-pressure mercury vapour lamp (HPMV) of 400 watts input has been the most popular because it has a fair luminous efficiency, is reasonable in cost and is a compact source. A high proportion of the emission is, however, in the green region of the spectrum, least efficient for photosynthesis; the thermal emission is also fairly high. New types such as the mercury fluorescent lamp have recently been developed, combining the high intensity and compactness of the HPMV lamp with the lower thermal emission and the better spectral composition of the fluorescent tube.

In the practical use of supplementary light, it is economically feasible to illuminate only relatively small areas at the necessary intensity. At the present cost of electricity in England, it is quite uneconomic to irradiate, for example, a growing crop of tomatoes or cucumbers. Many seedlings can, however, be massed in a small area and irradiated during the dark days of winter to accelerate growth and provide a better, stronger plant for planting out. The technique for irradiating tomato seedlings is described on p. 286. Cucumbers also respond to irradiation with less risk of harmful effects from the heat of the lamp. Lettuces have also been successfully irradiated for planting in winter and early spring.

When controlling light conditions in relation to the photoperiodic reaction of plants, the actual quantity of light which provides effectively long photoperiods varies according to the time when it is applied, the colour of the light, and the species being irradiated. For species in which control of daylength is used commercially, times and intensities of lighting have been determined empirically. Short-day plants are generally more sensitive than long-day plants. To prevent flowering of short-day plants, tungsten-filament lamps spaced to give 5 to 10 lumens/sq. ft are used for 2 to 5 hours in the middle of each night; to promote flowering of long-day plants, lamps spaced to give a similar or greater intensity are switched on from sunset to give a day of 17 hours or more. Low-wattage tungsten-filament lamps are almost universally used because they emit a high proportion of red light, and are the cheapest type to instal. The technique adopted for chrysanthemums is described on p. 274. The commercial application of photoperiodic regulation is limited to those plants for which some economic or other advantage is to be gained by altering the date of flowering by the use of artificial lighting or mechanical shading. So far, techniques for only a few crops have been worked out and are practised to a considerable extent in U.S.A., less so in Europe and Great Britain.

At the Nottingham Easter School, Canham (1957) presented spectral energy distributions of fifteen types of artificial light source, of which nine are given in absolute units.

Work at the U.S. Department of Agriculture laboratories at Beltsville,

Maryland, relates more particularly to the use of light to regulate flowering, and the 'exceedingly profitable use of artificial radiation' (Borthwick and Parker, 1952). It is now known that radiation in the red end of the spectrum is especially effective when used to prevent the flowering of many short-day plants or to promote the flowering of many long-day ones. Radiation within the blue range is also highly effective for most plants, but considerably less so than in the red. All wave-lengths in the visible part of the spectrum are usually effective at adequate levels of energy. During recent years, quantitative data have been obtained at the Beltsville laboratory for a number of plants, relating wave-length to energy required for a given flowering response, the results being expressed in the form of action spectrum curves. Four kinds of plants (Biloxi soybean, Wintex barley, *Xanthium saccharatum* and an annual variety of *Hyoscyamus niger*) were all responsive to very low energies of red radiation. In soybean the energy in the blue required for a given response was roughly sixty times that in the most effective part of the red; and in the violet, where the effectiveness was greater than in the blue, it was still approximately twenty times as great. For the other plants the differences in effectiveness of red and blue were very much greater, indicating that the plants vary widely in their requirements for blue relative to red.

Borthwick and Parker concluded that these facts may indicate a possible reason for the greater response to light from incandescent filament than from fluorescent lamps (although the latter are more efficient sources of light). Laboratory experiments on sugar-beet confirmed the practical experience of sugar-beet seed growers, that the incandescent filament lamps are far superior in spectral quality to the fluorescent lamps as a source of supplemental light to induce seedstalk formation during winter months.

In reviewing in the *Journal of Ecology* for March, 1958, the Proceedings of the Nottingham Easter School on the Control of the Plant Environment (Hudson, 1957 b), G. C. Evans states: 'One is not surprised to find a variety of units quoted for the expression of light intensity. It is, however, depressing to find a majority of the authors of the major papers concerned using foot candles or lux. One would have thought that the meaningless nature of such units as applied to effects of radiation on plants had already been sufficiently demonstrated. At the same time there is no unanimity among the users of meaningful units, a variety being quoted based on ergs, watts or calories. Much mental calculation would be saved if it were possible to agree on a common unit. In view of the very great utility of the *Smithsonian Meteorological Tables* to all workers in this field, the present writer would advocate the general adoption of the scheme of units based on calories which is the standard practice of this work. If it be objected that 1 cal/cm^2/min is too large a unit (J, the solar constant, or mean intensity of total solar radiation incident on the top of the atmosphere, being 1·94 cal/cm^2/min) the calorie/square decimetre/ minute is a very convenient size, midday summer sunlight in this country (U.K.) being between 50 and 60 of these units. Its use thus avoids the continual repetition of powers of ten and at the same time makes the contents of the *Smithsonian Tables* instantly available to the student.'

Chapter X

GENECOLOGY AND BREEDING

The crops in the following chapters have been classified in relation to the degree of manifestation of vegetative growth, reproductive development, or a combination of the two. Thus we have in one group the pasture and fodder crops, green vegetables, sugar-cane, tobacco, stem fibre crops and trees and shrubs; in a second group the crops grown for their storage organs; and in a third, the florist crops, cereals, grain legumes, oil crops, fruit trees and fruit vegetables. This is a logical grouping on the basis of the principles and experimental data which are under consideration in this book, and may well be suitable for more general application in reviews on research in economic botany.

The requirements of these different types of crops in respect of the primary, and also to some extent the secondary environmental factors are stated briefly in the chapters which follow. Again, the review is necessarily superficial in relation to the wealth of data which is now accumulating; brief reference is made to the more recent papers by a large number of specialists working on many crops in many countries, and through the use of their bibliographies it will be possible to obtain access to a much wider literature.

The extent to which the range and grassland manager, crop cultivator, horticulturist and forester may manipulate the environment, or utilize and develop genotypes capable of responding to a given environment in a required direction varies considerably. The manager of natural grass and shrub range can adjust his grazing, cutting and burning practices to the reproductive cycle of the species he wishes to favour. The crop husbandman can obtain from the plant breeder genotypes with a known response to light and temperature in harmony with the environment of the cultivated conditions in which they are to be grown, or possibly bred types from which a limiting or highly specific requirement or degree of sensitivity for temperature of vernalization or photoperiod has been bred out. The forester faces similar problems, depending on whether he is concerned with the management of a natural stand, or the use of strains produced by the forest tree breeder. It is the horticulturist, with his

167

glasshouses, frames and shading equipment, who can best utilize the available knowledge of the growth and reproductive processes of his crops for economic production, to create an artificial environment similar to, or better than that of the place of origin of his crop, or which changes

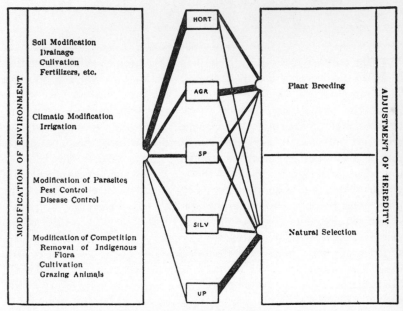

Fig. 28. Fitting of crop plants into new environments (Frankel, 1954).

(The parts played by modification of environment and adaptation of heredity in the main groups of crop plants. The relative intensities of adaptive influences are indicated by the thickness of connecting lines.)

Key to diagram:

HORT: horticultural crops
AGR: agricultural crops
SP: pasture plants in sown pastures
UP: pasture plants invading unimproved (indigenous) pastures
SILV: silvicultural crops

the normal pattern of growth and reproduction in a direction which will give a higher and/or earlier economic return.

Genecology

Those who are concerned with the current attempts to develop a more scientific or genetical approach to the age-old practice of plant exploration, collection and introduction (Whyte, 1958) must also consider the environmental conditions of the sites of collection and introduction. Reference has already been made to Stebbins' views on the relationship between cross- and self-fertilization in established and pioneer sites (p. 65), but the problem is much wider than that. Collections made at different latitudes throughout the photoperiodic range of a species or at increasing altitudes with or without increasing distance from the Poles must take into account whether, for example, a low temperature phase is an obligatory requirement for reproduction, or whether the species or genotype in question is sensitive to slight variations in photoperiods or not. This is a very fertile field for the reconsideration of established data and principles in the light of the experimental evidence quoted in this book.

Any such review must take into consideration the pattern of reproduction in relation to the primary or controlling factors throughout the latitudinal or altitudinal range of the strains within a species. Some thought should also be given to the validity of the distinction made here between primary and secondary factors. Do not all the environmental factors play a part at all times, but sometimes in a primary and sometimes in a secondary capacity? Might it be correct to say that there are *factors of existence*, against which a strain exhibits a range of tolerance, e.g. to excessive heat or cold, excessive wetness or drought, lethal salinity, and so on; *factors of maintenance and production*, such as soil fertility, water supplies, adequate light intensity for growth; and *factors of reproduction*, chiefly temperature, light and darkness in varying degrees and intensities, sequences, combinations and alternations?

Relevant studies include those by Olmsted (1952), whose earlier work on the range grass genus, *Bouteloua*, was reviewed in detail in the first edition; Sinskaya (1958) on the composition of the ecotypical and varietal populations of *Onobrychis*, *Bromus*, *Secale* and others; McMillan's work (see p. 196) on the flowering behaviour of various range grasses transplanted within a longitudinal range of conditions in Nebraska; and the work of the Carnegie Institution of Washington, stationed at Stanford in California, on the phenotypic expression of genotypes in contrasting environments (Clausen and Hiesey, 1958 a) and on the ecological race as a variable biotype compound in dynamic balance with its environment (Clausen, 1953).

The main example quoted in the first edition was the work of Evans, Allard and McConkey (1935), who made a study on the time of heading and flowering of early, medium and late strains of timothy at different

F*   169

latitudes, and noted the extent to which their results confirmed Hopkins' Bioclimatic Law (1918). This law states (as quoted by these authors) that, if other conditions such as those relating to longitude, altitude, distance to large bodies of water, and other factors that may have an effect on local climates are equal, then the time of flowering, or any other periodic event in the spring, should progress from south to north, in the northern hemisphere, over the entire range of latitude where any species

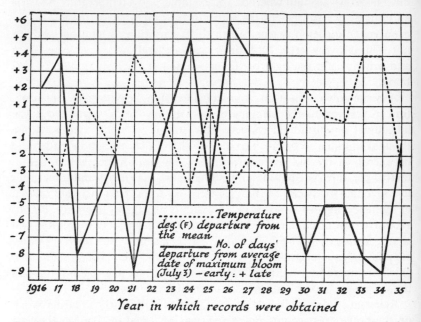

Fig. 29. Latitude in relation to growth phases in timothy (*Phleum pratense*). Relation of mean temperature during April, May and June to the date at which the maximum percentage of plants are in full bloom (Evans, 1939).

of plant under consideration may grow, at the uniform rate of one-fourth of a degree of latitude each day.

Before describing their experiments, Evans, Allard and McConkey refer to the fact that two of the strains used had also been grown in an earlier experiment, carried out at six stations, ranging from Savannah, Georgia, at 30° 6′ N., to Fairbanks, Alaska, at 64° 51′ N. latitude. The time when the first florets bloomed progressed from south to north, not at a uniform rate, but at a rate that was constantly accelerated as the season advanced. This effect Evans (1931) attributed to the greater lengths of day occurring during late spring and early summer at northern as compared with southern latitudes.

This earlier experiment indicated the desirability of conducting further investigations on the way in which the season for the appearance of the inflorescences or heads and the beginning of the flowering process progresses from one latitude to another. Thirteen strains of timothy were therefore chosen, showing fairly uniform gradations from very early to very late, and these were grown at three stations at different latitudes (see Table 3).

The plants of each strain had been propagated vegetatively from the same original plant, so that there were no possible genetical differences between them as there would have been if they had been grown from seed. The dates when the first florets bloomed are shown in Table 3.

Table 3

DATES WHEN THE FIRST FLORETS BLOOMED ON TIMOTHY PLANTS GROWN AT
STATIONS AT THREE DIFFERENT LATITUDES (IN 1933)

Strain number	Washington, D.C. N. Lat. 38° 54' Altitude 50 ft	North Ridgeville Ohio N. Lat. 41° 23' Altitude 750 ft	Guelph, Ontario N. Lat. 43° 33' Altitude 1,120 ft
19456	May 27	June 5	June 20
19458	June 2	June 8	June 20
15092	June 6	June 10	June 22
11902	June 8	June 12	June 25
6127	June 13	June 16	June 25
6743	June 14	June 22	June 28
9220	June 23	June 27	June 28
12421	June 28	June 29	July 3
15485	July 3	July 4	July 8
19416	July 10	July 5	July 6
15445	July 13	July 10	July 7
19459	July 25	July 15	July 8
19460	July 31	July 22	July 15

It is considered possible that Hopkins' Bioclimatic Law may apply reasonably well to all but three of the strains, but this does not explain why the season for heading and flowering of the latest three selections should progress from north to south. The explanation suggested by Evans, Allard and McConkey is that in very early strains heads develop and the flowering process occurs with days 10 to 12 hours long. In strains which are later under natural conditions, longer days are required for these processes, if the plants are grown under days artificially made of

171

uniform lengths. At the southern station the lengths of day during late spring and early summer are not as great as at the stations farther north. For the earliest strains, the lengths of day at the southern station are sufficient for the development of heads to begin before the temperature becomes high enough for active growth at the stations farther north. In very late strains of timothy, on the other hand, length of day apparently is the limiting factor at the latitudes where this experiment was conducted. Since the minimum length of day in the spring is attained, in the northern hemisphere at stations which are relatively far north, sooner than at stations farther south, the season for heading and flowering of these very late strains of timothy consequently progresses, in these latitudes, from north to south. These results have been expressed diagrammatically by Lona (1951) (see Fig. 30).

Olmsted (1952) selected the genus *Bouteloua* because it contains a number of widely ranging species, some which were known to show morphologically and, apparently, physiologically differentiated biotypes. Some are of considerable economic importance because of their abundance and palatability on native ranges, and for possible use in reseeding. The experimental data show that a widely ranging species may be so differentiated in its photoperiodic adjustments and requirements that its assignment to a particular photoperiodic class may be invalid unless based on material from a wide latitudinal range. Side-oats grama exhibits practically the entire range of reported photoperiodic responses. This has a bearing in turn on the nature of the physiological mechanisms of these responses. The existence of both long-day and short-day types in one species, linked by transitional ones, suggests that the qualitative differences between the extreme types are the visible expression of only quantitative differences in the mechanism which induces or permits flowering. Olmsted states that side-oats grama probably originated in low latitudes, in which the short-day response is typical, and spread to higher latitudes, evolving *en route* intermediate and long-day types with the elimination of the short-day types at the high latitudes. With more data on the genetic and evolutionary mechanisms, it might be possible to use photoperiodic behaviour as a clue to dispersal routes.

The work of the Institute of Plant Industry in Leningrad on *Onobrychis* is an example of an altitudinal study (Sinskaya, 1958). The following vertical belts of populations are clearly distinguishable in the Northern Caucasus, under identical photoperiods.

(1) The high mountain belt. Under cultivated conditions, plants from this belt do not blossom during their first year of life and in some cases not

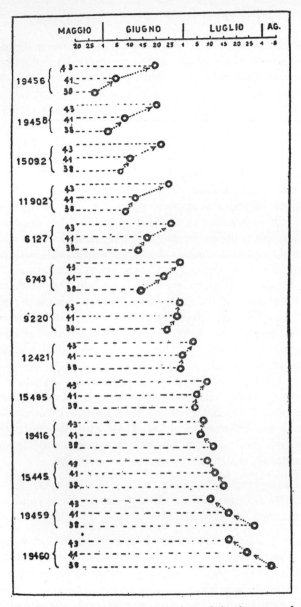

Fig. 30. Diagrammatic representation of development of 13 strains of *Phleum pratense* grown at three different latitudes (approx. 38°, 41° and 43°N.). Rings indicate time of first flowering of each strain in the different sites; maggio = May; giugno = June; luglio = July; ag. = Aug. (Based on data from Evans, Allard and McConkey, 1935) (Lona, 1951).

173

even in the second year, but when they do come to flower in the second and following years they are earlier than the plants from the lower belts. The high mountain belt is one of hardy, slow-growing, early-flowering, winter perennials.

(2) The middle mountain belt, where only very few plants come to blossom during the first year of their life. In the following years they begin to flower later, and their stems are considerably higher.

(3) The sub-mountain belt, where the majority of plants come to blossom during the first year of their life though their flowering is relatively late. These plants are late-flowering spring perennials.

(4) The belt of adjacent steppes, where are distributed plants which all come to blossom in the first year of their life. They are more or less drought-resistant and may be called spring perennials.

The morphological characters change very gradually; with decreasing altitude the size of the flowers and pods, and the dentation of the pods diminish; the petals become less bright in colour, the leaflets broader. It becomes extremely difficult to distinguish species on morphological characters, much easier, according to Sinskaya, to draw a line between vertical belt populations and to establish new species corresponding to these belts, mainly on the basis of biological and ecological characteristics.

Turning to cultivated plants of wide latitudinal distribution, Sinskaya describes the studies of her associate, A. M. Gorsky, on the composition of populations of over 200 local and bred varieties of winter wheat and rye grown in four different localities. These varietal populations, which were grown in conditions of unusually late spring sowing, fall into three main ecoelements or definite groups of biotypes:

(a) with early emergence of ears in the year of sowing,

(b) with late emergence of ears in the year of sowing, and

(c) those remaining vegetative in the year of sowing.

The plants belonging to the first group predominate in the south, and are usually more heat-resistant and less winter-hardy than analogous biotypes from farther north. The plants belonging to the third group are from the north of the range, and have the longest stage of vernalization, especially when they originate from districts with a comparatively mild climate and deep snow cover. The most complex populations occur in the middle latitudes and provide the greatest possibilities for selection.

The true varietal composition of a cultivar may be brought to light by growing it, for example, at different elevations at the same latitude, or by sowing in one site at a specified range of dates, or by transferring the cultivar to conditions very different from its home environment. When the Krasnodar variety of sunflower was grown in Siberia, it disintegrated into types varying widely in height and time of flowering, characters which had been held masked into uniformity in its usual environment; in other words, the natural length of day stabilizes the varietal population, while short days lead to its disintegration into separate components. When the complex of environmental factors is very unfavourable to all or to the great majority of biotypes of a population, visible differences among the components of the population usually diminish and consequently selection becomes difficult or impossible.

An incidental point noted in Sinskaya's experiments is that sudden changes of an effective factor may have much greater results than the constant action of the same factor. An 8- or 10-hour short day throughout the life of plants is less effective as a factor in disintegrating sunflower populations than the short-day regime applied only 25 or 30 days after the appearance of seedlings. The long-day factor applied before bud formation (as she says, before the end of the photo-phase) divides all biotypes of sunflower into short-day or long-day ones, according to whether the long-day or short-day regime has an accelerating influence on reproductive development. The short-day regime applied after bud formation accelerates the development of all biotypes and its disintegrating ability becomes greatly diminished or nil. Thus the disintegrating capacity of each factor depends also on the stage of development and age of components of a population.

Clausen and Hiesey (1958 a) review their own and other workers' experiences on phenotypic modification caused by the activation of latent genes. In a later publication, Clausen and Hiesey (1958 b) describe their work on the genetic structure of ecological races, dealing with response patterns at contrasting altitudes, genetic systems regulating biochemical and physiological effects and their expression in different environments, and genetic systems of ecological races; these authors conclude with a statement of their own concepts of the genetic structure of ecological races, which have frequent reference to environment.

Genes may be latent for several reasons. They can lack complementaries, can be inhibited or suppressed by other genes, or the environmental conditions may not be favourable for their expression. Many chemical and biological processes have temperature thresholds above and below which they do not function. Possibly all genes have thresholds at which they become activated. Living things of various kinds may possess latent or residual genes which become activated in environments differing radically from those in which the organism evolved and where long-range natural selection has occurred. Clausen and Hiesey illustrate this by three examples.

The tropical species, *Sorghum vulgare*, has a maturity gene Ma_1 which is inactive in a 10-hour photoperiod, but which becomes active in a 14-hour photoperiod; the effect is 'dramatic' since under these conditions the flowering of the Ma_1 biotypes is 2 weeks later than ma_1, the stem is longer, and the number of leaves below the panicle is increased by eleven (Quinby and Karper, 1945).

The Wimmera strain of *Lolium rigidum* is a spring annual which does not need low temperature for floral initiation. Seedlings germinated and grown out-of-doors in the cool English spring develop inflorescences at the 6th to 7th node from the base (Cooper, 1954). When grown in a heated greenhouse in a 24-hour photoperiod, a great deal of 'residual variability' is disclosed and the floral initiation takes place between the 5th and 21st leaf. When the strain is vernalized at 3°C for 6 weeks and then grown in a 24-hour photoperiod in the heated greenhouse, the variability is again masked and flowering is uniform from the 4th to the 6th leaf. The omission of moderate pre-cooling, combined with a 24-hour photoperiod, discloses the latent genetic variability of this otherwise uniform agricultural strain. 'Selection had never taken place in this kind of environment.'

In its native habitats, *Deschampsia caespitosa* is non-viviparous in contrast with the highly viviparous *D. alpina* of a different ecological zone. Vivipary is the character used for specific distinction. Seedling cultures of *D. caespitosa* from 56° N. latitude in southern Sweden, 60° N. in southern Finland, and 68° N. in Swedish Lapland were grown at Stanford in California at 38° N. Each culture then broke up into a mixture of viviparous, non-viviparous and non-flowering plants varying in height from 20 to 80 cm (Lawrence, 1945). The viviparous plants varied in degree from highly to only slightly viviparous. Flowering began in late June, but the inflorescences did not start developing viviparous plantlets before August and September, when the days had shortened. It would be interesting to study this character in the biotypes of *D. caespitosa* to be found growing naturally in the alpine pastures above 11,000 ft in the Himalaya, probably the southern limit of the species.

Latent genes 'are probably far more common than is generally realized because their study so far has been very limited. Ecotypes from contrasting climates differ greatly in the composition of their genes and

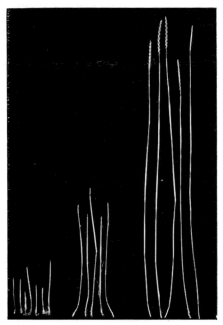

18. Effect of copper and length of night on head development in Thatcher Spring Wheat (Brown, Tiffin and Holmes, 1958). *Left to right:* copper-deficient, short night; copper-sufficient, long night; copper-sufficient, short night

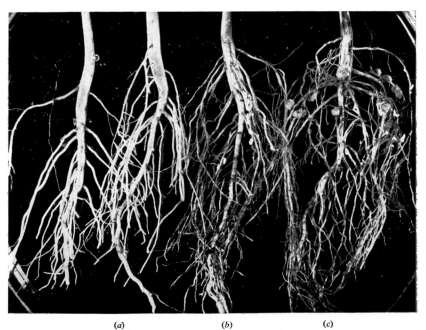

(a)   (b)   (c)

19. Effect of day length on nodule formation in soybean by a specific strain of *Rhizobium* (Bonnier and Sironval, 1956). (a) Roots of plants in 8-hour day, without *Rhizobium*. (b) Roots of plants in 8-hour day, with *Rhizobium* (no nodules). (c) Roots of plants in 16-hour day, with *Rhizobium* (heavy and numerous nodules)

(a)

(b)

20. Effects of gibberellin on plants
(a) Utah 10-B celery, grown at night temperature of 15° to 18° C. (Bukovac and Witt-wer, 1957). *Left:* control, not treated. *Right:* 100 micrograms applied for 20 consecutive weeks. (b) Gypsy Petunia (Linstrom, Wittwer and Bukovac, 1957). *Left:* Control, not treated. *Right:* Foliar spray containing 10 p.p.m. applied 45 days before photographing

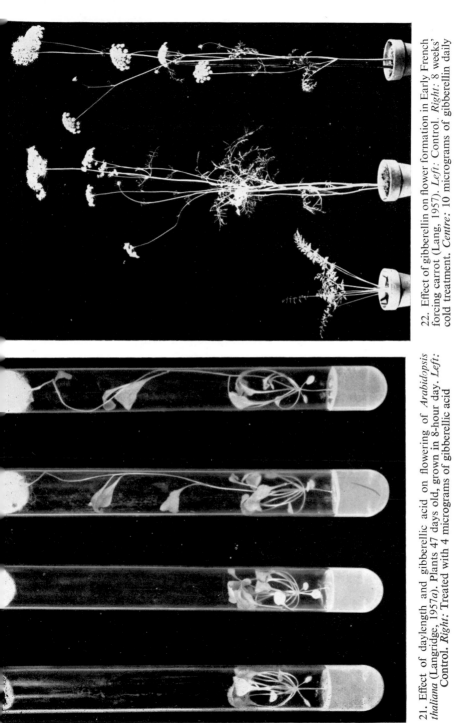

21. Effect of daylength and gibberellic acid on flowering of *Arabidopsis thaliana* (Langridge, 1957a). Plants 47 days old, grown in 8-hour day. *Left:* Control. *Right:* Treated with 4 micrograms of gibberellic acid

22. Effect of gibberellin on flower formation in Early French forcing carrot (Lang, 1957). *Left:* Control. *Right:* 8 weeks' cold treatment. *Centre:* 10 micrograms of gibberellin daily

23. Retardation of development of chrysanthemum (Fred Shoesmith) by treatment with Amo-1618 (see Chapter VII) (Cathey, 1958). Rooted cuttings placed for 0, 2, 4, 8 and 24 hours in 100 p.p.m. (at 50° F.) of Amo-1618. Cuttings then planted and placed immediately under short days

24. Bolting of *Brassica rapa* under Alpine conditions (Lona, 1957). *Left:* plant grown in mountains flowered before the end of summer. *Right:* Plant grown in plains remained vegetative. *Note:* Plants grown in mountains but given high night temperatures also remained vegetative

are especially rich in unexpressed genes. Such ecotypes have evolved independently, possibly for long periods of geologic time, and their adjustments to climate have been achieved in diverse ways. Their genes are nevertheless completely interchangeable. A high degree of variability becomes evident when the heredities of interecotypic hybrids are recombined, revealing great differences in the genic composition of the parental races. Inactive genes from one race may combine with their complementaries from another. Genes repressed by inhibitors in one race may be released by another race which has neither. Many characters are also regulated by genes of epistatic sequences in which the hypostatic genes are unexpressed. Recombinations may free the hypostatic genes to expression, but it may require several generations to release all the possibilities.

'Most gene systems are composed of several kinds of genes, such as those having complementary, cumulative and oppositional effects. The expression of a character often depends upon the balances of such a system, and it may vary with the environment as discussed above. The phenotypic expression of the gene system that regulates a character in wild plants is usually sufficiently fixed so that the character varies little from year to year. When such plants are moved to a radically different environment, however, striking modifications may occur such as those in *Deschampsia*.

'When contrasting ecotypes are intercrossed, the F_1 may exhibit some hybrid vigor. If sufficiently large F_2 and later generations are grown, the variability is highly increased and is often accompanied by transgressive segregation. An increase in vigor over the parental ecotypes may be retained, or even increased, in later generations. This is in contrast to the hybrid vigor of maize and rye in which the vigor of the F_1 is lost in subsequent generations and is replaced by inbreeding depression.

'Hybrid vigor changes with the environment, for the gene-controlled growth-promoting and growth-inhibiting processes vary in intensity with the environment, and otherwise inactive genes may become activated in new environment. An especially striking example was reported in the F_2 of the cross between subspecies *borealis* and *gigantea* of *Achillea borealis*. At the lowland station at Stanford there is no conspicuous hybrid vigor in the F_2 of this cross. At the mid-altitude Mather station, however, the high-latitude *borealis* parent tends to die during the summer, and the low-latitude lowland *gigantea* tends to become killed during the winter. The F_1 plants survive with great vigor, and more than 50 per cent of the F_2's are even more vigorous than the F_1. The parental characters complement each other in the F_1 and the greater part of the F_2, producing more vigorous growth and greater tolerance to both winter and summer seasons in this environment' (Clausen and Hiesey, 1958 a).

It would be expected that strains of agricultural crops which have been developed in contrasting climates should show behaviours similar to the natural ecotypes. Some strains may be expected similarly to have evolved distinct genetic systems that may complement each other when recombined after crossing. 'The hereditary structures of living things that successfully have been able to populate climatically diverse regions of the world are so constituted that they contain a great deal of unexpressed variability. Some of the hidden variability can be made evident by moving the organism to a highly different environment, where some of the inactive genes become activated. Another part may become manifest when genes of ecotypes from contrasting environments are brought to expression through crossing and recombination. Distinct species undoubtedly carry vast amounts of unrecognised variability, because only differences that can be genetically analysed can be identified. Living things are flexible in their environmental responses, but our knowledge of the potentialities of such responses is limited because only few investigations have been undertaken to study organisms in highly diverse environments' (Clausen and Hiesey, *loc. cit.*).

'The outward and visible form that a plant assumes on any particular habitat cannot necessarily be taken as a complete mirror of that plant's internal and ultimate genetical constitution' (Stapledon, 1943).

These considerations, combined with the numerous examples of the disintegration of economic strains when purchased for use in a contrasting environment, necessitate a review of past genetical studies on the inheritance of physiological characters or of those morphological characters which are merely an outward expression of physiological adjustment or maladjustment to the environment. It would appear to be inadvisable to draw conclusions in these respects or to specify the nature of segregation until the breeding experiments have been made at representative and contrasting sites throughout the actual and potential range of distribution of the species or cultivar in question. This is another way of saying that cultivars which are apparently uniform in growth habit or other characters have not generally been bred for the characters related to their reproductive physiology. Several examples of this are quoted in this volume. If reproductive physiology is accepted as the central problem of plant science, it will be essential to discover the real nature of a biotype in relation to the primary factors of the environment and to breed out recessive diversity before starting a conventional breeding programme.

Breeding on the Basis of Environmental Requirements

This is the part of the whole problem of developmental physiology which has caused most disagreement and controversy (Hudson and Richens, 1946). The basic criticism levelled by the supporters of phasic development at what they call the Mendelism-Morganism school of formal genetics would appear to be that the geneticists belonging to the latter have concerned themselves with a study of many purely morphological and growth-type characters, with little or no regard to the physiological characters. The claim is put forward that it is the physiological inheritance of a plant that is important, both genetically and economically, and that many if not all of the morphological characters that have been the subject of economic plant breeding for many years are merely the expression of the type of inheritance of the physiological (developmental) characters under the environment of the experiment. The natural sequence in this argument is to say that many if not all the pure lines that have been developed are not true pure lines at all, as they are thoroughly heterozygous for the physiological characters and segregate out for these as soon as the environmental or other conditions permit.

In place of the conventional methods of plant breeding based upon factorial analysis, cytogenetics, the gene theory and similar methods that have been the foundation of genetical research for so long, it is argued that plant breeding should now be based upon a thorough knowledge of the developmental period and phases (or environmental requirement), obtained by phasic analysis, and that intelligent crossing of parents with the required developmental phases will provide a progeny with the requisite seasonal behaviour, growth type, morphological characters, yield, etc.

An example was given in the first edition of the breeding of lettuce in the Soviet Union, based upon the analysis of environmental requirements, the purpose of which was:

(1) to determine the duration of the thermo- and photo-phases in the differing groups of lettuce varieties,

(2) to discover whether it would be possible to split these varieties into biological strains by the method of phasic analysis, and

(3) to ascertain the response to vernalization of germinated seeds or green plants of varieties differing in length of vegetative period.

The biological difference between the winter and summer varieties of lettuce is that the former have a short thermo-phase and a long photo-phase, while the latter have a long thermo-phase and a short photo-phase. Cultivation of lettuce plants at different daylengths has a marked effect upon the morphological characters and behaviour of different plants within a variety. Under a natural daylength as well as in a 24-hour day, plants of all varieties remain uniform in all respects; when grown under a 14-hour day, and even more so under a 10-hour day, their behaviour and appearance are very diverse. Plants belonging to one and the same variety now differ markedly in general shape and other morphological characters, as well as in time of shooting. Thus a variety that has been carefully selected under a normal daylength in one region is nevertheless a population or mixture composed of biological races differing with regard to their physiological properties. In other words, they are heterozygous for the phases of development, but this heterozygosity is not manifested so long as the strain is cultivated under the same conditions as those in which it was produced.

Other examples quoted in the first edition include the work of Bell (1945) on sugar-beet (see page 256), the studies of O. N. Purvis on the inheritance of spring and winter (or annual and biennial) habit, and the work of American physiologists on the inheritance of the duration of three stages of development in crosses involving varieties of tomato, namely (1) number of days from sowing to first bloom; (2) number of days from first bloom to first fruit set; and (3) number of days from first fruit set to first complete change of colour of any fruit. The sum of these three stages is regarded as a measure of the earliness-of-maturity character. The purposes of this investigation were to determine whether these natural biological periods in development are definite sub-characters and to ascertain the efficiency of the fit between obtained and theoretical means, based upon certain formulae, as a method of determining whether the effects of the genes differentiating the quantitative characters are arithmetically or geometrically cumulative. Throughout the study and interpretation of the data, an attempt was made to keep in mind the probability that the genes bring about the differentiation of a character by initiating, either directly or indirectly, developmental processes which no doubt in many cases interact among themselves.

The most recent review of this subject is that by Rudorf (1958) in the Second Edition of *Handbuch der Pflanzenzüchtung*. Rudorf appends to a review of the whole subject of developmental physiology in relation to plant breeding the following sections:

Genetics of developmental characters
Genetics of biennial and annual habit
Genetics of winter and summer habit
Genetics of early and late maturity
The use of photoperiodic response and vernalization in breeding
Use of photoperiodic response
Synchronizing flowering times of parents in crossing programmes
Obtaining earlier maturity and high seed yields in F_1 and F_2 generations
Transferring the active substance for ripeness-to-flower by grafting
Use of vernalization in breeding
Technical data on photoperiodic treatments with artificial light.

The introducer of new varieties, the agronomist, the crop ecologist and the plant breeder frequently use the term 'adapted variety' to mean sometimes adaptation to the primary and/or secondary characters proposed here, or to one or more of the factors of existence, maintenance and production, and reproduction. Dorst (1957) has reviewed the meaning and significance of the word 'adaptation' from the plant breeder's point of view. It is a dangerous word, since by its vagueness it is often not clear which conception is meant, 'and it is sometimes introduced when there is no clear conception at all'. It may refer to something which is either 'static or dynamic, an established state and a changing state, a situation and a process'. The terms of the plant sociologists, namely, ecological span or amplitude, might be more suitable. Adaptation of populations is a result of a shift in the collective genotype. After multiplication some genotypes will come to the fore, others will decrease in number or even disappear.

Adaptation of iso-homozygotes (pure lines of self-fertilizing plants) or of clones (e.g. potato varieties) is based on the ability of the phenotype to be modified, therefore on the physiological response of the genotype to the environment. Apart from sporadically occurring mutants, spontaneous cross-pollination with other genotypes or admixtures (with other genotypes), the environment does not affect the genotype of iso-homozygotes or clones. This adaptation, as a consequence of the ability of modification, of course also holds for populations of cultivated plants. In all breeding procedures the adaptability of the selections is of the utmost importance. The breeder will try to obtain a clear idea of the adaptability of his selections and on these grounds he will choose his selections for inclusion in trials set up for assessing agricultural value.

Breeding of Maladjusted Biotypes

For many practical, nutritional and other reasons it would be highly desirable to establish pastures with seed of non-flowering strains which would remain permanently vegetative within the regions of their agronomic adaptation (Peterson, Cooper and Vose, 1958), i.e. maladjusted in relation to flowering and reproduction by seed. Since vegetative propagation is impracticable on any scale, this would necessitate the production of seed in another environment with conditions favouring reproduction. Absence of heading may be associated with low vigour or with late spring growth, but these disadvantages may be compensated by the steady mid-season production of such strains.

Most grasses of temperate regions require long photoperiods for floral initiation and stem elongation, although the time from ear initiation to ear emergence is modified by spring temperature. Species and strains vary in their exact photoperiodic responses, the earliness or lateness of heading depending on the critical photoperiod. A number of studies, including parallel observations of the flowering behaviour of S.23 perennial ryegrass at Aberystwyth (52° N.) and Davis, California (38° N.) suggest that it is possible to select plants which fail to flower in a particular latitude because photoperiodic requirements are not satisfied. There is, of course, still the possibility that maladjusted biotypes may be carried part way towards floral induction in one season and receive the remaining requirements in the next.

There have been few detailed investigations of the inheritance of flowering behaviour in the herbage grasses, but in *Lolium*, Cooper finds the difference between the early-flowering group (Wimmera and Irish), and the late-flowering S.23 perennial ryegrass to be polygenically controlled with no evidence of one or a few main gene differences. In these outbreeding strains, most plants are highly heterozygous for genes controlling flowering date, and the genetic variance of progenies from selfing or crossing individual plants is of the same order as that of the whole population, making possible considerable response to selection.

Many temperate perennial grasses also possess a winter requirement for short-day and/or low temperature before floral induction is possible, little or no heading occurring after a late spring sowing. Differences again occur between strains and ecotypes. The response to low-temperature induction in *Lolium* is also polygenically controlled; considerable genetic variation is carried in the heterozygous state within individual plants and gradually becomes available for selection.

'In the temperate herbage grasses, therefore, at least two developmental mechanisms exist whereby the timing of inflorescence development can be controlled; a "winter" requirement for short-day and/or low temperature before floral induction is possible, and also a requirement for long photoperiods for floral initiation and subsequent development. Considerable genetic variation in all these responses has been shown to exist within species, its distribution being related to the climatic or agronomic origin of the material. It should therefore be possible to select, in a particular region, plants which remain vegetative indefinitely, because their requirements for either "winter" exposure or long summer photoperiods are not satisfied under local conditions. They may then be grown for seed production in districts or under artificial conditions favourable for reproductive development.

'A fundamental problem in the production of a non-flowering strain is to decide whether to concentrate on the photoperiodic response or the "winter" requirement, as the factor limiting inflorescence development. In this connection, the seasonal regularity of the limiting factor is important. Winter temperatures in one locality vary considerably from year to year, and the response to winter conditions in one season may not be strictly reproducible in subsequent years. The effective temperature-range for cold induction is not known for most herbage grasses, nor do the usual meteorological records give an exact measure of the temperature experienced by the growing point of the grass plant. It is clear that the regional mapping of effective winter temperatures may be rather difficult. On the other hand, the seasonal distribution of photoperiod is regular from year to year, and being based only on latitude, can be calculated accurately for any locality. Apart from the modifying effects of temperature during inflorescence elongation, flowering performance in any one season may therefore serve as a guide to future behaviour. Response to photoperiod thus forms a more reliable basis for the production of non-flowering strains' (Peterson, Cooper and Vose, *loc. cit.*).

The next step is to obtain plants with a critical photoperiod above that of the longest summer day in the region where the strain is to be used for pasture. An obvious source is the collection of late-flowering material from higher latitudes, relatively easy for Davis, California, more difficult in Aberystwyth with its maximum photoperiod of 18 hours; the choice of material in the latter case is restricted to arctic or sub-arctic latitudes. Another source of non-flowering material lies in selection from within existing late-flowering strains; outbreeding strains of *Lolium perenne* contain considerable potential genetic variation which is released in each generation by segregation and recombination. Finally it may be possible to find or produce non-flowering mutants.

'Even when non-flowering plants of satisfactory performance have been obtained, the problem arises of seed supply on an economic basis. Obtaining seed from small lots of non-flowering plants, either for breeding purposes or for the production of foundation seed, offers no problem. Flowering may readily be induced by extension of the day-length using incandescent lamps of low wattage, the plants being kept outdoors or in an unheated greenhouse. In long-day plants, it is the length of the dark period which is important in preventing flowering, and reproductive development can be induced by a short break in the middle of the dark period. Artificial light, therefore, need only be used for a short time at midnight, and has in fact been employed for this purpose in the production of sugar beet seed in breeding nurseries in the United States.

'For larger quantities of seed, artificial light is not practicable, and seed production would have to be carried out at higher latitudes, where the daylength is adequate for floral induction. In Britain, this would mean growing seed crops in the north of Scotland, preferably above latitude 58° N. A strain could probably be selected which would flower at that latitude, and yet remain vegetative in the south of England. The flowering and vegetative limits of such a strain would be an integral part of its description.

'The farther north the strain is to be used for pasture, the more difficult it will be to produce a non-flowering strain, since there will be fewer areas suitable for seed production. To obtain a strain which would remain vegetative everywhere in Britain, for example, seed would have to be grown on a commercial scale at latitudes above 60° N., probably in Scandinavia' (Peterson, Cooper and Vose, *loc. cit.*).

Chapter XI

HERBAGE AND FODDER PLANTS

Reactions Alone or in Mixtures

Aknowledge of the developmental physiology of the herbage grasses and legumes which make up natural grasslands or sown pastures and fodder crops is of the greatest importance in the management of these particular crops. In addition to the study of leaf area index in the pure stands or mixtures referred to in Chapter III, much evidence is now accumulating on the response of herbage plants to the environmental factors which govern growth and reproductive development. This research is concerned with the relation of light and temperature to pasture growth as such, with the change from a vegetative to a reproductive state in grasses and legumes, and even, as seen in the preceding chapter, with the possibility of producing non-flowering strains of pasture grasses. Since in pastures the leaves are lower in fibre, higher in protein content and more digestible than the stems, anything that can be done to apply our existing knowledge of the reproductive physiology of herbage species will be of major economic importance. A greater degree of control over vegetative and reproductive growth may be achieved either by using species which do not find conditions adequate for reproduction in the site where they are to be grown, or by basing cutting and grazing practices on a knowledge of the physiological processes in the plants, primarily flower induction and the formation of flower primordia, and also the reaction of roots to repeated defoliation.

Thus it will be possible to provide a physiological basis for purely agronomic data, such as the performance of strains of perennial ryegrass in Scotland (Copeman, Heddle, Hunt and Sampford, 1958): 'S.23 was decidedly the latest strain in the trial. In April, growth was less than that of Kent, as was its May production except in a phenomenally early season. Its May productivity in comparison with early strains varied widely from season to season and from station to station, an early season tending to favour S.23, a late season the earlies. By June, however, when

185

the earlies had passed their spring peak, S.23 remained more productive than they, although New Zealand sometimes entered its second period of productivity soon enough to rival S.23 in June production. During the June–July period S.23 was very similar in productivity to New Zealand, but in the following two months the latter tended to outyield it. S.23 responded strongly to nitrogen, but its total production, even at the high fertilizer level, never equalled that of the early strains, while at the low level it was even less productive than Kent. The high-tillering capacity of both S.23 and Kent enabled them to maintain themselves well in the sward during the three-year period of the trials.'

The work of Blackman and his associates at Oxford, e.g. Blackman and Wilson (1951), has shown that species differ in the light intensity at which the growth rate is maximal. Some species make fastest growth at about 80 to 85 per cent full summer daylight, a few shade plants have an optimal intensity below 80 per cent, while some have theoretical optimal light intensities greater than full daylight. Black (1957 a) has concluded on the basis of the literature that, while pasture grasses make best growth at or even above full daylight, pasture legumes are intolerant of even slight shade and would make optimal growth at very high light intensities (although one may refer to the fact that white clover was originally a plant of woodland fringes, and has adapted itself or produced ecotypes adapted to full light). Black (1955) found that the growth rate of the plant of Mediterranean latitudes, subterranean clover, at Adelaide is determined solely by the amount of light energy received, being independent of temperature; it is highest in summer, when more than 400,000 foot-candle hours were received in each of several 7-day experimental periods, and there is no evidence that light saturation had even then been reached. Benedict (1941) made an investigation on range grasses in Wyoming in the knowledge that the light intensities there were higher than elsewhere in the United States. It had been suggested that the Wyoming light intensities might be too high for optimal growth, but this was not confirmed; shading to 70 per cent full daylight reduced the growth of three species of range grasses.

Any arguments based on the major importance of the plant's ability to intercept all available light energy cannot be extended to arid or semi-arid environments, where soil moisture replaces light as the major factor controlling plant growth. High light intensity, high temperature, low humidity and low soil moisture are, however, so closely interrelated that their separate effects on growth can be assessed only in controlled conditions where each factor may be varied independently; it is, however, not possible to produce the required light intensities artificially (Black, 1956 b).

Mitchell (1956) is studying the influence of temperature on the growth of pasture plants at the Grasslands Division of D.S.I.R., Palmerston North, New Zealand, using three interrelated approaches, namely, field observations, studies of individual plants growing in pots in greenhouses or in the open, and measurements of rates of growth in controlled environments, where temperature, intensity and duration of light, nutritional status and moisture could be maintained at desired levels (Table 4).

Table 4

PERCENTAGE INCREASE PER DAY IN DRY WEIGHT OF SHOOT

Plants grown under controlled environment (Mitchell, 1956)

| | Temperature | | | | | |
	45°F	55°F	65°F	75°F	85°F	95°F
Lolium perenne	9·0	11·9	14·7	13·4	9·8	2·1
Dactylis glomerata	9·7	13·9	15·9	15·1	13·3	4·8
Paspalum dilatatum	1·8	7·1	14·4	20·5	22·1	19·2
Holcus lanatus	10·1	15·3	18·6	16·6	12·3	—
Trifolium repens	5·2	10·5	13·4	14·7	13·3	8·5
Lotus uliginosus	4·9	9·6	13·5	16·3	14·3	4·2
Trifolium subterraneum	7·6	10·8	11·8	11·5	8·1	4·0

During their vegetative growth, the species recorded in Table 4 have their meristematic centres close to or in direct contact with the soil surface, and their temperatures are largely determined by the temperature of the adjacent soil. As even a 3-in. pasture on a sandy soil substantially reduces the soil temperature, the importance of correct management to maintain a protective cover is obvious. An advantage of the tussocky growth habit may be the protection of meristematic zones from diurnal extremes of high or low temperature. Defoliation at higher temperatures checks the development of tillers and, with shading to 30 per cent full daylight, tillering eventually ceases almost completely. At lower temperatures, neither similar defoliation nor shading has so marked an effect. The influence of nitrogen status on survival is more complex under conditions of drought or high temperature, and is related to the fact that most of the available nitrogen is in the surface layers which dry up first. Thus plants are cut off from their supplies of nitrogen while still able to reach water at lower levels in the soil. In a more fertile soil, the nitrogen is available at greater depths and the more abundant and prolonged leaf growth helps to provide a green cover to minimize soil heating and hence also loss of moisture near the surface.

Some of the first measurements of microclimatic temperatures around the roots, stems and leaves of forage crops in the United States were made by V. G. Sprague at the U.S. Regional Pasture Laboratory in Pennsylvania. These revealed that the temperature climate in the air layer below the 4-ft height is much more rigorous than that at higher levels. Recent microclimate investigations by Beinhart, Plant Physiologist at the South Carolina Agricultural Experiment Station, show very large temperature gradients—as large as 30°F—within a distance of only one centimetre above a dry soil surface. Vegetation on the soil surface moderates these large temperature gradients. Thus grazing intensity, by modifying vegetative cover, changes the temperature to which forage plants are subjected. Temperatures taken within the plant tissues of Ladino clover indicate large differences between plant parts. With an air temperature of 76°, stolon temperatures of 98°, petiole temperatures of 80°, and soil surface temperatures of 86°F were measured. Soil moisture also has a marked effect on surface and air temperatures. Measurements show a 20°F gradient in the first centimetre above a dry soil, while uniform temperatures exist above a moist soil. Soil type, especially soil colour, has a pronounced effect on soil surface temperatures. Five soil types gave a 30°F range in soil temperature related largely to surface colour.

Work at Purdue University has shown that the growth response from increased light on lucerne, red clover and birdsfoot trefoil seedlings in growth chambers is curvilinear for tops and linear for roots (Gist and Mott, 1957). Root growth is affected more than top growth by reduced light intensity. The increasing of temperatures from 60° to 90° F reduces seedling growth. Reducing soil moisture causes a corresponding reduction in seedling growth. Red clover is less affected by reduced light than the other two crops.

Seasonal changes in temperature also affect forage plants. Workers in Florida have found that a slight drop in night temperature reduces growth of both Pangola grass (*Digitaria decumbens*) and Coastal Bermuda grass. Plants maintained at 60°F night temperature suffer a reduction of 20 per cent in stem elongation as compared with those at 70°F. Lowering the night temperature to 50°F results in a further reduction in stem elongation. The number of tillers resuming growth is also reduced at the lower night temperatures. Dry weight yields at 50°F are only half those at 70°F.

American workers also find that temperature and soil fertility interact to produce winter killing of pasture plants. The survival of Pangola grass decreases as nitrogen fertilization is increased, winter killing being almost complete with applications above 400 lb nitrogen per acre per year. The killing of Pangola grass is associated with insufficient root reserves, since root yields decrease with increased nitrogen.

Grazing Management

The extensive American literature on the evaluation of the physiological response of range plants to grazing use has been reviewed by Hedrick (1958). The emphasis has now changed from 'forage removal' to 'forage remaining'. Lack of knowledge on the response of individual plants to grazing is still hampering the application of correct range management. It is, however, known that too heavy, early or frequent removal has caused a decline in plant vigour, the greatest damage occurring during periods of minimum food storage, with marked effects on root growth before any effect on the tops becomes visible.

An important aspect of correct range or veld management is the resting of the stand to permit the grasses to produce seed. Scott (1956) has, however, stated that it is not generally realized that, if the period of elongation of the internodes before the appearance of the flowering culm is at all protracted, much damage can be done to the developing inflorescences by not starting the resting period early enough. A knowledge of the length of this period in the dominant grasses as well as some method of determining when elongation is about to start or has started would be invaluable. Another point of importance which appears to have been overlooked is that, if the periods of elongation and times of differentiation of the inflorescence are different in the most important species, it would be possible to rest the veld in South Africa for a certain period to encourage the flowering of a desirable species and mow or practise heavy grazing at a stage when an undesirable species is particularly vulnerable to defoliation. This important point has been overlooked in the past as, in practically all systems of veld management, rest periods have been such that desirable and undesirable grasses have had an equal opportunity of flowering and setting seed. The relative proportions of these grasses in such veld has then depended upon their ability to compete with each other for such factors as light, water and nutrients. There is no doubt that such systems of rest have aided the more palatable grasses to hold their own, but where the unpalatable grasses have already become dominant, some means of checking their growth whilst encouraging that of the palatable grasses is necessary.

It would appear then that the study of the development of the flowering primordia and the internodal elongation should be of particular value when applied to grasses of sour and mixed veld. It might be argued, however, that this would affect only the seeding and that, with the dense cover usually found in such veld, it would not affect its composition for some considerable time, if at all. It is at this point that a knowledge of the root behaviour of the different species with different heights and intensities of cutting would be invaluable and might provide a key to the management of the grazing.

The apparent cessation of the growth of roots with severe defoliation is easily understood, as the source of nutrients through photosynthesis is removed. Slowing down of growth with less defoliation is likewise easily explained. It is known, however, that when the plant is flowering and seeding there is translocation of nutrients to the flowering parts and hence it is possible that, at this stage of development, defoliation might affect both flowering and growth and lead to considerable weakening of the plant. It has been observed that such defoliation seriously affects *Aristida junciformis*, which, by nature of its unpalatability, is not usually defoliated after the early part of the season, and this may be the reason.

Scott has now planned a study of the development of the flower primordia and internodal elongation in a number of the principal palatable and unpalatable grasses in mixed and sour veld. In addition, the effects of defoliation in relation to the time of season and development of the internodes will be studied. This work will be carried out not only in the first season after germination of the seed, as has been done in the past, but over a period of years to observe the behaviour of perennial grasses. Parallel with this will be a study of root behaviour of the same species for a few years to determine whether there is any correlation between height of defoliation, stage of development of the plant and root behaviour. If there is, it should be possible to design systems of veld management on knowledge obtained in this way so that not only will the more desirable grasses be encouraged, but unpalatable types will be controlled. Should this work prove of value as far as the South African veld is concerned, it might also have an application in the management of mixed, cultivated pastures. Systems devised in this way would then be based on definite scientific facts and not on results obtained by trial and error.

Competitive Relationships

Competition between pasture species, already discussed in Chapter III, is such an important factor in pasture management that it deserves further reference here. Pastures composed of annual species are very important in Mediterranean environments, and in this connection Donald (1951) examined the influence of density, stage of growth, and fertility level on intraspecific competition. At sowing there is a linear relationship between density and yield (weight of embryos or embryo + endosperm per unit area). Competition is evident in dense populations shortly after germination and thereafter becomes operative progressively in populations of lower and lower density. Because of the extreme reduction in growth rate in dense swards later in the season and the high growth rate in sparse swards, the sparse sward tends to approach the more dense sward in its final yield. Final yield of dry matter is constant from moderate to high densities. There is no reduction in dry matter per unit area even in extremely dense swards. This maximum yield of dry matter for the environment is controlled by some factor of the environment. Donald considers that nitrogen was the factor in two of his experiments and light in the third.

These competitive relationships have considerable implications in pasture practices. In areas in which dependence is placed on winter annuals (as in many Mediterranean environments in Australia and elsewhere), the winter period is normally one of feed shortage. While stands of moderate density may give satisfactory or even maximal final yields for the environment, only stands of high density can give satisfactory early (winter) yields of herbage. In swards of subterranean clover or of Wimmera ryegrass and subterranean clover, high populations are essential for good early production. The results emphasize the need to permit sown annuals to seed sufficiently liberally in the first year to produce a high second-year population. The data on the density/yield relationship as affected by nitrogen supply suggests that the less favourable the environment, the smaller the number of plants required to exploit it. This is supported by current agricultural practice with both crops and pastures. Seeding rates for wheat are highest in the more favourable environments and lowest in marginal wheat areas. Similarly seed rates with pasture species are smaller in less favourable environments (Donald, 1951.)

Reproductive Development and Quality

There is a need to reconsider the data produced over many years by agricultural chemists on the seasonal variations in protein content or other nutritional characteristics of herbage, particularly if it is possible in so doing to compare early and late strains. One example will suffice. It is well-known that the percentage of protein falls as grasses mature. On a given date, a late-maturing plant is, as a rule, higher in protein than an earlier plant which has proceeded farther toward maturity. In a study of different grasses, Phillips *et al.* noted that the late-maturing species are lower in protein than early ones, and that a late orchard-grass clone is lower than an early one at a comparable stage of maturity. The significance of this observation is that, if early clones of a given species are superior to late ones in a character that makes for quality in forage, then, other factors being considered, emphasis should be placed on the production of early rather than of late-maturing strains.

Sullivan and Routley (1955) have reported on the protein content of three grasses harvested at comparable stages of maturity and the relationship between protein content and date of harvest. No significant relationships were obtained between protein content and earliness or lateness in reed canary grass or timothy. In cocksfoot, high protein is associated with earliness. This result does, however, require to be tested under grazing conditions. It would also be desirable to know the curve of protein content during the life of a sward or its component species, not so much in relation to arbitrary times of cutting but to recognizable stages of growth and reproductive development. It may well be found, for instance, that the nutritive value of a pasture is highest when shooting has begun or has proceeded for a certain time, rather than during the earlier growth phases. The frequently repeated idea of having non-flowering strains of grasses may therefore not have such great merit nutritionally. The pasture would certainly be easier to manage since it would not persist in going into head in the normal flowering season, but its quality needs to be investigated.

Reproduction in Pasture Grasses

This subject has been fully reviewed by Cooper in 'Grasses in Agriculture' (Whyte, Moir and Cooper, 1959), and the following paragraphs

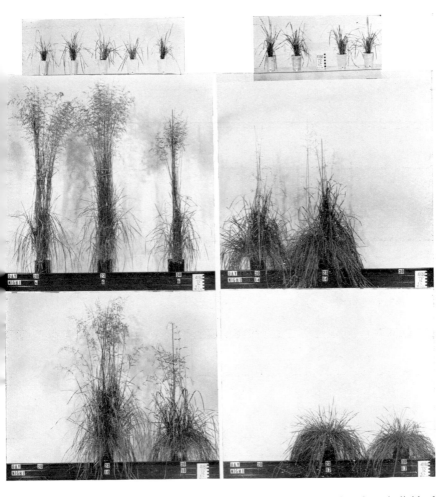

25. Temperature responses in the Earhart Laboratory of nine propagules of one individual *Poa ampla*, 4180-12, originally from near Spokane, Washington. *Uppermost row:* Status on 5 January 1950, prior to the temperature treatments. The propagules were numbered from left to right, 1–9, inclusive. *Centre row, left:* Propagules 1, 2 and 3 after having been exposed for 163 days to a night temperature of 6° C and day temperatures of 20°, 23° and 30° C, respectively. *Lowermost row, left:* Propagules 4 and 5 after having been exposed during the same period to a night temperature of 10° C and day temperatures of 23° and 30° C, respectively. *Centre row, right:* Propagules 6 and 7 subjected to a night temperature of 14° C combined with day temperatures of 20° and 23° C, respectively. *Lowermost row, right:* Propagules 8 and 9 subjected to a night temperature of 17° C and day temperatures of 23° and 30° C, respectively. Photographs in the lower two rows taken 15 June 1950, 163 days after the temperature treatments were begun. The black and white scale is 10 cm. long and the squares are 1cm.^{2}; reduction the same in all pictures (Hiesey, 1953 *a*).

26. Responses of a clone of a maritime race of *Achillea borealis* (*left*) as compared with those of a race from the San Joaquin Valley (*right*) when grown at four different combinations of controlled temperatures. *Left half: lowermost row*, four propagules of plant 5112-1 from Bodega, Sonoma County, California, on 7 January 1950, just prior to exposure to different temperatures; *middle row*, the same propagules 63 days after treatment; *top row*, the same on 6 June 1950, 150 days after treatment. Day and night temperatures are indicated in degrees Centigrade. *Right half:* Four propagules of plant 4074-26 from near Selma, Fresno County, California, treated the same as the maritime race. The topmost row, however, was photographed on 3 May, 116 days after treatment, when in full flower. All photographs reduced to the same scale; the scale beside the label is 10 cm. long (Hiesey, 1953 *b*).

are based on the section on reproductive development in that publication. Although for grazing purposes the maximum production of leaves and vegetative tillers is desirable, for the conservation of fodder, either as hay or silage, some elongation of stems is valuable, both in providing bulk and also for ease of handling. For the establishment of cultivated grasslands an adequate supply of seed is usually necessary. The timing and extent of inflorescence development vary greatly between species and strains, and since they determine both the season of flowering and the duration of the life cycle are of great adaptive importance.

The general sequence of development of inflorescences is similar in all grasses (Evans and Grover, 1940, Sharman, 1945, Cooper, 1951). During vegetative growth, the growing point continues to produce leaf primordia in a regular alternate sequence, the leaf primordia later elongating to form expanded leaves. The first morphological sign of formation of an inflorescence is the appearance of 'double' primordia ridges on the growing point, resulting from the development of buds in the axils of the leaf primordia. Shortly afterwards, these leaf primordia are completely suppressed and their axillary buds grow out to form spikelets or panicle branches. Spikelet development is accompanied by elongation of the stem internodes, followed by emergence of the inflorescence, which occurs some 30 to 40 days after the first appearance of 'double ridges'. At the same time, the development of new tiller buds and nodal roots from the lower nodes is inhibited. The onset of head formation on a tiller therefore puts an end to the production of new leaves and vegetative buds on that shoot, and also prevents the formation of new tillers from buds already present.

Response to daylength: One of the most important environmental factors controlling reproductive development is the length-of-day or photoperiod, the exact daylength requirement varying with the species and strain (see Table 5).

Most grasses from temperate regions of moderate and high latitudes are long-day plants, i.e. they cannot form heads until the hours of daylight exceed a certain critical value. Even if the temperature is adequate for vegetative growth during the winter months, no heads can be produced until the required photoperiod is reached in the spring. On the other hand, grasses from lower latitudes, where the optimal seasons for flowering and seed production may coincide with shorter daylengths, are often short-day plants with an upper critical photoperiod, above which heads cannot be formed. In South African bluestem, *Hyparrhenia hirta*, flowering is delayed by long days and by high night temperatures,

Table 5

REQUIREMENTS OF HERBAGE GRASSES IN RESPECT OF DAYLENGTH

Long-day species

Andropogon scoparius	Larsen, 1947; McMillan, 1956 b.
Bouteloua curtipendula (in part)	Olmsted, 1943 and 1944.
Bromus inermis	Allard and Evans, 1941; Evans and Wilsie, 1946; Gall, 1947; Sprague, 1948; Newell, 1951.
Cynosurus cristatus	Wycherley, 1952.
Dactylis glomerata	Tincker, 1925; Allard and Evans, 1941; Sprague, 1948; Wycherley, 1952; Gardner and Loomis, 1953.
Festuca pratensis	Sprague, 1948.
Hystrix patula	Allard and Evans, 1941.
Lolium perenne	Tincker, 1925; Sprague, 1948; Cooper, 1951; Wycherley, 1952.
L. multiflorum	Cooper, 1951.
L. rigidum	Cooper, 1951.
Paspalum notatum	Knight and Bennett, 1953.
Phalaris arundinacea	Allard and Evans, 1941.
Phleum pratense	Tincker, 1925; Allard and Evans, 1941; Sprague, 1948.
Poa bulbosa	Allard and Evans, 1941.
P. compressa	Allard and Evans, 1941; Sprague, 1948.
P. pratensis	Allard and Evans, 1941; Sprague, 1948; Peterson and Loomis, 1949.

Short-day species

Bouteloua curtipendula (in part)	⎫
B. eriopoda	⎪
B. filiformis	⎬ Olmsted, 1943.
B. gracilis (in part)	⎪
B. hirsuta	⎪
B. rothrockii	⎭
Hyparrhenia hirta	Mes, 1952.
Muhlenbergia scheberi	Allard and Evans, 1941.
Sorghum halepense	Knight and Bennett, 1953.

Indifferent to daylength

Acroceras macrum	Mes, 1952.
Bouteloua gracilis (in part)	Olmsted, 1943.
Eragrostis lehmanniana	Mes, 1952.
Muhlenbergia mexicana	Allard and Evans, 1941.
Tripsacum dactyloides	Allard and Evans, 1941.

while several species of *Bouteloua* from southern Arizona show short-day flowering responses. Some grasses are indifferent to daylength and will flower equally readily in long or short photoperiods. These include the South African species, *Acroceras macrum* and *Eragrostis lehmanniana*, and the American range grasses, *Muhlenbergia mexicana* and *Tripsacum dactyloides.* In these grasses the season of flowering is evidently controlled by factors other than photoperiod.

Many African grasses are characterized by poor flowering and seed setting. Three promising South African species, *Setaria tenuiseta*, *Digitaria eriantha* and *Echinochloa pyramidalis*, have been used in a study on the influence of environmental factors on growth and reproduction at the Plant Physiological Research Institute of the University of Pretoria. Failure to set seed in the species of *Digitaria* and *Echinochloa* appears to be due rather to genetic factors. With *Setaria tenuiseta*, either long days or cold nights favour an erect habit of growth, and the plants kept outside during the day tend to form greater amounts of a purple pigment in the leaves and internodes than plants in the other treatments. Relatively long days or, to a lesser extent, relatively short, cool days with cool nights favour flowering. Normal, viable pollen is formed. When the experiment with *Setaria tenuiseta* was repeated the following season, the plants flowered equally well under all conditions. The difference in the results of the two experiments may have been due to the age of the plants and to the conditions to which they had been subjected prior to the experimental treatments. Full-grown plants were therefore being kept at three different climatic conditions during the winter, and again subjected during the summer to a variety of climatic conditions (Pretoria, 1955/56). Further work at Pretoria confirmed the earlier results, but still only a few seeds were formed on the plants grown under a 16-hour day or natural photoperiod. As crossing with plants of other South African origin was not successful, it is suggested that perhaps all the material in the country is from one original clone and that further introduction from Central Africa is necessary to reduce the apparent self-sterility.

Even in grasses which are sensitive to photoperiod, the flowering responses may be modified by temperature. Using controlled day and night temperatures, Hiesey (1953 a) found that a night temperature of 17°C completely prevents heading in certain ecotypes of *Poa ampla* and *P. compressa*, although these flower freely at a night temperature of 6°C (Plate 25). Conversely, in the southern grasses, *Axonopus affinis*, *Paspalum dilatatum*, *P. notatum* and *Sorghum halepense*, Knight and Bennett (1953) report that night temperatures below 55°F tend to inhibit flowering in all four species.

Although a particular species may be classed as long-day, short-day or indifferent, local strains or ecotypes within the species will differ in their exact response to daylength. The relation between geographical origin and photoperiod requirement has been analysed by Olmsted (1944, 1945 and 1952) using populations of the range grass, sideoats grama (*Bouteloua curtipendula*), from different regions of the United States. Strains from the southernmost areas, south Texas and south Arizona, consist largely of short-day plants, heading only with a photoperiod of below 14 to 16 hours. The most northern strains from North Dakota contain almost entirely long-day plants requiring a daylength above 14 hours, while populations from intermediate localities show a gradation between the two extremes. A similar ecotypical range occurs in *Andropogon scoparius* (Larsen, 1947), although typical short-day plants are not found in this species.

In a comparison of strains of timothy (*Phleum pratense*), Evans and Allard (1934) and Allard and Evans (1941) observed a close correlation between latitude of origin and daylength requirement. Strains of the pasture type from high latitudes, 50° to 60° N., have critical photoperiods over 15 hours, and do not head normally under natural daylengths at Washington, D.C. (39° N.). As the latitude of origin decreases, so does the daylength requirement, the Canadian strain, Huron, needing 13½ hours and the early strain, Marietta, from Ohio only 12 hours. Early and late maturing strains from the same latitude differ in flowering responses, the earlier strains having the lower critical photoperiods (see diagrammatic interpretation by Lona, 1951, in Fig. 30). Similarly, in perennial ryegrass (*Lolium perenne*), Cooper (1951) found a close correlation between date of heading in the spring and photoperiod requirement. The early flowering strains have critical photoperiods below 12 hours and can start to form heads in Britain in late February, while the later flowering pasture strains have a higher requirement, over 13 hours, and cannot initiate heads until the beginning of April.

From the ecological point of view, the response to photoperiod determines the season of the year at which flowering and seed production occur. In each locality, ecotypes have been selected the daylength requirements of which result in flowering at the optimal season, usually early to mid-summer for temperate species. Quite close adaptation to local variations in climate is possible.

McMillan (1956 a) has made transplant studies of variation within five Western grasses (*Bouteloua curtipendula*, *B. gracilis*, *Panicum virgatum*, *Andropogon gerardi* and *A. scoparius*) in relation to their position in a broad habitat gradient across Nebraska. When clones were transplanted in a uniform garden at Lincoln (in the east of the State), it became apparent that clones from western longitudes are early flowering, while those from the east are late flowering. Populations from intermediate geographic positions are intermediate in flowering behaviour. Some of the variables in this habitat gradient, from an altitude of about 5,000 ft in the west to about 900 ft in the east, include: increasing probability of greater rainfall, increasing summer humidity, reduced probability of late spring frosts, later initiation of a dry season, and a longer wet season (Visher, 1954).

Clones of *Andropogon scoparius* in particular representing five community sites in Nebraska were grown in the uniform garden and in the greenhouse under different photoperiods (McMillan, 1956 b). In the uniform garden the eighteen clones from the most westerly site flowered 2 weeks before the first clones from the easternmost site began flowering. Ten clones of the westernmost population flowered under both 14- and 16-hour light periods, and five clones flowered only under 16-hour light periods. During the same growth period, only four of the eighteen easternmost clones flowered under the 14- and 16-hour periods and ten flowered only under 14-hour periods. The westernmost clones in their community habitat were the latest to begin growth in spring and the earliest to flower, a characteristic which was maintained in the uniform garden. The easternmost clones were the earliest to begin growth and the latest to flower. Clones from different positions on a steep bluff in western Iowa varied in response to light periods.

The data suggest (McMillan, 1956 b) that variations in temperature as well as in length of photoperiod may have an effect. The growth and flowering of the western clones in the uniform garden at Lincoln occurred during a fairly cool June. During this period, the Lincoln clones were themselves vegetatively vigorous, but there was no elongation of stems during the subsequent period when all the eighteen western clones reached anthesis; the warmer night temperatures of July may be significant in the flowering of the Lincoln clones. The sequential effect of different day and night temperatures noted by Hiesey (1953 a) in *Poa* will now be studied in *Andropogon scoparius*.

McMillan (1957) later separated the habitat effects from genetic controls within the community by the reciprocal transplanting of members of a prairie community and a sandhill community. This separation of habitat and genetic controls proved to be valuable in interpreting community phenomena in non-experimental habitats. An evaluation was made of behaviour in the two transplant gardens, in a greenhouse under 14- and 16-hour photoperiods, and at the community collection sites. Observations during 1955 and 1956 of the 10 clones of each experimental population indicated that a period of 2 weeks separated the initial flowering of the two populations of most taxa. This difference appeared in most gardens, but the flowering sequence of the various populations occurred at Halsey (sandhills) approximately 2 weeks later. These differences allowed the separation of genetic and habitat effects. The genetic conditioning within the individual dictates the earliest time of flowering. The actual time of flowering of any individual is the result of

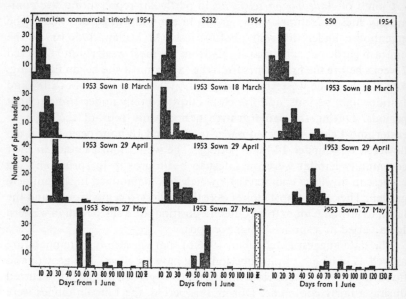

Fig. 31. Influence of date of sowing on head production in timothy (*Phleum pratense*) in United Kingdom. Variation in heading date in sowing year (1953) and in first harvest year (1954). NH=non-heading plants (Cocks, 1958).

the date of inception of growth coupled with this genetically-controlled maturity factor. The earlier flowering of Halsey clones in either garden is due to the influence of the shorter maturity factor. The later date of inception of growth of those clones assures later flowering dates at Halsey. Whether a clone actually flowers appears to be determined by the immediate availability of moisture. The differences in daylength and temperature during the major part of the growing season at these two gardens do not appear to govern time of flowering. This was suggested by the light period studies which reproduced differences between the populations of equal magnitude to those in the gardens or at the community sites. The similarity of species lists at each of the community sites results from the presence of ecotypic variants within each of the species. The overlapping patterns of ecotypic variation have resulted from the selective forces which prevail in the habitat gradient across Nebraska.

In cultivated grasses, the optimal season of flowering, and hence the response to photoperiod, may have been modified by agronomic requirements. For grazing, the maximal production of leaves and vegetative tillers is desirable, and in humid temperate species such as *Lolium perenne*, intensive grazing has selected ecotypes with a high photoperiod requirement, which delays heading as long as possible. Regular harvesting for hay or for a seed crop, on the other hand, selects types with earlier and more uniform heading and hence with a lower critical photoperiod.

If local strains are transferred to regions of different latitude, even though other climatic factors are similar, the seasonal distribution of photoperiod may not be adequate for flowering and seed production. Trumble (1952) states that some north European and northern American ecotypes of *Agropyron tenerum*, *Arrhenatherum elatius*, *Bromus inermis*, *Dactylis glomerata*, *Lolium perenne*, *Phalaris arundinacea* and *Phleum pratense* fail to flower and set seed at Adelaide, South Australia (35° S.) with a maximum photoperiod of 14·3 hours, although ecotypes of the same species from south Europe or southern United States flower normally. Seed production is also likely to be a problem when north temperate species are grown at high elevations in such equatorial regions as Kenya. Conversely, species from lower latitudes, like Wimmera ryegrass (*Lolium rigidum*) which has a long vegetative growing season in South Australia, run to head rapidly in the higher latitudes of northern Europe.

Winter requirement: Although the response to daylength is usually the environmental factor determining the date of flowering in the spring or summer, many grasses of cool temperate regions cannot respond to photoperiod and form heads without previous exposure to winter conditions. If sown in mid or late spring, few or no inflorescences will appear in the same season, although the daylength may be quite adequate. This winter requirement involves either a response to low temperature (vernalization) or to short daylengths, or both. In the United States, Gardner and Loomis (1953) find that the northern species, *Agropyron cristatum*, *Agrostis alba*, *Dactylis glomerata*, *Festuca rubra*, *Phalaris arundinacea* and *Poa pratensis* need exposure to winter conditions before heading, but the southern or range species, *Andropogon gerardi*, *Bouteloua curtipendula*, *Elymus canadensis*, *Eragrostis curvula* and *Panicum virgatum* do not. Winter requirements also occur in the cool temperate grasses, *Bromus inermis* (Gall, 1947, Newell, 1951), *Cynosurus cristatus* (Wycherley, 1952) and *Lolium perenne* (Cooper, 1951, Wycherley, 1952), but not in the range species of *Bouteloua* studied by Olmsted (1943). The physiological responses involved have been analysed in more detail for certain grasses. Peterson and Loomis (1949) find that *Poa pratensis* requires both short days and low temperature, while in *Dactylis glomerata* the short days must accompany or precede the low temperature (Gardner and Loomis, 1953).

As with response to photoperiod, the winter requirement may vary considerably between strains of the same species. In the ryegrasses (*Lolium* spp.), which include a range from summer annual to extreme perennial forms, Cooper (1951, 1957) finds a close correlation between the requirement for low temperature and the annual or perennial habit. The summer annuals, such as Westerwolth ryegrass, show no response to low temperature. Although heads of the winter annual, *Lolium rigidum*, are formed eventually without exposure to cold, reproduction is accelerated by low temperature, while in the biennial *Lolium multiflorum* many of the plants must be exposed to cold before heads can be initiated. Most strains of perennial ryegrass have an obligatory requirement for low temperature, this being greatest in the persistent pasture strains and least in the shorter-lived 'commercial' types. It has been possible to classify ryegrass strains into distinct ecological groups on the basis of their responses to controlled low temperature treatments.

From the ecological point of view, a winter requirement, either for low temperature or for short days, controls the extent of heading and the duration of the life cycle. Where only a short growing season is possible because of climatic or agronomic limitations, short-lived annual grasses will be favoured, for example, the drought-escaping species, *Lolium rigidum* and *Phalaris minor* in Mediterranean regions, or the temperate catch crops, Westerwolth ryegrass and spring oats, none of which have an obligatory winter requirement. In more humid regions, where moisture supply is adequate for growth throughout the year and where continued production of fodder for several seasons is usually required, perennial species are better adapted. To persist as a perennial in cool temperate regions, a species must produce an adequate number of vegetative tillers or buds in late summer or early autumn to live through the winter, and must also lay down sufficient carbohydrate reserves for growth next spring. In species with a winter requirement before heading, the tillers produced after a certain date in the spring cannot form heads in the same year, will continue active assimilation during summer and autumn, and persist through the winter. Even so, not all the over-wintered tillers will necessarily produce heads in the following spring. In *Bromus inermis*, for instance, Lamp (1952) found that a proportion of the tillers present in the autumn remained vegetative throughout the following summer. The extent of the winter requirement controls the proportion of vegetative to fertile tillers and can therefore influence both the nutritive value of the herbage and resistance to cutting and grazing. Where the strain is to be grown for hay or for conservation, a fairly high proportion of fertile tillers maturing at the same time is often desirable. For grazing, on the other hand, a continued production of leaves and vegetative tillers is required and a high winter requirement will be favoured, as in the pasture strains of *Dactylis glomerata*, *Lolium perenne* and *Poa pratensis*. Not all cool temperate species, however, depend on a winter requirement for the attainment of the perennial habit. In *Phleum pratense*, for instance, there is no requirement for either short-day or low temperature, but heading ceases in mid to late summer, although photoperiod is quite adequate (Langer, 1956).

In tropical and sub-tropical species, which are not exposed to winter conditions, the extent of flowering and seed production is presumably controlled by other mechanisms. The effect of night temperature on southern grasses has already been mentioned, and in Kikuyu grass (*Pennisetum clandestinum*), Carr and Eng Kok Ng (1956) find that heads can be initiated only when the plants are severely defoliated and the in-hibiting influence of the main growing points is removed by decapitation. Inflorescences are then formed on short axillary branches. A similar type of control may occur in some other stoloniferous or rhizomatous species such as *Cynodon dactylon*, which normally produce few heads.

Although the season and extent of inflorescence development in cool temperate species are controlled mainly by photoperiod and low tempera-ture, the proportion of heads produced can also be modified by nutrition and defoliation. In an established sward, for instance, the number of tillers is strongly influenced by the nitrogen status of the soil. Where the content of available nitrogen in early spring is low, there will be com-paratively little production of new tillers. Most of those present will have received adequate exposure to winter conditions, will form heads in the spring, and will have a high proportion of fertile to vegetative tillers. An increase in the available nitrogen will encourage the production of new tillers in mid to late spring, and most of these will remain vegetative until the following year, thus increasing the leaf/stem ratio and the

G* 201

nutritive value of the herbage. Similarly, close grazing will, by removing the young inflorescences as they start to elongate, bring to an end the inhibition of the lower axillary buds by the main growing points and so encourage the production of new tillers.

Summer dormancy: Of some twenty perennial grasses in the Mediterranean climate of Davis, California, seven become summer-dormant in the field even when supplied with water throughout the dry season (Laude, 1953). *Stipa cernua, Oryzopsis miliacea* and *Phalaris tuberosa* var. *stenoptera* make vigorous vegetative growth in September after being summer-dormant and before effective autumn rains. Field observations confirmed by greenhouse studies indicate that, in *Poa scabrella*, high temperatures and long days are related to the initiation of dormancy, and moderating temperatures and availability of water are associated with the breaking of dormancy. Plants dormant for 20 months in a greenhouse resume growth 5 days after being placed at temperatures not exceeding 75°F daily and receiving water.

Proliferation: It is generally accepted that the term 'true vivipary' should be restricted to the germination of a seed while still attached to the living mother plant, while the appearance of leaves from floral organs in the absence of the seed should be referred to as vegetative proliferation. Certain grasses regularly reproduce by the latter means, the leafy portion of the proliferated spikelet becoming detached and serving as a diaspore for propagation; Wycherley (1954) states that in certain plants this proliferation is a hereditary character little modified by environment. These races survive in most areas and habitats, but since transplants remain constant in their proliferation, humidity is not the cause.

Proliferation of spikelets also occurs ephemerally in plants which are not members of these races, namely, *Agropyron repens, Alopecurus pratensis, Arrhenatherum avenaceum, Cynosurus cristatus, Dactylis glomerata, Deschampsia caespitosa, Festuca rubra, Lolium perenne, Phleum pratense* and *Poa trivialis*. These plants normally produce flower-bearing culms, but occasionally the spikelets in all or part of an inflorescence are proliferated. The proliferations may be used as cuttings and reared into adult plants, but the character is not inherited in normal conditions. If, however, plants are subjected to photoperiods intermediate in effect between normal flowering and vegetative growth, or if plants are removed from long days which would eventually cause them to produce perfect inflorescences, proliferation in normally seed-setting grasses may be experimentally induced. This effect has been produced in *Cynosurus cristatus* (Wycherley, *loc. cit.*), S.48 timothy (Langer and

Ryle, 1958) and other grasses. Reference is appropriate at this point to the studies of Jeater (1958) on the production of malformations of leaves and ears of grasses following treatment with growth-regulating weed-killers.

Reproduction in Pasture Legumes

RED CLOVER

The distinction between early and late flowering red clovers (the single and double-cut, or spring and winter types of European literature) is based on their developmental physiology, but an exact interpretation has not yet been given. An early type may produce a considerable percentage of flowers in the seeding year, and two cuts in the first harvest year. It would be desirable to know the age of the buds that produce the second cut; are they buds that have over-wintered and thus received their cold requirement, or has the type only a slight need for preliminary low temperature, in which case even physiologically young buds might be able to develop and reach maturity between the first and second cuts. It is interesting to note that it is possible to cut white clover as late as May and yet obtain a seed yield in the same season.

Important work in this connection is that of the late R. D. Williams at Aberystwyth, reviewed by his successor, Watkin Williams (1945). A map is given in this publication indicating how the cultivated strains of red clover are distributed in Europe. The cultivated early-flowering types are found south of a line which roughly corresponds to the 50° N. latitude and are therefore more adapted to warm southerly latitudes. Countries south of this line, that is France, Spain, Italy, Switzerland, Hungary and Czechoslovakia, rely mainly on early-flowering types, and, except at high altitudes in Alpine and sub-Alpine regions, few late-flowering types appear to be cultivated. North of about 60° N. the late-flowering types prevail, while between 50° and 60° N., for example, in the British Isles, both early and late-flowering red clovers are grown. These facts are of great importance in the production of strains suited to a particular environment or type of use.

Schulze (1957) has observed the photoperiodic behaviour of varieties of various origins within Europe, with what he calls a constant assimilation potential—a maximum of 12 hours per day. Plants raised under 12-hour days remain shorter, form larger, dark green leaves, form more stems and cover the ground earlier; they do not form flowers. Plants raised under 18-hour days grow taller, their leaves are smaller, coarser, and light green, they form fewer stems and cover the ground later and less densely; buds and flowers are formed in all strains under 18-hour days, although to a very varying extent according to the 'northerliness' of the region of origin. Varieties from Germany, Holland and England (49° to 52° 30′ N.) flower abundantly or even very abundantly and fairly early under 18-hour days; varieties from Denmark (55° N.), Sweden (56° N.) and particularly from Norway (61° N.) flower later and less. The number of shoot and flower primordia is clearly dependent upon the duration of daily light application.

In Swedish and Norwegian (Resistenta and Molstad) strains, the highest yield of leaves and stems is obtained under 18-hour days, while maximum root development and storage of reserves take place under 12-hour days; the content of crude protein decreases and that of N-free substances increases with increasing duration of light, both in the shoot and the roots. Maximum and earliest flower initiation (in Resistenta and Molstad)—under 24-hour days—coincides with the greatest protein/carbohydrate ratio; at the beginning of flower formation the shoot contains more than 80 per cent, if flowering is relatively abundant even 90 per cent of the reserve substances (Inhaltsstoffe) of the whole plant.

Particularly wide deviations caused by photoperiodism were observed in the two varieties, Steinacher (Germany: origin about 49° N.) and Molstad (Norway: origin about 61° N.). For optimal development Molstad needs longer photoperiods than Steinacher, roughly corresponding with the more northerly situation of its area of origin; the same is true of Molstad as compared to Resistenta. The longer the daily photoperiod, the earlier Molstad and Steinacher flower; Molstad flowers almost as early under 24-hour days as Steinacher under 15-hour days.

Schulze notes a distinct connection between the 'northerly' area of origin or of multiplication of a variety on the one hand, and the duration of light required for good or complete flower formation of all the forms occurring within a variety, on the other. If, for instance, the critical value for light duration required for complete flowering is not reached, selective effects are to be expected, i.e. there will be a selection for those plants whose photoperiodic requirements are still just being met. The critical value for the induction of complete flower formation increases with the more northerly location of the area of origin. Experience suggests that a deviation, in either direction, from the daylength required for optimal flowering and seed production during the growth period may lead to harmful selective effects. Red clover plants pre-treated with different photoperiods showed definite after-effects—even after all aerial

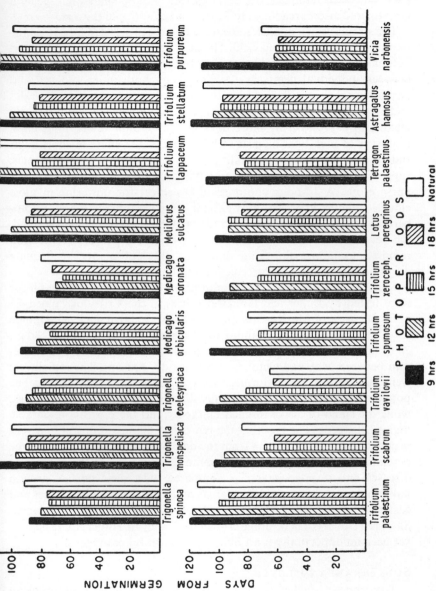

Fig. 32. Legumes in Israel. Effect of photoperiod on time of flowering (Landau, 1957).

parts had been removed—in development of new shoots and general growth, and also in readiness to flower and quantity of flowers.

The strains grown in Eastern Canada have been selected largely on the basis of winter survival and yield. The early and late types show, however, not only differences between strains but also even larger differences between individual plants in a single strain, both morphological and physiological (Bird, 1948). Using the Dollard variety, Ludwig, Barrales and Steppler (1953) found that inherent morphological variability shows maximum expression in short days and minimum under long days. Exposure to high light intensity tends to mask the effect of short days. Individual lines vary in their ability to survive under low light intensities, suggesting the possibility of selecting types suitable for cultivation under nurse crops. A 14-hour photoperiod is critical for flowering in most clones, 16 hours in others. Flowering is more profuse in 16-hour photoperiods than in 14-hour photoperiods in all but two of the lines studied, the reverse in these two. The duration of photoperiodic stimulation required to induce flowering differs in different plants; inadequate duration often causes the production of abortive inflorescences.

Kenland medium red and mammoth red clovers and alsike clover were tested by Buller and González (1958) in the Valley of Toluca, 25 miles due west of Mexico City (altitude 8,800 ft above sea level; climate cool with maximum, minimum and average temperatures of 80·2°, 26·6° and 54·9°F respectively; frosts common during winter; 32 inches rain between May and October, 6 months dry season). The red clovers were cut fourteen times during 3 harvest years, the alsike eleven. The populations of red clover thinned only slightly after the fourteen cuttings, while the stand of alsike thinned markedly and there was considerable ingress of weeds. The fact that the red clover stands were still in a very productive condition 4 years from the date of planting indicates the true perennial habit of medium and mammoth red clovers in the absence of diseases and severe winters, as compared with their normal growth habit in the red clover-producing areas of the northern United States and eastern Canada, where the species behaves as an annual or biennial. Since red clover is a new forage crop in the Valley of Toluca, there has not yet been an opportunity for a build-up of harmful pathogens.

SUBTERRANEAN CLOVER

The chance arrival of *Trifolium subterraneum* from the Mediterranean region in Australia and its subsequent spread over some 30 million acres of pasture land is one of the outstanding examples of plant introduction.

This species has now acquired such great economic importance that intensive research is in progress at a number of centres. Incidentally it is in this species that the problem has arisen of the effect, chiefly in Western Australia but subsequently also in New Zealand and the United Kingdom, of pasture plant oestrogens in the reproduction and lactation of grazing animals (Pope, 1954); most of the British work has been done on red clover.

At the Waite Institute in Adelaide, apart from the work on leaf area index already described in Chapter III, Black has studied the interaction of light and temperature in determining growth rate, the influence of seed size and depth of sowing on pre-emergence and early vegetative growth, and seed size as a factor in growth under spaced and sward conditions (Black, 1957 b). In the Victoria Department of Agriculture, Millikan (1957 b) investigated the effects of day and night temperature, photoperiod, light intensity, and phosphate level on the total growth $(T+R)$ and top/root ratio (T/R) of the Dwalganup and Mt. Barker varieties in a water culture experiment. The individual or combined effect of increases in photoperiod and in light intensity is to increase $(T+R)$ in both varieties. With a 16-hour photoperiod, varietal difference in the response of $(T+R)$ to day temperature occurs, depending on the level of phosphate in the solution. In general, T/R increases with day temperature, although the magnitude of the increase is affected by photoperiod, phosphate level and variety.

The response of total growth $(T+R)$ in each variety to phosphate is independent of day temperature at 8-hour photoperiod, but at 16 hours it is greatest at 17°C for both varieties. The growth $(T+R)$ response to phosphate is greater for Dwalganup than Mt. Barker, the condition favouring the greatest difference being high light intensity, or a 20°C day temperature combined with long photoperiod. These varietal differences in total growth due to different level of phosphate in the presence of other variables are associated with differential effects on the relative top/root (T/R) growth within and between the varieties. Different night temperatures have no differential effect on total growth of plants at an 8-hour photoperiod, but at 16 hours there are highly significant interactions between day and night temperature in both varieties. The sense of the interaction is reversed by an increase in phosphate level in the substrate. Runner stem development is a more sensitive indicator of the interaction than total growth $(T+R)$.

The value of this clover in southern Australia is greatly enhanced by the existence of a range of varieties differing in the length of their growing season, which is closely connected with the time of commencement of flowering. In an annual, the period from sowing to maturity can be divided into: sowing to flower initiation, flower initiation to flowering, and flowering to seed maturity and death of the plant. The first is most subject to variation in length, and so most important in its influence on the full period (Aitken, 1955).

Depending on the cold requirement of the variety, an insufficient period of low temperature retards or prevents flower initiation (Plate 10). The mild winter of southern Australia does not provide an adequate amount of low temperature for rapid flowering, the growing season is longer than in southern Europe, and the production of herbage is therefore greater. The low temperature requirement, however, reduces the value of the species as a self-regenerating annual when the temperatures of both the summer and the winter seasons are too high for flower initiation; this occurs when the later varieties are sown in northern Australia. Temperatures of the summer growing season in the tropics are likely to be too high even for the short low-temperature requirement of the earliest flowering group, with its high critical upper margin of about 75°F mean weekly temperature. If the dry winter months are cooler and water is available, flower initiation may occur, but is retarded with consequent leafiness of the plants. Hence, only varieties of the early flowering group may be of use in the pastures in northern Australia, and then only in the cooler districts. The range of early to late flowering groups is due to genes controlling the requirements of low temperature and photoperiod for flower initiation. There are similarities with other crop plants; the over-summering in the vegetative state of the late-flowering groups resembles that in late varieties of peas, wheat, perennial ryegrass and sugarbeet.

Important fundamental genetical and physiological studies are also being made in the Division of Plant Industry, C.S.I.R.O., Canberra. The genetical responses to the Australian environment have been reviewed by Frankel (1954). The presence of genic and structural sterility barriers suggests that many of the varieties were reproductively isolated long before they were introduced to Australia. Major varietal differences are unlikely to have arisen from selection of locally adapted ecotypes. There is thus ample justification for a programme of hybridization and selection to improve and to extend the range of the species. Such a programme would be impeded, but not prevented, by the presence of reduced fertility in some segregates (Morley, Brock and Davern, 1956). In order to discover the real nature of the varieties of this clover, and

208

particularly their reaction to environmental factors, physiological studies are being made in support of the genetical work.

Genotype-environment interactions noted in the flowering time of a number of varieties grown in different places are interpreted in terms of the effects of photoperiod and temperature on flowering (Morley and Davern, 1956). Sensitivity to photoperiod may be independent of sensitivity to temperature. Flowering times of some strains, although simultaneous in one environment, may differ in another environment, due to variation in the relative importance of different components of the environment in controlling flowering time; these strain differences are related to the climate of the strain's natural habitat.

In a study of the inheritance of flowering time, Davern, Peak and Morley (1957) found that heterosis and dominance did not occur, and that genetic variation was polygenic. An F_1 diallel analysis and F_2 two-way analysis showed that approximately 90 per cent of the total variance was attributable to additive genetic effects. An estimate of the repeatability of strain performance over two seasons showed that small but significant strain-year interactions were occurring. Strain repeatability, as measured by intra-class correlation, was 86 per cent. A breeding test involving F_2 selections and their progeny gave a mean parent-offspring regression of 0·86 over the six crosses studied, which agrees well with expectations of breeding behaviour based on these analyses.

While working at the Earhart Laboratory in Pasadena, Evans (1958 b) studied the influence of various temperature and light regimes on flowering and flower initiation in eight strains. Flower initiation appears to be under the control of three interacting partial processes, two of which are synergistic and promotive while the third is inhibitory. The promotive processes are possibly both light-independent, one being favoured by high temperatures and the other (the vernalization process) by low temperatures. The inhibitory process, on the other hand, is restricted to the diurnal dark period and is favoured by high temperatures. The interaction between the vernalization and dark inhibitory processes is such that in the absence of dark inhibition no vernalization is required by any strain, while on the other hand sufficient vernalization can apparently overcome all dark inhibitory effects. Treatment with gibberellic acid eliminates the need for vernalization by plants grown in short days at high temperatures. Strains differ markedly in their responses to the three partial processes. In their response to the dark inhibitory process two strains are more affected by night temperature than by night length, while in two other strains the opposite is the case: this suggests that the dark inhibitory process could be resolved into more than one component.

In a second study on flower initiation, Morley and Evans (1959) removed plants of five strains from the field at Canberra, to receive a series of daylength and temperature treatments. The times to inflorescence initiation in all treatments were determined by dissection. As vernalization proceeded the requirement of all strains for long days was progressively reduced until, by mid-winter, all had become virtually daylength-independent. At this stage, induction is no longer retarded by vernalization or by the dark inhibitory processes, but probably by a light-independent process which is limited by low field temperatures. This latter process may be operative during or immediately following the absence of the dark inhibitory reactions. The literature on wheat and lettuce suggests that this process may be general in long-day plants.

White Clover

Trifolium repens is a perennial which may behave as a winter or summer annual or as a biennial depending upon the interactions of favourable or unfavourable environmental factors (Gibson, 1957). Different responses to daylength have been observed between plants from seedstocks of Ladino clover grown for several generations under different daylengths. Northern American strains of common white produce only scattered flowers in the southern States while naturalized southern strains flower profusely. Although it is generally accepted that flowering and forage production are competitive, little is known about the effect of flowering on longevity; it has, however, been noted that persistence of clones is conversely related to the amount of flowering under various clipping and irrigation treatments. Gibson (*loc. cit.*) compared the persistence of plants growing in a long light period with those under normal day in Alabama; the long light period was adopted to induce flowering of genotypes which normally produce only a few blossoms at that latitude. Plants of the flowering group (Louisiana white) reached a peak intensity of flowering earlier than usual, while non-flowering types (Oregon Ladino and Pilgrim) blossomed profusely (see Fig. 33). The non-flowering clover under the normal daylight period persisted longer than the same clover under the extended light period or the profuse-flowering clover under the normal daylight period. The profuse-flowering clover under the extended light period persisted longer than the non-flowering clover under the same light period. This profuse-flowering clover under the extended light period had apparently passed the peak intensity of flower-

210

ing and had reverted to vegetative growth prior to the occurrence of the adverse summer conditions. The critical minimum for flowering of Ladino white clovers is within a few minutes of 14 hours 15 minutes. Geographically this critical minimum photoperiod is to be found near latitude 32° N. Thus Ladino strains from northern latitudes will flower sparsely, if at all, below this latitude.

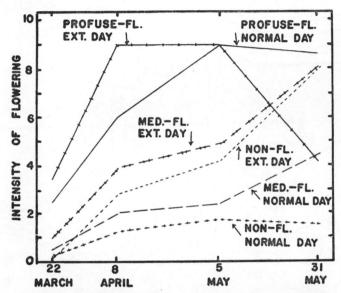

Fig. 33. Flowering intensity of three groups of white clover growing under normal daylight and daylight extended by Mazda lamps from sundown to midnight. Intensity ratings were made using a 0 to 10 scale, with 0=no flowers and 10=profuse flowering. Values plotted are averages for two entries in four replications (Gibson, 1957).

Daday (1954) studied the distribution by latitude of gene frequencies in wild populations from a wide range of habitats. Generally speaking, the types from southern Europe are erect, with large leaves, thick stems and early flowering; the northern European (Norwegian) type is prostrate, with smaller leaves, thinner stems and late flowering. By means of a modified picric acid test, Daday classified his material into four phenotypes:

(a) glucoside and enzyme,   (b) glucoside only,
(c) enzyme only,   (d) neither glucoside nor enzyme,

according to the presence of glucoside, lotaustralin, and enzyme linamarase genes in dominant or recessive conditions (Figs. 34 and 37).
A continuous gradual decrease in the frequency of these genes was noted
over the whole range from 100 to 0 per cent, as the source of the samples

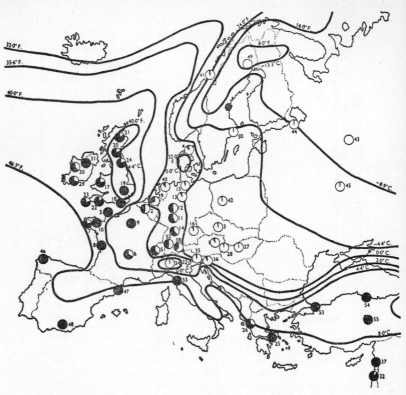

Fig. 34. Distribution and frequency of the glucoside lotaustralin gene in European
and Near Eastern wild populations of *Trifolium repens* (Daday, 1954).
   Black section: Dominant gene frequency.
   White section: Recessive gene frequency.
   ——January isotherm. (Figures at circles refer to sites quoted in the original
text.)

moved from the Mediterranean to north-eastern Europe. As the distribution of the dominant allele frequencies is closely related to January
isotherms, it is concluded that these temperatures have played an important role through natural selection in the evolution of subspecies.
In a later study on a global basis, Daday (1958) finds that natural

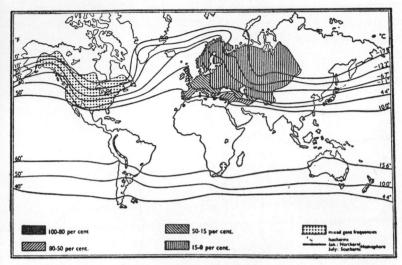

Fig. 35. Distribution of lotaustralin gene frequencies in world populations of *Trifolium repens* (Daday, 1958).

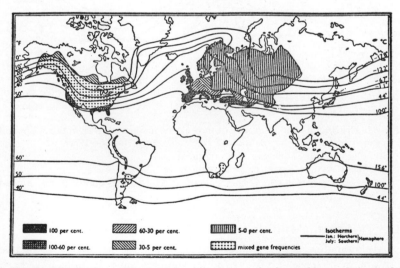

Fig. 36. Distribution of linamarase gene frequencies in world populations of *Trifolium repens* (Daday, 1958).

213

selection has already produced a balanced equilibrium in Europe and the mainland of Asia, and that this selection is still in progress in North America and Japan (Figs. 35 and 36).

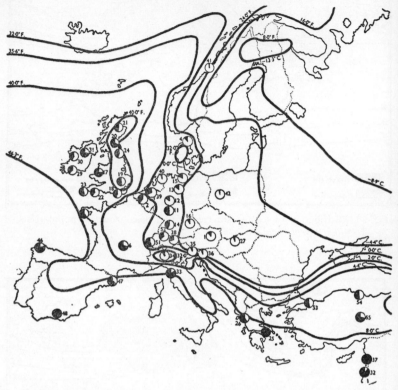

Fig. 37. Distribution and frequency of the enzyme linamarase gene in European and Near Eastern wild populations of *Trifolium repens* (Daday, 1954).

Black section: Dominant gene frequency.
White section: Recessive gene frequency.

———January isotherm. (Figures at circles refer to sites quoted in the original text.)

LUCERNE AND MEDICS

Although few if any studies have been made on the reproductive physiology of these important fodder legumes, investigations have been made in a number of countries and conditions on the relation between environmental factors, primarily low winter temperatures, and physiology, persistence and yield. Recent studies by R. J. Bula at the Indiana

Agricultural Experiment Station show that the dry weight accumulation of lucerne is essentially proportional to light intensity over the range of 750 to 3,000 foot-candles. The shape of the curve suggests that light saturation is in excess of 3,000 foot-candles, an important consideration in species competition in forage mixtures. For any particular species or mixture, there is a ceiling yield imposed by competition for light. Swards have to be managed so as to maintain the optimal leaf area. This aspect is now being studied on a quantitative basis.

In the first paper in a series on quantitative inheritance in lucerne, Morley, Daday and Peak (1957) studied the problems of inheritance and selection for winter yield in Australia. When spaced plants derived from ten strains and 44 F_1 plants were grown in the field at Canberra, they exhibited discontinuous variation in winter growth. Some were completely dormant, others grew at over 40 per cent of their summer rate. Strains differ with respect to combining ability for growth rates, both in summer and winter, but differences between strains in combining ability are much more evident in winter than in summer. The correlation between winter and summer growth rates is markedly affected by differences in winter dormancy. Thus the Canadian creeping-rooted strain, which had the highest combining ability for summer growth, was among the poorest for winter growth. Within strains or crosses, winter and summer growth rates were strongly correlated ($r = 0.77$), presumably because genotypes within such lines were relatively homogeneous with respect to winter dormancy. The Hairy Peruvian strain, and to a lesser extent Hunter River, Provence, and an Australian selection showed high combining ability for winter growth.

Winter dormancy may be broken either by increased temperatures (heated glass-house) or by supplementing the natural day-length with low-intensity artificial light. These treatment effects were supplementary without interaction. In one set of material a highly significant genotype (clone) × temperature interaction, and the absence of a genotype × day-length interaction, indicated that genetic differences in dormancy could be determined largely by the response to low temperatures. For the present, neither short days nor low temperatures alone seem sufficient to distinguish between winter-active and winter-dormant genotypes.

The productivity of pastures in many areas of southern Australia is limited by a virtual cessation of growth in winter, even though moisture is frequently adequate. Morley, Daday and Peak find that the growth rates of some genotypes in winter are promising for the introduction, selection and management of lucerne and other species for increased winter production. The results of these workers and those of Buller, Pitner and Ramirez (1955) on lucerne in Mexico show that winter dormancy is characteristic of strains from sub-arctic and cool-temperature environments. Similar observations have been made by Kolomiec (1955) in red clover and by Nobs (1955) in *Mimulus*. Strains with a satisfactory type of winter growth are most likely to be found at the warmer end of the distribution of a species. Bula, Smith and Hodgson (1956) have noted that cold resistance in very hardy *falcata* and hardy Ranger alfalfa develops faster and at higher levels at Palmer, Alaska, than at Madison, Wisconsin. The level for non-hardy Arizona Common is very low at both locations. Trends of water-soluble protein nitrogen appear to follow those of cold resistance in Ranger and *falcata*. Arizona Common shows the highest level of total available carbohydrates at both locations; Ranger is intermediate, and *falcata* lowest.

A number of studies have been made on the relation between latitude and growth and reproduction, as for example, the testing of northern European strains in Mediterranean countries, in the hope that it may be possible to build up a source of seed without experiencing any change in the genotypes due to the marked change in latitude. Smith (1955) made studies in Wisconsin on the performance of populations of Ranger alfalfa derived from seed which had been produced in several States within and outside the variety's northern region of adaptation. Significant differences in performance are not apparent among the Ranger plant populations derived from seed lots of the same class (foundation, registered, or certified) of seed produced in the same State or produced from different ages of stands in the same State. The significant differences are among the different State origins of seed. Ranger alfalfa seed (certified) originating from one generation of increase in southern latitudes produces a greater number of tall plants and fewer short plants in the populations following early autumn cutting and shows more winter injury than populations derived from seed originating from one generation of increase in northern latitudes (foundation or registered). These contrasts are even more apparent when the populations are derived from seed lots originating from a second generation of increase in a southern latitude.

When plants from each lot are grouped into four categories, viz., those with stems that grow short, medium, tall, and extra tall under the shortening days and cooler temperatures of autumn, the amount of winter injury increases in each group as the seed originates from a more southern latitude. Regardless of latitude, winter injury is more severe in the taller than in the shorter height groups. The observed differences in perform-ance between the populations derived from certified seed of Ranger pro-duced in the southern latitudes of the United States and seed produced in the north are, however, not large. Certified seed originating from the southern latitudes therefore seems to be suitable for fodder production in Wisconsin and other northern areas.

When eleven varieties were tested in the Valley of Mexico (7,600 ft above sea level in a temperate climate), the non-hardy types were found to be early maturing, quick recovering, active in winter, highly suscept-ible to top injury from frosts, and generally weak in persistence. The winter-hardy types were the contrary in all these respects (Buller, Pitner and Ramirez, 1955).

Some species of annual medic are already established in the Mallee of southern Australia and others are regarded as potential components of pastures (Aitken, 1955). The search for better types for these low-rainfall pastures is based on the isolation of early flowering types with non-objectionable burrs and as high a yield of leaf and seed as possible. When sowings of *Medicago tribuloides* are made in the field throughout the year, the flower initiation of the winter sowings is the most rapid and that of the late summer sowings most delayed (due to the absence of sufficiently low temperature following germination). Low temperature and long photoperiod accelerate flower initiation as in subterranean clover. Five types of annual medic that persist in the Mallee resemble the 'second-early' varieties of subterranean clover in the character of their flower initiation.

BIRDSFOOT TREFOIL

Lotus corniculatus has a relatively prostrate growth habit and very limited flower production in Pretoria. In controlled experiments, flower-ing occurred only in 18-hour days, while temperature had little effect (Pretoria, 1957). An unusually high percentage of abortive buds is aggravated by high night temperature and maintenance under glass during the day. In later experiments, it was found that at least 15 hours of light are necessary for production of normal flowers, but total flowering increases with longer photoperiods. In 15-hour days, forty photoperiods are necessary for appearance of first flowers; in 16-hour days, only twenty-two photoperiods are required. The minimum number of con-secutive 18-hour photoperiods necessary for floral induction is only four, but these plants do not produce visible buds. When seven long days are given, vestigial buds do develop but not normal flowers. The requirements

217

for floral induction are therefore not the same as for floral development. Plants in full bloom under long days cease to produce flowers one or two weeks after transference to short days, indicating that photochemical induction is not maintained. An erect growth habit accompanies floral induction in this legume.

VETCH

The seeds of vetches may be soaked in a certain amount of water, made to swell at room temperature (18°C) for 24 hours, and then vernalized with low temperature (1° to 5°C) for 30 to 35 days (*Vicia villosa, V. pannonica*) or 14 days (*V. sativa, V. faba*). The results obtainable with winter vetches differ little from those with winter cereals, but vernalization has a marked effect on the seed production of hairy vetch, despite the shortening of the vegetative period (Kurth, 1956 a and b). The photoperiodic reaction of long-day plants may be largely eliminated by vernalization.

In studies on *Vicia sativa* at the University of Pretoria, it was noted that: (*a*) plants grown outside during the day are markedly smaller than those in the greenhouse, although they may have the same dry weight as plants several times their height in the greenhouse; intensity and quantity of light may be concerned; (*b*) an increase in night temperature from 15° to 21°C reduces dry weight and N content, but an increase in percentage N may occur; (*c*) a 16-hour photoperiod stimulates elongation, as compared with a 12-hour photoperiod, and causes an increase in dry weight, particularly at the lower day temperature of 18°C; (*d*) the highest dry weight and N content occur under natural light in full days; and (*e*) a day temperature of 27°C reduces the percentage N in non-flowering plants.

LUPINS

In the yellow lupin (*Lupinus luteus*), self-fertile flowers are produced abundantly but only a small proportion produce mature pods with seeds. Terminal racemes bear about 40 to 50 flowers, basal laterals have 10 to 30 and apical laterals from 5 to 20 flowers. The flowers are grouped in whorls with 5 flowers each. Normally flowers on one or two whorls will open each consecutive day until all the flowers of an inflorescence are in full bloom (Van Steveninck, 1957 b). Under field conditions mature pods are produced only on the lowest two or three whorls of the main inflorescence, rarely on the basal laterals, and never on the apical laterals. Flowers situated in any whorl of the main inflorescence are capable of producing pods; developing pods on earlier flowers have an abscission-producing effect on later flowers of the same inflorescence. It is improbable that competition for nutrients is the primary cause of abscission, but rather that the results might be explained by the more recent theories of hormonal regulation. Flowers at the apex do, however, lack efficient vascular connections, while these are present at the base of the inflorescence. This and the lower growth rate of pods at the apex are considered to indicate that possibly nutrients cannot be transported in sufficient quantities through the upper part of the stalk to support normal growth of pods. This may accentuate the abscission-producing effect of the developing pods at the base.

Pea-mosaic virus has an interesting effect on the reproductive capacity of the yellow lupin. Unusual pod-setting characteristics were noted by Van Steveninck (1957 a) in two types of plants:

A. twice as many pods as usual, atypical in shape, containing a normal number of seeds only half the usual size; and

B. plants almost sterile, entire plant with none to about six pods, each with only one or two large seeds, growth and flowering continuous.

Van Steveninck confirms an earlier observation of Troll (1952) and records that both the A and B plants were infected with a common species of pea-mosaic virus. No genetic difference in reaction was found between the two types. Early infection causes plants to produce more flowers per inflorescence, but these are usually sterile and growth continues through the production of lateral shoots. Plants infected later, after the appearance of inflorescences, produce about double the number of pods and seeds on their main inflorescence. The growth of pods on infected plants is limited in longitudinal and median directions; they contain almost as many seeds as pods on healthy plants, but they are 40 per cent smaller than normal. Pods on plants infected early have usually one or two seeds larger than normal. The virus does not limit the size of the seeds directly, but indirectly through limiting the size of the pods. There are a number of facts to indicate that the virus disturbs auxin metabolism: shorter internodes on the inflorescences, increased number of flowers at early infection, and the two-fold increase in pod-setting at later infection.

There is a close connection between weather and yield (Schulz, 1958). Rainfall at end May/early June is of special importance for seed setting. The number of plants which set seeds on the side shoots is also dependent on rainfall. There is marked relationship between size of seed and establishment, vigour, height, time of flowering and yield. Kurth (1955) states that the requirements for vernalizing yellow sweet lupin and *Lupinus angustifolius* are 60 per cent moisture, followed by exposure to 3° to 6°C for 10 to 15 days. Ritzel (1957) noted gibberellin activity in *Lupinus*, not only from the seed but also from both the inner and outer wall of the pods. Activity increases with increase in seed size, and decreases only after seed has approached final size.

Chapter XII

OTHER LEAF AND STEM CROPS

Green Vegetables

V egetables are considered in different sections of this book, depending on whether the economic product is the leaves, fruits or storage organs. It is not possible to review all the literature relating to leafy vegetables which has appeared since F. L. Milthorpe and B. Horowitz in 1943 attempted to define the environmental conditions in which a number of vegetables, including cabbage and lettuce, produce the vegetative organs required for marketing, or premature and undesirable seed heads in a vegetative crop, or a crop of seed for reproduction of the line. Reference should be made to *Horticultural Abstracts*, and to reports of work at centres such as the Horticultural Branch of the U.S. Department of Agriculture in Beltsville, or the National Vegetable Research Station in England, where studies are made to determine the separate effects of physiological and climatological factors in plant growth.

Several long-day annuals such as leaf and head lettuce, endive, spinach and dill grown under non-inductive short (9- to 11-hour) photoperiods, but treated with gibberellin, show marked stem elongation and may be induced to flower and produce seed. Some long-day plants (lettuce, endive) grown under an 18-hour photoperiod and treated with gibberellin flower earlier than controls, others (spinach and dill) do not (Wittwer and Bukovac, 1958).

Brussels Sprouts

The seed cannot be vernalized; the plants are day-neutral. There is a juvenile phase during which seedlings cannot be made to flower, and which is distinguished from the adult form by physiological and morphological characters which change with the attainment of ability to flower. A period under low temperature is necessary for flower initiation in adult vegetative plants. Cold for 6 to 9 weeks is necessary to bring about full flowering in all plants. Flower primordia are initiated and developed in the cold (Stokes and Verkerk, 1951) (Fig. 38). Auxin application during cold treatment of otherwise juvenile plants can promote floral initiation at an unusually low node, with an acceleration evident both in 9- and 11-week-old plants, and with a resultant increase in length of the flower stalks as well. De Zeeuw and Leopold (1955) quote this as a further example in the growing body of evidence that auxin treatments associated with low temperature are promotive of flowering, and suggest that the completion of the juvenile phase may be in part the

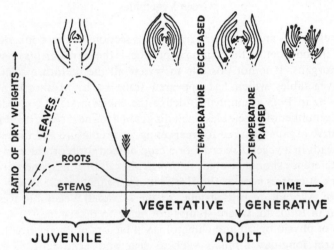

Fig. 38. Flower formation in Brussels sprouts. Diagram showing the changes in structure of apical growing point and distribution of growth during juvenile, vegetative adult and reproductive stages. Dry weight of leaves and roots are represented as multiples of stem dry weight (Stokes and Verkerk, 1951).

accumulation of a sufficient auxin level at the apical meristem to bring about the condition receptive to cold.

CABBAGE

Seeding in cabbage is influenced chiefly by exposure to low temperature; length of day is believed to have no effect. Although vernalization by low temperature is effective, such treatment accentuates the need for high temperatures in the post-vernalization stages. The most important modifications as regards the economic utilization of the cabbage are related to morphological anatomical variations in vegetative organs which are restricted to the main shoot axis, to the leaf blade, the midrib and the lateral buds. Corresponding biochemical changes increase if morphological changes influence the basic physiological processes; this is true if a normally branched main axis (e.g. kale or Brussels sprouts) is modified to a large terminal bud as in white cabbage. The cabbage head is the result of marked contraction and moderate swelling of the main axis which diminishes towards the base, forming a cone-shaped part of the stem. The exclusion of normal atmospheric conditions of which lack of light may be the most decisive factor, in the shell-like sessile leaves of this large terminal bud produces considerable changes in the percentage of important biochemical substances, which in turn have a considerable effect on the nutritive value of the cabbage (Schuphan, 1958).

The production of seed is sometimes a difficulty. For example, a variety of head cabbage from Indonesia has been found to flower and set seed at low elevations in Hawaii much more easily than the European types with their greater cold requirements. One of the problems of the Polish vegetable industry before the Second World War was to develop the production of seed of early varieties, all of which had to be imported. The heads of late varieties required for seed are over-wintered in trunks or cellars, but early varieties of the Ditmarsh type decay under these conditions. When this variety is sown on 20 July and 10 and 31 August, and kept under relatively low temperatures (0° to 10°C) from 17 November and 8 January until 22 March, the percentage of seedstalks developed from the first two dates of sowing is 100, that from the latest 86 (Chroboczek, 1955). Plants exposed earlier to the cold treatment form seedstalks about 3 weeks earlier, but the older and larger plants in the later lots form stronger seedstalks and give a higher yield of seed.

The cabbage has been the subject of highly detailed biochemical studies, for example, the chromatography of hormones and hormone precursors (Housley and Bentley, 1956), and the photocontrol of anthocyanin formation (Siegelman and Hendricks, 1957). A single photoreceptive pigment is present in red cabbage seedlings leading to action maxima at 6,900 Å and near 4,500 Å.

CAULIFLOWER

Haine (1955) has studied the improvement and maintenance of winter varieties at the National Institute of Agricultural Botany, Cambridge, following the early breeding work of F. R. Horne in Devon in 1927/28, undertaken with the object of extending the range of maturity of Roscoff seed introduced from France. In 1937, four varieties were made available which gave a succession of broccoli from mid-December until early May. In order to overcome certain difficulties in seed production a technique has been developed which provides sufficient quantities of seed and can be used to ensure the continuation of uniform and reliable stock seed from year to year. The technique is based on observations that winter cauliflower produces profuse bracts on the inflorescence when temperatures are relatively high. Flower buds fully visible to the naked eye are suppressed at 20° to 30°C, turn brown and drop off. The same condition may occur occasionally during exceptionally hot weather in early summer in England, or regularly in Mediterranean climates where for some reason flowering is not completed before the temperature rises steeply in late spring. By adopting the method of vegetative propagation of cuttings of small portions of the inflorescence, it is possible to maintain a valuable plant perpetually, and portions of the plant can be removed when required for flowering and seed production.

CHICORY

The progress of growth of Witloof chicory has been studied by Lecrenier, Tilkin and Runchaine (1955) for 2 years in weekly observations. The period of strongest growth occurs in July and August. Then the leaves stop growing, their number becomes stable and the root retards its growth in weight and dimensions. Differences in morphological characters between types then decrease and disappear. The conditions necessary for dormancy before forcing require study in a controlled environment. In forcing trials at 18° to 24°C, leaf width increases uniformly, length and weight increase more rapidly; raising of the temperature causes this growth to be more rapid without changing the general process.

ENDIVE

Methods of forcing have also been studied on this plant (Pécaut, 1957). The reaction to forcing is found to differ both between varieties and within varieties, and the latter should be made the subject of selection. A remarkable acceleration of reproduction is obtained by exposing germinating seeds to low temperatures (Rappaport and Wittwer, 1956 b). The specific cold requirement during early growth stages is similar to that for head lettuce; it was demonstrated by first placing germinated seedlings at 40° F for 20 days, transferring them to a greenhouse night

27. Effect of temperature on chrysanthemums (Encore) (Cathey, 1954). Plants grown at a minimum temperature of 60° F. Propagated from stock grown at (1) 80° F, (2) 50° F, (3) 55° F, (4) 50° F, all in long photoperiods. Crown pinched. Photographed 20 May

28. Light for an hour in the middle of the dark period delays the blooming of chrysanthemums. Photo: Bureau of Plant Industry, Soils and Agricultural Engineering,
U.S. Department of Agriculture

temperature of 60°F and finally transplanting the vernalized and the control seedlings in the field on 21 May. The vernalized plants developed the morphological characteristics of overwintered plants and flowered on 12 July, while the non-vernalized produced vegetative heads and showed no sign of flowering before 1 September.

LETTUCE

The seeds are a favourite subject for studies of germination. The botanists in the Hebrew University, Jerusalem, in particular (Blumenthal-Goldschmidt, Cohen, Evenari, Kamson-Rappaport, Mayer, Poljakoff-Mayber, Neumann, Zacks), have published a series of studies in the Bulletin of the Research Council of Israel, on questions such as: influence of gibberellic acid and kinetin on germination and seedling growth; auxin and anti-auxin on germination; eosin on germination; red light and gibberellic acid on temperature-inhibited germination; direct oxidation of glucose in germinating seed; growth active substance extractable from dry seeds; interaction of thiourea and ascorbic acid; respiration of seeds germinated at high temperature; mechanism of germination stimulation by alternating temperatures; interaction of thiourea and coumarin; respiration of seeds imbibed for long periods; ascorbic acid content of germinating seeds; breakdown of phytin and phytase activity in germinating seeds. Borthwick, Hendricks, Toole and Toole (1954) have studied the action of light on germination, and Miller (1958) the relationship of the kinetin and red light promotions of lettuce seed germination.

Dullforce (1956) has demonstrated the effects of environment on the growth rate of leaves of seedlings, of Cheshunt variety 5b, raised in a glasshouse, or in growth rooms where temperature, light intensity and daylength were varied independently. When the relative growth rate was analyzed into the component functions of net assimilation rate and leaf area ratio, it was found that these were affected in opposite ways by temperature and light intensity, net assimilation rate being affected negatively by temperature, but positively by light intensity, whereas the leaf area ratio was affected positively by the former and negatively by the latter. In observing the effects of injury on seedling growth it was noted that seedlings recover rapidly from removal of one cotyledon or virtually all the primary root, when the injuries are inflicted during transplanting at the cotyledon stage. Recovery of the normal relative growth rate is associated with the re-establishment of normal shoot/root ratios, net assimilation rates and leaf area ratios. The effect

H   225

of injury can be expressed as the time lag between the growth curves of injured and uninjured seedlings once normal rates of growth have been established.

Rappaport and Wittwer (1956 a) studied the effect of seed vernalization, temperature and photoperiod on flowering in head lettuce (Plate 17). Using leaf number and days prior to the appearance of the developing inflorescence and days to anthesis in Great Lakes head lettuce, it was found that night temperatures above 65°F subsequent to seed vernalization accelerate flowering and result in seedstalks without preceding head formation. Below 65°F, vernalized plants first produce a high percentage of firm, vegetative heads and then flower. Non-vernalized plants flower only at night temperatures above 65°F. At high root temperature (64° and 71°F) flowering is promoted, while at low (50° and 57°F) flowering is delayed. The minimum night temperature following vernalization at which early flowering was favoured was reduced from 65° to 60°F when plants were grown at a daylength of 16 hours. With a 9-hour photoperiod irrespective of vernalization, plants produce firm heads which eventually flower. A combination of high air and root temperatures and long days appears to promote flowering in seedlings vernalized in excess of 13 days at 40°F. The same workers have studied the effects of night temperatures and photoperiod on flowering of leaf lettuce.

Following the demonstration by Rappaport and Wittwer that temperature, photoperiod and chemical growth regulators, separately and interacting, markedly influence seedstalk development in lettuce, Fukui, Weller, Wittwer and Sell (1958) fractionated ethyl ether extracts of vernalized and non-vernalized lettuce seedlings into acid and 'neutral' fractions. Paper chromatographic separation followed by bioassay with the *Avena* straight growth test demonstrated the presence of twice the amount of IAA (3-indoleacetic acid) in the acid fraction of the non-vernalized seed as compared to that which was vernalized, and two growth-promoting substances in the 'neutral' fractions of both the vernalized and the non-vernalized seed.

Bremer (1931) and Bremer and Grana (1935) crossed short-night varieties with indeterminate summer varieties, and found that the photoperiodic response in short-night plants is controlled by a single gene. In the F_2 generation of a cross between a winter variety, Maiking, and a summer salad variety, Deacon, 1092 of 1473 plants resembled Maiking by flowering early in the summer on short nights.

The growing of seed in the Swedish climate is a very risky enterprise.

226

The early-bolting long-day varieties succeed best, but day-neutral varieties only rarely, due primarily to the weather conditions in August. Gullåkers Plant Breeding Station in Hammenhög has demonstrated that, by prolonging the day to 24 hours, bolting and seed ripening may be moved forward enough to avoid the bad weather at the end of August. When a long-day variety is exposed to 10 hours white light and 8 hours supplementary coloured light, the plants remain vegetative in all cases (Wassink, Stolwijk and Beemster, 1951).

Spinach

The yield is largely dependent on the proportion of male plants, the composition of varieties varying from poor-leaved, early withering male plants to whole female plants. As this is a pronounced long-day plant, the further north, in Sweden, for example, it is cultivated, the earlier the bolting becomes. Long days and a temperature of about 20°C are the most important factors for a short life cycle; flowering can be accelerated somewhat by vernalization. Studies in the Netherlands have shown that a strong photoperiodic response exists in the Nobel variety to the green, yellow and red regions of the spectrum, whereas violet, blue and infra-red are much less active (Stolwijk, 1952). Petioles in violet, blue, and infra-red irradiation are longer than those in the dark and white controls. An antagonistic effect of spectral regions appears to be conceivable only if at least two pigment systems are involved in the reactions (see also Borthwick, Hendricks, Toole and Toole, 1954).

Tobacco

This was one of the plants in which Garner and Allard first recognized photoperiodism; they found that the Maryland Mammoth variety was entirely vegetative in the normal days of summer and early autumn at latitude 39° N. In the greenhouse, with a shortening day and a lengthening night the variety came into flower even when the plants were very young. Floral induction of these 'short-day' plants could be suppressed by shortening the dark period with light of low intensity. On the other hand, the Connecticut Broadleaf variety was found to be independent of daylength, and was called by Garner and Allard 'indeterminate' or 'day-neutral'.

Investigations of inheritance of photoperiodic response have been made with tobacco. Before the discovery of photoperiodism, Allard in

1919 described crosses of Maryland Mammoth with White Burley Connecticut Broadleaf and other varieties now known to be indeterminate. In all cases, the non-flowering characteristic of Maryland Mammoth as grown under field conditions was inherited as a unit character. Of 1820 F_2 plants, 439 were of the Maryland Mammoth type. In 1948, Lang crossed Maryland Mammoth with the indeterminate variety, Java; of 467 F_2 plants, 128 were of the long-night type. Smith (1950) noted a differential photoperiod response from an interspecific gene transfer Nicotiana rustica was crossed with a line of N. tabacum Maryland Mammoth in order to obtain the maximum leaf development, in long days, transmitted by the recessive gene which Garner and Allard had noted in Maryland Mammoth. After a number of crossings, the Mammoth gene was transferred to the genotype of N. rustica. In the crosses lines with the residual genotypes tabacum or rustica Mm and mm flowered in long or short days; tabacum mm flowered in short but not in long days rustica mm did not flower under any conditions. The cumulative action of modifying genes is postulated, and it is suggested that the rustica Mammoth might be a useful plant for the study of the substance determining flowering.

The responses of two varieties (N. tabacum Harrison Special, and N rustica, Matihari) to different times of sowing, vernalization and photoperiodic treatment have been studied at the Presidency College, Calcutta (Sen Gupta, 1955). The best vegetative and reproductive growth was found in the sowings of both species of 10 and 25 September (tobacco is grown as a summer and autumn crop in the South Indian plateau, and as a spring and summer crop in the regions near the foothills of the Himalaya). Pre-sowing cold treatment had no effect on Harrison Special, delayed flowering in Matihari. Although both the species may be said to be indeterminate in photoperiodic response, flowering is promoted by long days in Matihari and by short days in Harrison Special. The leaf area of both increases with increases in light periods. In general, photoperiodic treatments are much more effective after rather than before transplantation.

Experiments have been made in controlled conditions at Wageningen on the influence of environmental factors on growth and development of Delcrest Virginia tobacco (Coolhas, 1955). Formation of flower buds is delayed with increasing day temperature; this shift is most marked between 21° and 30°C, but is no longer apparent between 33° and 36°C. The weight of dry matter also increases with rising day temperature, to an optimum at 33°C. Day temperature has a marked effect on the number of leaves. Visible formation of flower buds is not affected by relative humidity of the atmosphere, but the opening of the first flower is delayed at 80 per cent as compared with 50 per cent relative humidity. The production of dry matter increases with increased duration of exposure to light. The number of leaves is smaller in the shortest exposures. The day on which flower buds form and the first flower appears is later when light is applied for longer periods.

The pollen tubes of tobacco supply to the style and ovaries additional amounts of enzymes which oxidize tryptophan to indoleacetic acid and hence initiate fruit development (Lund, 1956). The effects of darkness on the constitution of leaves and susceptibility to virus have been studied by Humphries and Kassanis (1955), and the relation between the effect of darkening and changes in ascorbic acid content on susceptibility by Wiltshire (1956).

Peppermint

Night interruption studies have verified that peppermint (*Mentha piperita*) is a long-day plant with a critical daylength between 16 and 18 hours (Langston and Leopold, 1954 a). Gross morphological changes occur during and following photo-induction. Variations in light intensity over a broad range have no appreciable effect on the photoperiodic response and its accompanying morphological changes under the conditions of this study. Length of day and light intensity are important factors in flower development as distinguished from floral differentiation. Fresh weight increases are attributed to the photoinductive mechanism. The greater the length of day, the greater the number of oil glands per unit areas of the lower epidermis. Under the conditions of this study no measurable oil quantities could be obtained in daylengths of 14 hours or less.

Sugar-Cane

Since the extensive review in the first edition, considerable progress has been made in Hawaii, both in developing methods of controlling tasselling, and in applying Clements' (1953) foliar diagnosis or crop logging system (see Fig. 39) as a guide for estimating irrigation and fertilizer requirements for the 200,000 acres of the crop in the island. It has been very difficult to control the ripening of sugar-cane in Hawaii, where the crop is harvested more or less throughout the year. In earlier

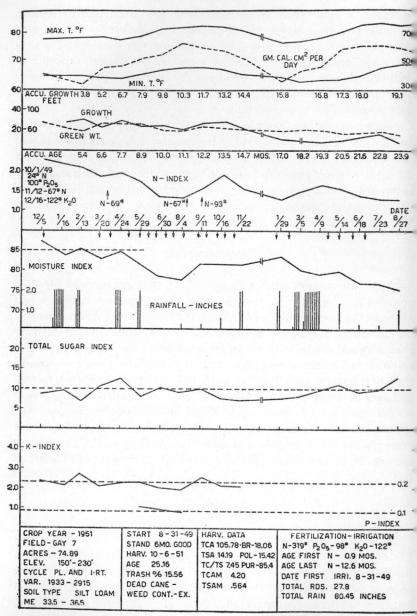

Fig. 39. Crop logging of sugar-cane. Actual record for a particularly difficult field in Hawaii, which gave its record yield when managed completely on the log (Clements, 1953).

work, it was apparent that irrigated crops of good quality were character-ized by final moisture index values in the vicinity of 73 to 74 per cent (in the young leaf sheaths); the crop logs showed that this final figure had to be approached gradually. A third factor in the quality obtained was the moisture status during growth; it is more difficult to obtain good juices from a crop that is lush throughout its history than from one which is grown somewhat dry.

In attempting to arrive at a programme for ripening, it had first been necessary to demonstrate that sugar is actually accumulated by the plant during this period. Some have held the belief that sugar is deposited in the internodes only until the leaf attached to the node dies, after which it ceases. Observations in Hawaii show that there is a very large increase in the sugar content of the internode long after the leaves have fallen from the corresponding nodes. A ripening programme can therefore increase the sugar content of sugar-cane stalks very materially. Fields of cane may be divided into three categories: (a) those kept at a high mois-ture level throughout their cycle, and especially during the second season of growth, which generally give heavy tonnages of mediocre quality, (b) those kept at a very low moisture level, which usually give light tonnages and do not necessarily yield good juices, but which are easy to ripen, and (c) those between these two extremes. It is easy to start ripening a partic-ular crop on time if it is known into which category it falls (Clements, Shigeura and Akamine, 1952).

Floral development has been studied by Engard and Larsen (Hawaii Agricultural Experiment Station, 1948), and tasselling in relation to breeding and production by Mangelsdorf (1956). Tasselling represents a dissipation of energy and also marks the end of growth of the terminal growing point. An economical method of preventing tasselling in heavy-tasselling varieties would help the grower by reducing losses in yield, and the breeder by providing seedlings without excessive tasselling. A positive method of inducing flowering or of keeping stored pollen alive is needed to permit crosses between early and late-tasselling varieties. The sugar-cane breeder looks enviously at the procedures adopted by the pineapple grower to induce flower initiation.

In both the Northern and Southern Hemispheres, the change from a vegetative growing point to a tassel bud occurs during the period of shortening days. Early varieties such as POJ 2878 first shows the micro-scopic indications when daylength including twilight has fallen to about 12·5 hours. The primitive form of *Saccharum spontaneum* requires a long day for tassel differentiation; it flowers in August in Washington, D.C.,

231

but fails to tassel near the Equator. Another variety which grows wild near Tokyo flowers in late summer, but does not flower in the 14-hour day in Formosa. Attempts to induce flowering in these long-day forms by extending the natural daylength artificially in Hawaii have so far failed.

Workers at the Central Sugar-cane Research Station in Bihar (Sharma *et al.*, 1956) found, in their studies of wild *Saccharum* as suitable progenitors of commercial canes, that smaller forms flower earlier in the season, while tall ones arrow towards the end. The correlation coefficient between height of plant and number of days from germination to flowering is as high as $+0.94$. No correlation was obtained between time of flowering and relative growth rates.

Mangelsdorf believes that each variety has a daylength range within which tassel differentiation can proceed and beyond which no differentiation occurs. Some varieties are precise and exacting in their requirements for tasselling, and have a short tasselling season; others can produce tassels over a wide range of daylengths, and have a long tasselling season. The tasselling time of the latter group may be somewhat controlled by age. The flowering date of most varieties is affected only slightly, if at all, by the date of planting. At the Kailua breeding station, the interval between the first microscopic evidence and the emergence of the tassel from its 'boot' ranges from 50 to 70 days; this interval may be influenced by temperature and probably by other conditions related to rate of growth. While a suitable length of day or rather night is the first prerequisite for tassel development, other factors may also operate. For example, stalks which are too young when the appropriate daylength arrives fail to tassel, the stage of maturity varying with variety. The presence of a considerable number of mature internodes is essential for floral differentiation in many shy tassellers. Tasselling may also be prevented by drought even when all other requirements have been met.

Sugar-cane tassels more freely under the cloudy, rainy conditions of the windward districts of Hawaii than under the sunny conditions of the leeward districts, perhaps because of differences (*a*) in the quality or quantity of sunlight, or (*b*) in minimum temperature, or in the range between minima and maxima. The optimal elevation for tasselling is somewhat dependent upon latitude, and may again be associated with a maximum temperature. The higher the soil fertility and the more rank and succulent the growth, the less likely is tasselling to occur. Ratoon cane tassels more heavily than plant cane.

232

OTHER LEAF AND STEM CROPS

Stem Fibre Crops

Crotalaria

Early work by the Indian scientists, Singh, Kapoor and Choudhri, on the response of *C. juncea* to light and particularly photoperiods was reviewed in the first edition, pp. 333–4. When the crop is to be used for green manure, it is presumably desirable to provide conditions optimal for growth; the best photoperiods for growth vary from 6 to 20 hours, for reproduction from 11 to 26 hours. It would thus be an advantage to use this species for green manure in regions with long days of 16 to 20 hours, provided frost damage is not likely to occur. Fibre length in crops grown for fibre is a characteristic of great technical importance. Studies at the Benares Hindu University showed that the production of high-class fibre from *Crotalaria* is favoured by long days and that latitude and seasonal characteristics should be considered when the crop is to be grown for this purpose.

Sen Gupta and Talukdar (1955) also studied this crop at the Presidency College, Calcutta. *C. juncea* was grown in pots at intervals of one month for 12 months, commencing from 21 April, 1951. Growth and development of plants in these 12 sowings were greatly influenced by time of sowing. For widely different sowing times between April and September (150 days), flowering occurred within September and until mid-October (44 days); the vegetative period thus became progressively shorter with the later sowings. There was a reduction in height, number of internodes and circumference at base of stem with the later sowings; those made between October and February made poor growth, due probably to the lower temperatures. A favourable time for sowing the variety C.12 in West Bengal is in the months of April/May.

Vernalization induces late flowering. Sunn hemp C.12 is a short-day plant; the climatic factors of the different seasons influence the photoperiodic behaviour; the effect is remarkable in 10- and 12-hour photoperiods, due perhaps to the additional action of temperature. A clear induction effect is noted, the plants responding earlier after the beginning of treatment when they are 30 and 45 days old.

Studies have been made at the University of Pretoria on the growth, yield and nitrogen content of species suitable for green manuring and perhaps also for fodder. *C. intermedia* is higher in yield than *C. juncea*, is palatable and non-toxic, but at first grows more slowly. *C. recta*, a perennial not killed completely by frost, gives a higher yield of dry matter in its second growth season than any other species in the first (Mes *et al.*, 1957). Plants of this species growing in the University plots flower very

H*   233

late in the season, and are killed by frost before the seeds ripen. To determine their sensitivity to daylength, well-grown plants were exposed to 12- and 16-hour photoperiods respectively; both groups were kept in a day temperature of 27°C and a night temperature of 15°C and later 18°C (Pretoria, 1957). Plants flowered under a short, but not under a long photoperiod until transferred to a short photoperiod.

FLAX

Observations have been made at the Biological Laboratory of Dacca University on the vegetative shoot apex and the origin and development of leaf and bud primordia and foliar traces (Mia, 1955). The Australian worker, Millikan (1957 a), designed an experiment at the Earhart Laboratory in Pasadena, Cal., to obtain information on the effects of variable day (20° and 26°C) and night (14° and 20°C) temperatures on growth, and to determine whether any interaction occurs between phosphate level in the substrate and the response to temperature of the variety Liral Crown. Height of main stem is increased by high day temperature and reduced by high phosphate, whereas these variables have reversed effects on tillering (both mean number and total length per plant). However, high phosphate improves tillering when the day temperature is 20°C, but not when it is 26°C. High phosphate also increases total length of tillers when the night temperature is 20°C, but not when it is 14°C. Total growth (top + roots) is reduced by increases in either day temperature or phosphate, but there are differential effects on tops and roots. An inverse relationship occurs between day and night temperatures with respect to their effect on total growth and height of the main stem, but only where the day temperature is unfavourable for total growth. Thus, night temperature is unimportant when the day temperature is low (20°C), but at the high day temperature (26°C) the plants grow best at the low night temperature (14°C). Thus, differences which may occur between the results of fertilizer trials with the same soil in the greenhouse and in the field may be attributable in part at least to variations in the temperatures under which the two types of experiments are conducted.

In experiments at the University College of Wales, Aberystwyth, Durrant (1958) found that remarkably large differences can be produced in the weight of plants as a result of the effect of the environment on previous generations. The inheritance of such large differences to at least the fourth generation is believed to be due to cytoplasmic change rather than to maternal effects, a conclusion which is supported by other experiments. A hypothesis which is proposed is that, with relatively high temperature and low light intensity, cell division can proceed rapidly; but the number of cytoplasmic self-duplicating particles falls, due to a shortage of photosynthetic products, the utilization of these products being also influenced by mineral supply. The altered cytoplasm stimulates the nucleus to synthesize different substances, or different amounts of the same substances, to establish a new equilibrium between nucleus and cytoplasm. The new equilibrium could be at least as stable as the old, and the new plant type to which it gives rise would have the appearance and constancy of a distinct genotype. Such a cytoplasmic-nuclear interaction may further stimulate genetic change by the nuclei themselves having an effect on the difference between reciprocal crosses of environmentally conditioned types, the pollen nucleus complementing any small effect of the pollen cytoplasm. In short, plants may remain differentiated as a whole over several generations in addition to the normal differentiation of parts of plants within a generation. Durrant states that temperature/light relationships will probably play an important part in future investigations.

HEMP

Photoperiodic studies were made at the Plant Industry Station, Beltsville, to find procedures which might facilitate the breeding of the crop and perhaps suggest improved methods of field production. As already noted in Chapter II, hemp is dioecious and normally produces male and female plants in about a 1:1 ratio; in many cases, however, the females may exceed the males. Plants which are predominantly either male or female may also produce floral structures of the opposite sex; within a single strain, the extent to which these intersexual forms occur varies with respect to both the percentage of the population concerned and the degree to which the character is exhibited by an individual plant.

Borthwick and Scully (1954) used the variety Kentucky in all but one experiment, in which half of the plants were of the Chile variety and the rest were Kentucky. They find that photoperiodic control can be useful to the breeder in that several generations can be produced each year by using short photoperiods. It is also possible to synchronize flowering dates of plants that differ in earliness, and perhaps most important, to stimulate the production of male flowers on female plants for the purposes of self-pollination. Selection of plants for abundant production of male flowers on female plants might be successful, because of the varying tendencies of certain female lines in this respect.

The work of Heslop-Harrison on sexuality in plants has been mentioned

in Chapter II; the same worker (1956) has investigated the effect of
α-naphthaleneacetic acid on sexuality in hemp plants flowering after a
period of minimum photoperiodic induction. In genetically male plants,
female flowers were formed in sites which would normally be occupied
by males, a result which appears to provide evidence that flower sexuality
may be normally regulated by the level of native auxin in the vicinity of
the meristems during the period of differentiation of flower primordia.
Secondary effects of auxin treatment are seen in an overall reduction in
the intensity of the flowering response, and in the modification of the
course of heteroblastic development, the trend towards a reduction of
leaf lobbing and serration which normally accompanies flowering being
reversed sooner in NAA-treated plants passing through a period of
flowering than in untreated controls.

In Japan, Yoshida (1955) has studied the photoperiodic responses,
particularly in relation to the changes which occur in leaf shape.

HIBISCUS

Studies on the fibre-bearing species of this genus have been made by
Sen Gupta and his associates and are described in a review of 12 years'
work on the physiology of growth and development in fibre plants,
oilseeds, pulses, sorghum and tobacco at the Presidency College, Calcutta (Sen Gupta, 1955). *H. sabdariffa* or roselle fibre is an important
Indian crop which is strongly influenced by length of day (Talukdar,
1952), flowering 53 days earlier than the control in short photoperiods of
10 hours. *H. cannabinus* flowers in 34 days in 10-hour photoperiods,
earlier than normal by 124 days, and earlier than under 14-hour treatment
by 126 days. Observations have been made on the height of *H. sabdariffa*
and *H. cannabinus* in relation to time of sowing; the usual decrease in
height at flowering time with lateness of sowing from April onwards is
noted.

JUTE

This crop has been studied at the Presidency College, Calcutta, and by
the Indian Central Jute Committee. Sen Gupta (1955) has reviewed the
results of work at Calcutta to that date and gives a full bibliography.
Again, the effect of time of sowing has been studied, using the two species,
Corchorus capsularis and *C. olitorius*. For widely different sowing dates
between April and August (a range of 120 days), flowering occurs between
mid-August and end of September (a range of 45 days); the environment
during September is thought to be very favourable for flower initiation.

Both species are clearly short-day plants; in a normal growing season, C. olitorius flowers in 21 days of 10-hour photoperiods, 104 days earlier than the control, C. capsularis in 33 days, 97 days earlier than the control. A clear induction effect can be observed, more marked when plants are 30 days old before treatment. Other experiments have concerned the relation between fertilizers and photoperiodic response (none), the effect of different photoinductive cycles of light and darkness, transmission of photoinductive stimulus by grafting (none noted), the inheritance of photoperiodic effect (none found), and the effect of vernalization at low temperature (2° to 4°C) for 30 days and high temperature (30°C) for 7 days (some earliness in flowering). Talukdar (1955) recorded the ratio of soluble sugar and nitrogen in normal and photo-periodically induced plants. The sugar/nitrogen ratio is comparatively higher in plants induced to flower early. Both the sugar and nitrogen contents fall at the flowering stage, and rise again after the first initiation of flowers.

The Indian Central Jute Committee has also studied the response to vernalization and photoperiodic treatment. Pre-sowing cold treatment alone brings about an earliness of 15 to 18 days in flowering in C. capsularis varieties, but a lateness of about 8 days in C. olitorius varieties. Both species respond greatly to variation in daylength, particularly when short photoperiods are given in the early seedling stage. First flowering is delayed about a week by long photoperiods. April sowings of either type give the highest yields. Late varieties of both C. capsularis and C. olitorius are significantly superior to early varieties.

Trees and Shrubs

This section deals only with trees and shrubs grown for the production of stems. Flowering ornamentals and fruit trees are discussed in Chapters XV and XVII. The latest review on woody plants is that by Wareing of Manchester University (1956), in which he considers eighty-seven papers under the general headings of:

(a) types of photoperiodic responses,

(b) locus of photoperiodic perception in relation to dormancy,

(c) the partial processes of photoperiodism in woody species, and

(d) the ecological and practical importance of this knowledge.

Wareing states that most experiments quoted in the literature up to September, 1955 dealt with the effects of daylength on various aspects of dormancy, although a few experiments had been made on the flowering responses of certain shrubby species. Vegetative effects can be conveniently studied in seedling trees, whereas flowering does not occur in many forest trees during a juvenile period which may last for many years, by which time the trees have become too large for convenient experimentation.

Vegetative processes in woody species which have been shown to be affected by daylength include the duration of extension growth, leaf growth in conifers, time of leaf abscission, duration of cambial activity, time of bud break, and seed germination. Reports on the flowering responses of woody species to photoperiodic conditions are few in number; there are some data on the relation between daylength and the duration of the juvenile period.

In discussing the locus of photoperiodic perception in relation to dormancy and on the basis of the evidence that photoperiodic induction of flowering in herbaceous species is determined primarily by the daylength conditions to which partially or fully expanded leaves are exposed, Wareing considers the available data in relation to the following questions:

(a) Are the fully expanded leaves also sensitive to photoperiodic conditions in woody species? If so, how far is the response of the buds affected by the presence of mature leaves in dormant seedlings which still retain mature leaves?

(b) What is the locus of photoperiodic perception in actively growing seedlings for the induction of dormancy by short days? Is the actively growing shoot apex directly sensitive to daylength conditions, or does the stimulus for the formation of resting buds arise in the mature leaves under short days?

What is believed to have been the first major symposium on tree physiology was held at Harvard Forest, Petersham, Mass., from 8 to 12 April, 1956, under the sponsorship of the Maria Moors Cabot Foundation (Wareing, 1957). The meeting was attended by physiologists and research workers from the United States, various Commonwealth countries and Europe. In a session devoted to photoperiodism in trees, Downs (U.S. Department of Agriculture, Beltsville) indicated the broad range of photoperiodic phenomena in tree seedlings. Wareing gave a comparative study of photoperiodism in seeds, buds and seedlings of *Betula pubescens*, and considered the possible role of growth inhibitors in both seeds and buds. Pauley (Univ. Minnesota) emphasized the importance of photoperiodism in forest tree breeding. 'Thermoperiodism' in loblolly pine (*Pinus taeda*) was demonstrated by Kramer (Univ. New Hampshire); best growth is made when the difference between day and night temperatures is greatest; species of oak show similar effects;

'thermoperiodism' may be important in limiting the range of some species. Sax (Arnold Arboretum) described experiments to elucidate the physiological basis of methods long used by horticulturists to induce earlier flowering of trees, namely, the use of dwarfing rootstocks, bark inversion and knotting of the stem. Flower initiation in spruce in relation to various external conditions was described by Fraser. Stanley (Calif. Forest Exp. St.) is carrying out a biochemical study of male, female and vegetative structures of pine, and attempting to identify differences in metabolites and enzyme patterns. Wareing outlined observations on the reproductive development of Scots pine and attempted to relate this to the 'ageing' of the tree as a whole and of the individual branches. The second symposium in this series was held at Harvard Forest in April 1957 (see Thimann, 1958, and review by L. Leyton, *Nature*, **182**, 1698, 1958).

Photoperiodic response has great significance in forest tree breeding, particularly when selecting northern genotypes of pines, birch and poplars for cold resistance. On transplanting these long-day forms to the short day of southern latitudes, a serious disturbance of growth results and the trees usually become stunted and of little value. In order to correct this, long-day illumination may be supplied artificially or long-day trees may be crossed with short-day forms in the hope of obtaining a hybrid combining the desirable qualities of the northern genotype with the short-day photoperiodicity of the southern plants. The photoperiodic response of poplar species may be of considerable importance to breeders as the maximum rate of growth in any type will be achieved only when it is grown under the conditions of illumination to which it is adapted. Detailed studies have been made on *Populus tremula* in Sweden; genotypes from northern provenances are characterized by adaptation to long-day illumination while southern races are characterized by adaptation to short days. Trees from Norbotten are homozygous for long-day response while those from Småland and Scania are homozygous for short-day reaction. Types from the geographically intermediate stations at Vasterbotten and Medelpad are heterozygous in respect of photoperiodic characters. Short- and long-day types were crossed and the progenies grown under the short-day conditions of southern Sweden. The F_1 hybrids were dwarfs and had inherited the adaptation to long-day illumination of the northern races as a dominant character, showing that the elimination of the undesirable long-day reaction must be effected before northern aspens can be utilized in the production of new forms suitable for southern zones.

Similar ecotypic variation has been noted in the North American species of *Populus*, in which the time of cessation of extension growth is inversely correlated with the latitude of origin. Ecotypic variation has also been reported within species of *Populus* collected from the same latitude, but from different altitudes; these are probably, according to Wareing (1956), primarily adaptations in the endogenous mechanism determining the duration of extension growth with respect to length of the frost-free period and other external conditions. Photoperiodism has important implications for the breeding of forest trees, since new types must show 'the same delicate adjustment to daylength as is found in natural ecotypes'. Further, by appropriate photoperiodic treatment it may be possible to reduce the delays, by shortening the juvenile period, as has been demonstrated in the photoperiodic breaking of dormancy in *Rhododendron*.

The cultivated poplars introduced into Hungary from Western Europe (*Populus serotina* and others) are not fully suitable for cultivation in that country, especially, it is said, because of photoperiodic conditions (Kopecky, 1956). Hybridization between species or varieties and between different species of black poplars has been very successful. It has, for instance, been possible to combine the juvenile growth of balsam poplars with the continuous growth of black poplars. The photoperiodic requirement is a hereditary character.

Reference will now be made to some more recent work, but omitting the numerous studies on light intensity in relation to photosynthetic activity in woody plants. Growth of many tree seedlings is promoted by exposure to long photoperiods, whereas very short photoperiods induce abnormally early dormancy. Information on this phenomenon has been taken a stage further by Vaartaja (1957) in an investigation of the photoperiodic responses of the seedlings of northern tree species. Seedlings of ten tree species were tested under two widely differing photoperiodic conditions in an environment otherwise near optimum. The amount of light given was the same under both conditions. Under conditions simulating long photoperiods, the seedlings of all species grew well and continued growth during the 8-month experimental period. Under the short photoperiod, the following species remained nearly or fully dormant for several months beginning soon after germination: *Larix laricina*, *Ulmus americana*, and two provenances of *Picea glauca*. The following species either remained nearly dormant or grew significantly slower than under long-day conditions: *Betula lutea*, *B. verrucosa* and *Pinus banksiana*; *P. resinosa* was considered sensitive to photoperiods, but its responses in appearance and growth were small; *Caragana arborescens, Thuja plicata* and *Acer negundo* showed no significant response.

Dormant Bigcone Douglas fir trees placed under a 20-hour photoperiod expand their buds within 2 months (Hellmers, 1957). The shoots elongate rapidly and set new buds. These expand and within 5 months several plants produce their third flush of growth. Under an 8-hour photoperiod (natural light), the buds on only 5 of the 26 trees in the experiment had started to expand. The shoots had not elongated. Coulter Pine trees placed under long days continue to develop their already lengthening candles. Needles are produced and new resting buds develop. There are no additional flushes of growth. Under short days, the growth of the terminal candles is arrested. Eight of the 28 trees under the short photoperiod developed a few needles on the already lengthening candles. Photoperiod can be a controlling factor to prevent growth during the warm periods that frequently occur in mid-winter over the natural range of the species.

Downs and Borthwick (1956 a) find that, in general, long days prolong growth and short days induce growth stoppage, but species differ markedly in the details of their response. American elm, red maple, *Catalpa*, Asian white birch, tulip poplar, and dogwood apparently grow continuously on 16-hour days, whereas horse chestnut, *Paulownia* and sweet gum do not. Stoppage of growth by treatment with 8-hour days seems to require about 4 weeks for the majority of the species, but fewer weeks for tulip poplar and horse chestnut and many more for elm. Some tree species, such as *Catalpa*, birch and tulip poplar, may be induced to resume growth by transfer to 16-hour days or to natural daylengths plus a 3-hour interruption near the middle of the night. Resumption of growth of *Catalpa* occurs on 16-hour days only if the transfer from short days is made soon after growth stops. A delay in transfer results in prolonged delay in growth resumption unless low temperature treatment is introduced. Resumption of growth in sweet gum occurs on continuous light but not on 16-hour days, while in *Paulownia* it does not occur under either condition. Defoliation of sweet gum and *Paulownia*, however, results in immediate resumption of growth but is ineffective on dogwood, elm and *Catalpa*.

As already stated, recent discoveries have added seed germination to the long list of life processes which are affected by duration of alternating light and dark periods. Seed of Eastern hemlock, *Tsuga canadensis*, seems peculiar in showing how markedly the optimal photoperiod may vary with temperature. This interaction poses interesting problems in the study of the physiology of germination, and the response to controlled light and temperature among seeds from widely scattered sources suggest possible evolutionary adaptation to contrasting climates. Such physiological diversity within a superficially homogeneous species may be more common than is usually appreciated. Stearns and Olson (1958) found that germination of unchilled seed of eastern hemlock varies remarkably with photoperiod as well as with temperature. Also, temperature modifies the most favourable photoperiod: 8 (or 12) hours at 17°C to 22°C versus 16 hours at 27°C (and perhaps 12°C). Rapid germination of excised embryos, unaffected by photoperiod or temperature, suggests that the endosperm (megagametophyte) or nucellus is important in seed inhibition. Moist chilling (stratification) for 10 or more weeks hastens germination and eliminates most light-temperature effects. As compared with northern (Quebec and Maine) seed, southern (especially Tennessee) seed, given a favourable photoperiod, shows less need for chilling; given stratification it has higher optimal germination temperatures.

The need for preliminary stratification helps to prevent germination immediately after seed is shed in late autumn. Adaptation to low soil temperatures of early spring permits rapid germination of stratified seed while moisture conditions are still favourable. In northern climates this is essential if full use is to be made of the brief growing season, especially under coniferous stands where the sun is relatively ineffective in warming the soil. Lower requirements for stratification and greater tolerance to high temperature by southern seed may be an adaptation to rapid warming of soils of deciduous forests in southern parts of the species' range. Stearns and Olson consider that acceleration of germination by light may in some cases increase survival of uncovered seed which is least protected from drying later in the season. If weather and seedbed circumstances are unfavourable for quick germination, increasing temperature reduces the probability of late spring germination followed by death during hot, dry summers. Such seed can germinate in a later year if weather is then more favourable or if burial in the soil in the meantime has protected the seed from high temperature and desiccation. After adequate moist chilling, such seed may germinate rapidly without light, when other conditions are favourable.

Experiments on the use of synthetic growth substances in the stimulation of the yield of latex of *Hevea brasiliensis* (rubber) at Kuala Lumpur and Bogor are described by Baptist and De Jonge (1955) and Wiersum (1955).

Chapter XIII

ROOTS AND TUBERS

POTATO

Reference was made in the first edition to Driver's review of the literature on the environmental relationships of this crop, and to Hawkes' account of the photoperiodic reactions of South American potatoes (see Cambridge, 1943). The best conditions for maximum vegetative activity are long, warm days of moderate light intensity. Flowering would seem to be favoured by long days and moderate temperatures and to be greatly depressed by short days. A long day does not markedly increase the number of flower primordia differentiated, but rather increases the number of flowers that attain maturity. Pollen from flowers of equal maturity grown under long- or short-day conditions appears to be equally fertile and capable of effecting a similar percentage of successful pollinations. The photoperiod has a lower effect once the berries have been formed, although they tend to grow faster and to have a higher percentage of seeds under long days. Southern mountainous regions of the U.S.S.R. and the Andes region of South America are in some way especially favourable for flower production, in spite of their short days.

Economic value depends upon production of tubers, and this is dependent upon stolon growth and the production of reserve materials. Stolons are long and there are numerous lateral and branched ones in long days. They frequently turn their ends above the soil surface and may form leafy shoots. Stolons under short-day conditions are shorter and limited to those required for tuber formation. Very short-day types may have difficulty in producing stolons under long-day conditions and may produce a greater number under short-day conditions. As the daylength decreases, ability to utilize the products of photosynthesis for growth decreases more rapidly than the decrease in photosynthetic activity. There is thus a larger surplus of available carbohydrates, and tuber formation is consequently much increased. Total yield, however, depends upon total available carbohydrate; it may happen that highest yields are obtained under long-day conditions in which, although the proportion of available carbohydrate is low, the plants are so large that the total carbohydrate available may be greater than from the smaller though more efficient short-day plants. The best conditions for maximum tuber yields appear to be long days to stimulate vegetative growth, followed by short days to turn the activity towards efficient tuberization, that is, the conditions under which potatoes are grown in temperate latitudes. No explanation has been found for the fact that the commercial varieties of higher latitudes do not grow well at the low temperature and in the short days of the Andes.

The experiments by Hawkes on the photoperiodic reactions of South American potatoes (see Cambridge, 1943) were carried out on part of the Empire Potato Collection made by an expedition sent to the South American Andes by the Commonwealth Agricultural Bureaux. The clones came from the department of Puño in the Lake Titicaca region of Peru, and also (in the case of *Solanum demissum* only) from Mexico. Assessments were made on tuber weight, tuber number, stolon production, time of maturity, height of plants, and flowering. The material used can be classified on the basis of stolon production in relation to daylength:

(a) short stolons in short day, none in long day;
(b) short stolons in both short and long day;
(c) short stolons in short day, long stolons in long day; and
(d) long stolons in both short and long days.

The clones take on the average about one and a half times as long to mature under long day as they do under short day, but the height of the plant is two and a half times as great. Short days have a depressing influence on flowering, although flowering is extremely abundant in the high Andes under short-day conditions. This may be due to the fact that flowering is dependent on the quality of the light received. A 12-hour day is sufficient in the intense light of tropical mountains but not in temperate regions, where a full summer day of 15 to 18 hours is required before flowering can take place.

Hawkes compares the potato with tobacco and soybean, where flowering does depend upon a photoperiodic stimulus. The photoperiodic mechanism may apply only to the dominant method of reproduction. In potatoes reproduction is almost entirely vegetative and tuber production is controlled by a photoperiodic response. With soybeans and tobacco, reproduction is by flowers and seed, produced only in an appropriate light period.

More recent work has been concerned with the factors governing tuberization and yield in relation to sowing dates, latitude, etc., with flower production and induction, and with the use of certain characteristics to indicate the photoperiodic reactions of breeding material at an early growth stage.

By modifying either the dates of planting or the storage, it has been possible in French experiments to obtain plants which show the same differences in behaviour as is noted in plants of different origins (Madec and Perennec, 1956). The environment during vegetation may emphasize or attenuate these differences. The effect of origin may be largely related to factors acting directly or indirectly on the evolution of sprouts. Yields in England and Wales are reduced by delay in planting maincrop varieties after about 11 April at the rate of about 0·4 tons/acre per week. This effect is rather greater in years with fine springs and on high yielding fields (Dyke, 1956). In Rothamsted experiments, responses to dung and fertilizers are greatly reduced with delay of planting.

Workers at the University of Helsinki have analyzed the nature of the difference in earliness manifested between some clones and varieties (Pohjakallio et al., 1957). The long day retards the onset of tuber formation in all varieties and clones investigated. For a short time after the onset of tuber formation, the short photoperiod has an accelerating effect on the development of the tubers. The haulms of plants also develop more rapidly and decline relatively early in short days. After the decline of the haulms, the tuber yield can no longer increase. Thus, in the latter part of summer, the increase in tuber yield is greater in long-day than in short-day conditions. Photoperiodic treatment applied at the time of sprouting also affects the rate of development of the plant considerably. Potato blight infects the haulms of the early potato varieties earlier, and thus more strongly, than the late ones, and it likewise appears earlier in the haulms of varieties grown in conditions of short daily exposure to light.

In the U.S.S.R., Žurbickiĭ and Vartapetjan (1956) believe that to a certain extent it is possible to counteract the unfavourable influence of the long day and to speed up tuber formation and increase the carbohydrate content by providing readily available nitrogen before flowering, followed by potash and phosphate during tuber formation. Also in German trials, Grosch (1956) found that the combined effect of daylength and nitrogenous fertilizers is such that it pays to give heavy dressings of

N to early varieties. In pot experiments, Schulze (1958) found that with increasing photoperiods (12, 18 and 24 hours) with the same conditions for growth and assimilation, the onset of tuber formation is progressively delayed, and yields diminish. With increased applications of N, tuber formation is further delayed. The 12-hour day gives the best utilization of N. The time of first tuber formation does not necessarily coincide with the onset of flowering. The longer the light periods and the greater the doses of N, the greater is the haulm yield at final harvest, but the smaller the amount of tuber formation. With a 12-hour day, assimilation is used primarily for tuber formation, with longer photoperiods mainly for leaf formation. Mature plants are more disease-resistant under long than under short day, but the higher tuber yield is always obtained under short day. The greatest root formation, obtained in long day with heavy dressings of N, is not associated with greater tuber formation.

Van Schreven (1956) has studied the factors affecting premature tuber formation and the influence of organic compounds and growth substances on tuber and sprout formation in the dark. Experiments at Beltsville (Gregory, 1956) indicate that:

(a) the tuber-inductive state appears to be promoted by a graft-transmissible stimulus arising under specific conditions of temperature and photoperiod,

(b) the effect of induction persists for some time even if the inducing conditions are no longer present, and

(c) the stimulus is found throughout the entire plant, and is not restricted to the underground parts.

Experiments in sterile culture show that a tuber can be grown from the axillary bud of an induced stem piece, or a shoot from the axillary bud of a non-induced one, simply by using sucrose. However, sucrose is not thought to be the determining factor.

As an outcome of experiments which showed that iron and potassium are interrelated in the metabolism of the potato plant, and that the nature of this relationship is dependent upon phosphorus status, Bolle-Jones (1954) made some incidental observations on flower production. Increased iron reduces the number of flowers produced per plant, particularly at high potassium levels. Increased potassium increases flower production of plants maintained at low levels of iron, but reduces it at the high iron or low phosphorus levels. Increased iron delays time of flowering and reduces the duration of the flowering period.

The grower is little interested in whether a variety does or does not flower, but a breeder can include a variety in a crossing programme only if it produces true seed. Thijn (1954) has made studies at the Potato Breeding Station in the Netherlands, on the variety Bintje, which hardly ever produces berries. Grafting on tomato and planting on bricks have a very favourable influence on flower formation, with double grafting, incising or the use of ligatures as useful auxiliary techniques. Flower induction is probably caused by an accumulation of assimilates.

Investigators at the Institut für Pflanzenbau und Pflanzenzüchtung of the Hochschule für Bodenkultur in Vienna have been particularly interested in the early recognition of daylength types as an aid in breeding programmes. Shading experiments with seedlings from crosses and selfed lines proved that short-day types occur among the seedlings of certain European cultivated varieties (Kopetz and Steineck, 1954). In a number of seedlings, the artificial shortening of daylength to 10 hours produces not only changes in leaf shape, but also considerable increases in tuber yield and a simultaneous decrease in aerial growth. The short-day treatment also results in a change and an improvement in the shape of the tubers. All the seedlings with strong short-day response in tuber formation had abundant leafy growth, flower and berry formation, as well as over-developed stolons and little tuber formation when exposed to normal daylength. On the basis of Kopetz' hypothesis concerning photoperiodic phenomena in summer annuals, it appears possible to separate at an early stage daylength-neutral types from short-day types (which are of no value under European cropping conditions) by growing seedlings under artificial or natural long days.

Another characteristic of possible value in breeding is the correlation between photoperiodic requirement and the length of the meristematic zone of the stem; the shorter the photoperiod, the shorter the meristematic zone, and also the distance from the apex at which tetraploid cell nuclei are found (Steineck and Czeika, 1957). Further, with decreasing photoperiods, the proportion of seedlings with geotropic stolons increases. Thus the direction of growth of the stolons indicates the photoperiodic requirements of the seedlings. The number and weight of tubers also increases with decreasing photoperiods. These facts are promising for use in breeding, in that they permit the elimination of photoperiodically undesirable types among seedlings grown in the greenhouse (Steineck, 1958).

There may be a thermoperiodic effect on the concentration of cell sap in the leaves and stems. Lona et al. (1952) found this concentration to be clearly higher in plants subjected to 4° to 8°C night temperature and 22°

to 25°C day temperature, than in plants grown in a 20°C night temperature and a 22° to 25°C day temperature.

SUGAR-BEET

Considerable attention was given in the first edition to the environmental factors which govern sugar production and flowering respectively, to the location of seed producing areas in North America, and to the work at Cambridge and elsewhere on the problem of bolting. The economic value of the crop depends upon those physiological functions and processes that lead to a maximum sugar content, while the production of seed requires to be carried out under conditions that will ensure the correct quota of temperature and daylength at the appropriate time in the life of the plant. According to Brandes and Coons (1941), whereas sugar-cane requires 8 to 9 months to attain adequate tonnage and satisfactory quality (for which suitable conditions are found only in tropical and subtropical latitudes), the sugar-beet is a relatively cold-hardy plant, grown for sugar production as an annual which in 160 to 200 days is capable of producing a large tonnage of roots of high sucrose percentage. In the northern hemisphere, sugar-beet is grown from an extreme southern limit of about 30° N. to an extreme northern latitude of about 60°.

The Soviet workers (Vavilov, 1935) place the centre of origin of the genus *Beta* in the Near East, possibly Asia Minor or the Caucasus. From this general area its distribution has been westward along the Mediterranean, northwards and eastward in the arid steppe regions, and as a littoral plant northward along the Atlantic and North Sea coasts. The distribution of sugar-beet in the southern hemisphere is confined largely to areas crossed by the corresponding January 70°F isotherm.

Summer temperatures probably affect yield and quality less than does water supply, but autumn temperatures have a marked effect on the storage of sugar. In the humid area and in general in irrigated areas in U.S.A., a plant that has made luxuriant root and top growth has usually a sucrose percentage of about 12 by 1 September. With the cool days and frosty nights of late September or October, growth is checked but there is an increase in photosynthetic activity and storage of sugar. Sucrose percentages rise, reaching averages of 15 or more by mid-October, and as high as 18 or more in November, if severe frosts do not occur. On the other hand, in southern areas sucrose percentages may

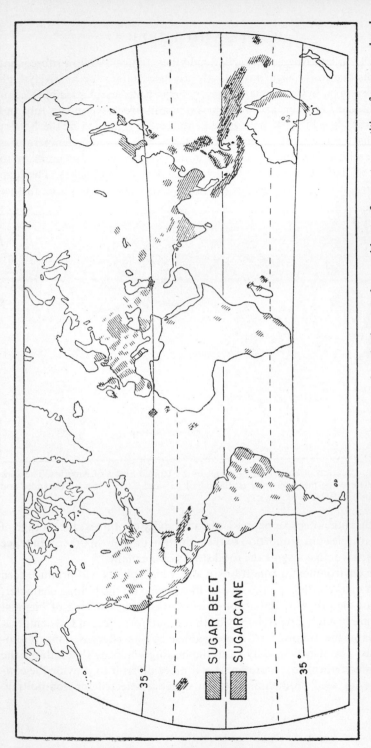

Fig. 40. World distribution of sugar-cane and sugar-beet. Potential areas of production are shown without reference to quantities of sugar produced (Brandes and Coons, 1941).

reach 12 in late August or early September, but may fall in subsequent months due to the vigorous growth produced under the relatively high temperatures. In California, however, sugar-beets are planted in December, January or February, and harvested and processed in late July and onwards. The highest sucrose percentages are achieved in the hottest months, and sucrose accumulation takes place at day temperatures frequently above 100°F. The common practice in these areas is to withhold irrigation water as the harvest period approaches. The high temperatures and decreased water supply may operate to check further

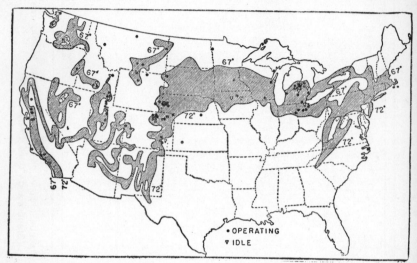

Fig. 41. Location of beet-sugar factories in the United States of America. The zone between the mean summer isotherms of 67° and 72°F is shaded (Brandes and Coons, 1941).

growth while intensive photosynthetic activity continues; the storage of sugar increases in proportion to the reduction in growth, the continuance of which would consume the food stocks of the plant.

The environmental conditions under which plants will produce seed have a marked effect on the seed yield and also on the bolting characteristics of the progeny. Initiation of seedstalks and flowering of biennial beets are brought about mainly by the cumulative effect of low-temperature exposure followed or accompanied by the effect of long photoperiods. The selection away from the bolting tendency that reduces the economic return from a crop makes it more difficult to provide the conditions for seed production. Within varieties selected for non-bolting, there still remains a small proportion of individual plants which will go to seed readily even when exposed to mild conditions. In a mild winter, the individuals with a tendency to bolt go to seed, those that have greater requirements of low temperature do not. Thus, if seed production is carried on in mild winters, there will be a tendency for the variety to show an increased percentage of 'bolters' in subsequent years, since only those individuals with a low requirement of low temperature hours will perpetuate themselves. The production of seed is best adapted to regions that provide a long exposure to prevailingly cool weather, not necessarily below freezing, followed by the appropriate length of day required for this long-day plant to produce flowers and seed.

Workers at Rothamsted Experimental Station (D. J. Watson and associates), Department of Plant Nutrition of the University of California at Berkeley (Albert Ulrich and associates) and at other centres have studied the nutrition of the crop *per se*, and to some extent also in relation to the so-called primary factors of the environment. 'Under practical conditions in the field, the major impediment to predicting the amounts of nutrients needed by the crop, and the amount to be supplied by the soil, is the lack of an accurate weather forecast . . . the crop log system of Clements (1953) for sugar-cane, or of Nightingale for pineapple, holds great promise for fertilizing the current year's crop in terms of important growth factors (sunlight, temperature, moisture, carbohydrate reserves, etc.) and in providing useful plant nutrient information for subsequent crops in the same field or area' (Ulrich, 1952).

Certain European workers have agreed that, under field conditions, the beet plant during the first season goes through a leaf development stage, a period of storage root formation, and finally a ripening stage. The Rothamsted workers conclude, however, that there is no clear distinction between phases of growth and of storage in the root, for the young roots have already a high sucrose content; that growth and sucrose storage therefore proceed together. During the second years' growth, if intervening temperatures are neither too low nor too high, and are of sufficiently long duration, plants flower readily, especially at cool temperatures and long photoperiods. Recent studies in controlled environments have indicated that growth and reproductive development may be closely related to the sucrose economy, namely, sucrose formation and utilization (Ulrich, 1955). The sugar formed first by the leaves is used to maintain the basic metabolism, and then to form more leaves and more fibrous roots; when these requirements have been met, the sugar formed is used to increase the sucrose concentration of the main root,

251

and at concentrations of 6 to 8 per cent the surplus sugar is then diverted primarily to storage root formation. The response of plants to controlled

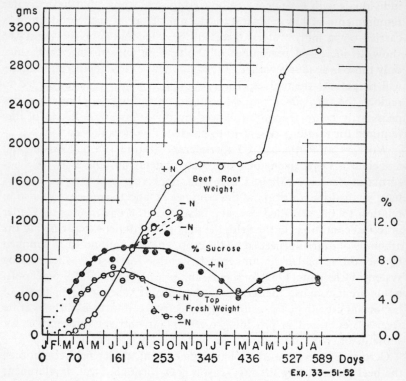

Fig. 42. Sugar-beet. Influence of time and nitrogen upon root weight, sucrose concentration and the fresh weight of tops of sugar-beet plants. The plants were grown with ample supplies of water and nutrients for natural daylengths in a greenhouse kept at 23°C from 8 a.m. to 4 p.m. and at 17°C from 4 p.m. to 8 a.m. During a period of 83 weeks the plants high in nutrients (solid lines, +N) failed to 'ripen' or to 'sugar up'. 'Ripening', however, was induced by watering comparable plants with a nitrogen-free culture solution starting 31 July 1951 (broken lines, −N). The maximum sucrose concentration of these plants (12.1 per cent on 6 November 1951) compares favourably with the maximum value of 9.3 per cent of plants high in nitrogen (31 July 1951), but this value is still far short of the sucrose concentrations of beets grown commercially. Beet roots (roots + crown) failed to increase in weight during the winter months (Ulrich, 1954).

temperatures in natural daylength at two levels of nitrogen was studied by Ulrich at the Earhart Plant Research Laboratory (see Fig. 42).

Other experiments at this laboratory involved different light intensities and photoperiods (Went, 1954; Went, 1957); under less favourable growing conditions, heterozygosity showed its greatest expression in differences of growth rate between individual plants. There is evidence that beyond a certain density of foliage there is no advantage to the plant in developing a large leaf area. Other results confirm the long experience of farmers with regard to the connection between night temperature and

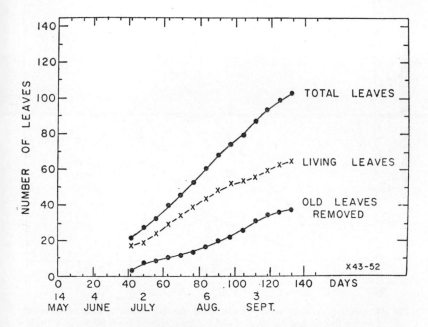

Fig. 43. Sugar-beet. Relation of time to total number of leaves formed, number of leaves living, and number of old leaves removed from plants in a 'cold climate' (63°F, 8 a.m. to 4 p.m. and 54°F, 4 p.m. to 8 a.m.). The leaf counts are for two plants per pot, using 12 pots per climate (Ulrich, 1956).

growth and sugar content; the sugar content increases with decreasing night temperatures, 7 per cent at 86°F, 12 per cent at 36°F. The weight of roots increases rapidly with rising night temperature, reaching a maximum between 57° and 79°F. Thus, when the beet is approaching maturity, low temperatures are economically desirable. Again at Pasadena, Ulrich (1956) studied the influence of antecedent climates on the subsequent growth and development. Experiments at Beltsville on quality of light in relation to flowering showed the great superiority of incandescent filament lamps over white and daylight fluorescent type (Borthwick and Parker, 1952).

In breeding it is useful to have a rapid succession of generations, and this may be achieved by appropriate treatments with temperature and light, even to the extent of five generations per year. Extended exposure to low temperatures increases the percentage of plants induced to flower

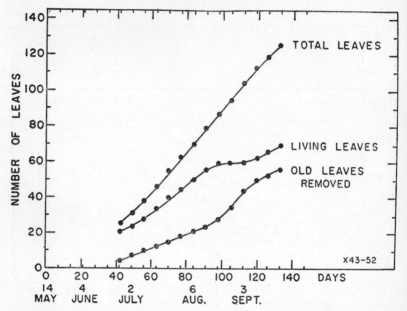

Fig. 44. Sugar-beet. Relation of time to total number of leaves formed, number of leaves living, and number of old leaves removed from plants in a 'mild climate' (73°F, 8 a.m. to 4 p.m. and 63°F, 4 p.m. to 8 a.m.). The leaf counts are for two plants per pot, using 12 pots per climate (Ulrich, 1956).

and reduces the period to first flower (Banga, 1948; Curth, 1955). The younger the plant in which flowering is induced, the longer the cold treatment must be in order to obtain the same amount of flowering at the same time as in older plants. Continuous light considerably increases the number of plants induced to flower and reduces the period of induction. The time differences compared with plants under normal days disappear with increasing age, but the proportionate difference remains.

The literature on vernalization has been reviewed by Margara (1954); temperature appears to be decisive in the photothermal induction of flowering; treatment with low temperature, while capable of accelerating flowering when applied at the seedling stage, becomes progressively effective the later the cold treatment is applied. Bolting is said to be promoted by vernalization, provided the vernalized seeds are planted in an environment sufficiently favourable for flower induction to proceed. Devernalization due to high temperature after planting has been

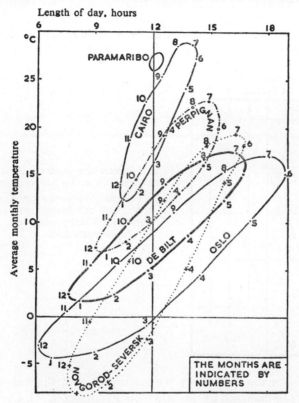

Fig. 45. Photothermographs in climatic studies of vegetable ecology (Ferguson, 1957).
Climate-photothermographs of six different places.

reported (Banga, 1948). Poor yields of seeds are usually obtained by producers in Israel in seasons following a mild winter, even in the cooler hilly regions. Landau (1958) ascertained whether bolting can be promoted by vernalization of seed, when subsequent development takes place under very high temperatures combined with suitable photoperiods, as would occur with very late planting. It appears that in some varieties bolting can be secured by long exposure of germinated seed to low temperature, even with high temperature during the growing period. German workers find it possible to vernalize beet at 0·5° to 5°C in the seedling stage and thus to obtain flowering and seed production in the first year (Kurth, 1955). They achieve 100 per cent bolting in the first year, whereas at Wageningen treatments of less than 20 days' duration (on fodder beet) do not appear to have been used.

Bolting is a very important problem in economic beet cultivation; if the percentage is high, there is loss of yield at harvest, mechanical

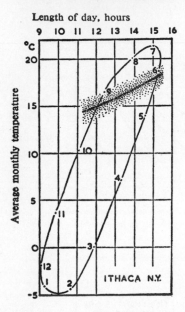

Length of day, hours

Fig. 46. Photothermographs in climatic studies of vegetable ecology (Ferguson, 1957).

Climate-photothermograph of Ithaca, N.Y., with the neutral zone for vernalization for Crosby table beet, according to Chroboczek's data.

harvesting is made difficult by the seedstalks, and the knives at the factory may be damaged by the hard woody roots. G. K. G. Campbell of the Plant Breeding Institute, Cambridge, told the 16th Meeting of the Institut International de Recherches Betteravières in Brussels in February 1953 that some selection against the tendency to bolt may be made in a population of physiological types comprised in a commercial variety, but selection by sowing early and then rejecting bolters is not always successful. Bell (1945) showed that these physiological types in a population may be separated; seedlings that failed to bolt after exposure to continuous light for several weeks in the winter were reserved for breeding and it was found that the progenies from such plants were more resistant to bolting than the population from which they were taken. To make full use of the new material, it is of course necessary to

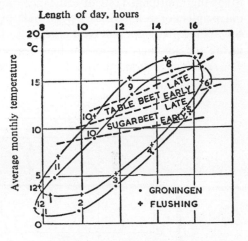

Fig. 47. Photothermographs in climatic studies of vegetable ecology (Ferguson, 1957).

Climate - photothermo - graphs for Groningen and Flushing, with an estimation of the neutral lines for vernalization, for late and early table beet and sugar beet.

select only those progenies that germinate satisfactorily at the low temperatures experienced before the normal sowing date (Table 6).

Table 6
COURSE OF SELECTION FOR NON-BOLTING TYPES IN A COMMERCIAL VARIETY (Campbell, 1958)

Year	Seedlings given Continuous Light for 8 weeks		
1	(1) 84 per cent Bolted, flowered and set seed	(2) 9 per cent Began to bolt but did not flower	(3) 7 per cent Remained vegetative
2	Seed held over	Flowered and set seed	Flowered and set seed
3	Seed of (1) and (2) sown early with parent variety as control gave: (1) 11·8 per cent (2) 1·7 per cent bolters against 12·6 per cent for control		Progenies tested and selected on sugar content
4		(2) 0 per cent bolters, control 5·5 per cent	Flowering and seeding
5			Test of yield and resistance to bolting

The planning of adequate tests of resistance to bolting of any breeding material selected by this process depends greatly on weather conditions following brairding. Tests of resistance may, however, be made largely independent of spring weather by stimulating bolting artificially, done by sowing the progenies in a cool glasshouse in December or January and giving the seedlings additional light for some weeks after emergence. The seedlings are transplanted to the field where, during the summer, a

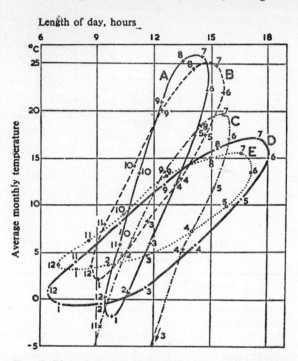

Fig. 48. Photothermographs in climatic studies of vegetable ecology (Ferguson, 1957).

Climate-photothermographs of: A, Dodge City, Kansas, U.S.A., 38° N.; B, Bologna, Italy, 45° N.; C, Grand Forks, N. Dak., U.S.A., 43° N.; D, Göteborg, Sweden, 58° N.; E, Hull, England, 54° N.

larger proportion bolt than can be expected after an early sowing in the field. A single figure has been used to assess bolting, based on counts made in September. However, plants that bolt early are, at the time of lifting the crop, more mature than those which start to bolt later; the early bolters are therefore the most important to record.

A variety produced by the Plant Breeding Institute in Cambridge in 1951, called KNB, was to be issued to farmers in spring, 1959, in trials of the National Institue of Agricultural Botany, under the name of Cambro. When sown early, this variety is very much more resistant to bolting than any of the commercial varieties at present available. In addition to the main variety trials conducted annually at the factory areas and summarized in the *British Sugar Beet Review* by E. G. Thompson of the N.I.A.B. (see issue for June, 1958 and earlier), early-sown observation plots on bolting have been continued since 1951, and also summarized in the *Review*. It appears that the general level of bolting has been reduced as a result; two of the worst offenders have been withdrawn.

Chilling equipment is now available at the Plant Breeding Institute, which should simplify testing for resistance to bolting. But Campbell (1958) states that there may be a place for gibberellic acid. In the doses tested, this substance can only partially replace the normal cold period required for vernalization in the physiological types used. In the field, however, it may be possible, by using a carefully controlled dosage, to distinguish between types more or less resistant to bolting, even in the absence of the climatic factors which normally induce bolting. The field trial was repeated in 1958, using separate isolations for testing the responses to cold natural conditions and gibberellic acid of plants selected on the basis of response in the field trial on gibberellic acid in 1957. In the Netherlands, Kloen and Speckmann (1956) found that the percentage of bolters in their tetraploid varieties is considerably lower than that of the diploid commercial varieties. Consequently they could be sown successfully at an earlier date.

Results of studies on the effect of sowing normal and 'non-bolting' types at different dates in the spring have been published by V. McM. Davey in the Reports of the Scottish Plant Breeding Station, Roslin, Midlothian, for 1957 and 1958. The incidence was as follows:

Sowing date	Percentage of bolting in	
	Normal	*Non-bolting Stock*
Mid-March	31 to 47	2 to 8
Early April	3 to 16	1 to 6
Mid-April	1 to 6	nil to 1

Where plant stands are approximately equal, the weight of unbolted plants of the early-April sowing was decidedly higher than that of the late sowing. By comparison with the mid-April crops—and taking bolting and stand into account—it was estimated that 7 cwt of sugar were lost by sowing normal beet in mid-March, and 3 cwt were gained by sowing in early April. On the other hand, the non-bolting stock showed a mid-March gain of 2·7 cwt and an early April gain of 3·5 cwt.

The Irish breeders are confident that all seed available to farmers will soon have a high degree of resistance to bolting, and will be suitable for sowing after mid-March. The quantity of seed of resistant strains is steadily increasing. Under the contrasting conditions of Nebraska, 2 and 16 April are the best sowing dates.

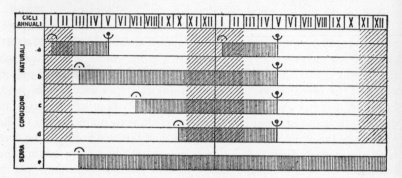

Fig. 49. Development of 'biennial' beet as influenced by sowing date, under natural conditions and in the glasshouse (Lona, 1954 a):

Semicircle open below: sowing time.
Semicircle open above: flowering time.
Vertical hatching: vegetative period.
Oblique hatching: period of natural vernalization.

JERUSALEM ARTICHOKE

Tuber formation in cultures of nodal pieces of *Helianthus tuberosus* is promoted by reducing the temperature or the light intensity (Marsden Ray, 1958). In short days and in a day temperature of 16 to 18°C, tubers and no long shoots are formed when the night temperature is 13°C, but when night temperature is 19°C about half the cultures form tubers, many of which soon bolt; all the aerial shoots which develop have con-spicuously shortened and often swollen internodes coloured purple with anthocyanin, suggesting an incompletely expressed tendency towards tuber formation. No conspicuous difference in the proportion of cultures forming tubers is observed as between 8- and 16-hour days. If there is any daylength effect, it is much less marked than that of temperature under the culture conditions.

MISCELLANEOUS ROOT CROPS

Space does not permit detailed consideration of the results obtained from experiments in many countries on fodder and garden beet, sweet potato, *Brassica* roots, carrots, turnips and radish.

Chapter XIV

BULBS AND CORMS

U nder this head we may consider the onion and its close relatives, and also the bulbs and corms of plants grown for their flowers, for example, daffodils, tulips, iris, gladiolus, etc. For the latter, however, only a few examples will be quoted. No attempt has been made to summarize the vast practical and experimental experience on these plants in the Netherlands or elsewhere.

ONIONS AND RELATED CROPS

Working at the Research Institute for Plant Physiology at South Kensington, O.V.S. Heath (now University of Reading) and his associates studied the physiological effects of daylength and temperature, and their interactions, in controlling the developmental morphology of the onion plant—especially the processes of bulb formation, and flower initiation and development. Bolting is again a problem, in this case the undesirable flowering of onions grown from sets. 'We must recognize that an onion cannot read the calendar, but rather that it behaves the way it does because it is a certain kind of onion growing in a certain kind of weather' (Asgrow, May, 1956).

Heath and his colleagues summarize the effects of environmental factors on flowering as follows.

First, a direct effect of high temperature on flowering may be distinguished. Inflorescence initiation *and* emergence are inhibited, partially or completely, by exposure of the plants to temperatures above about 21°C, either during the whole period of growth from seed to set, during the whole storage period (October-March) or the earlier part, or throughout the second season of growth from replanted set to mature onion. The effect from seed to set *may* be solely due to the reduction of set size consequent on earlier bulb development; the effect in the second season is independent of daylength and hence of bulbing. When high temperature is applied during the last part of the storage period it delays but may not ultimately reduce flowering. The effects of high storage temperature are not in the main due to drying of the sets.

Very low temperature (0°C) throughout the storage period or for the first part only reduces flowering, but low temperature for the last part results only in a sudden flush of inflorescence initiation on return to normal temperature and appears actually to increase flowering. Medium temperatures (10° to 15°C) at any time during the life history are apparently the most favourable to flowering, except for the accelerating effect of late cold storage.

On flowering, length of day has an indirect effect associated with bulbing as well as a direct effect. At temperatures high enough to encourage rapid bulbing in plants grown from sets, long days suppress inflorescence emergence; at temperatures low enough to prevent or delay bulb formation, long days accelerate the emergence of inflorescences by increasing the rate of scape elongation. The former effect of long days may thus be considered as indirect and due to the promotion of bulb development. Daylength is apparently without effect on flower initiation, and affects only the further development and emergence of the initials.

The more important effects on bulbing and ripening are: the onset of bulbing is a response to the stimulus of long days and there is an interaction with temperature such that at lower temperatures longer days are needed. Seedlings apparently need a longer photoperiod for bulbing than do plants grown from sets. At high temperatures bulb development is rapid and the emergence of new leaves ceases abruptly with its onset; at lower temperatures one or occasionally several more leaves may emerge. With a return to short days and/or low temperature, bulbing may be arrested and leaf emergence recommence without the usual dormant period. Long days and high growth temperatures not only stimulate rapid bulbing onset and development but also expedite ripening. Bulbing onset and ripening are delayed in plants grown from sets stored at high temperature, either throughout the winter (October-March) or for the last part only; heat treatment for the first part only of the storage period has little or no effect. Such delay is increased if drying of the sets in store is prevented by high humidity. There is a striking effect of size of set; large size is the outstanding characteristic leading to bolting, and the experimental fact that artificial reduction in size by the removal of swollen leaf bases prevents or delays bolting points the way to further progress in the analysis of internal rather than external factors.

Working in the Soviet Union, Reimers (1957) finds that an increase of daylength reduces the period of active vegetation in *Allium proliferum* within the limits of a given annual cycle of this perennial plant. A long day accelerates and a short day retards formation of underground and aerial bulbs. Formation of pedicels is accelerated by a long photoperiod. During a short day, actively growing daughter plants which do not possess a dormant period are formed on the pedicels instead of the aerial bulbs. The duration of the dormant period of aerial bulbs formed in sufficiently long photoperiods is proportional to the daylength employed during cultivation.

In garlic (*Allium sativum*), an increase in the photoperiod accelerates formation of the bulb but retards the formation of new leaves; this response is less pronounced than in the common onion, because of the difference in morphogenesis and the higher degree of autonomy in the growth of leaves and bulb in garlic (Reimers, 1957). The range in daylength within which bulb formation occurs is much larger for varieties of garlic which form flower stalks. A short day increases the duration of the active life period of flower-stalk-forming garlic within the limits of a given vegetative period and thus promotes the appearance of pedicels in them in the year in which the aerial bulbs are sown.

The shallot, *A. ascalonicum*, is grown during the autumn, winter and spring months in North Carolina. Best prices are often received for the early autumn crop. The bulbs are usually planted in early September and the plants are pulled and sold from about 1 November onwards. When growers try early August plantings, the plants grow normally for a few weeks, then form bulbs and die down instead of continuing to make vegetative growth and dividing. Plants grown from dry bulbs or from the division of field-grown plants produce bulbs when exposed to 15 hours of light daily and to temperatures of 70°F or higher (Jenkins, 1954). Plants grown at minimum temperatures of 70°F form small bulbs even at daylengths of 10 hours, but plants grown at low temperatures (28° to 40°F minimum temperatures) do not form bulbs under either long or short day conditions. An exposure of only 7 days to 15 daily hours of light and temperatures of 68°F or higher causes bulb formation to be initiated, but the bulbs are much smaller than those formed by plants that received 12, 21 or 28 long days. This indicates that long days and relatively higher temperatures are necessary for bulb formation in shallots, and that the effects of long days are cumulative. For economic production, therefore, in the Southern States of U.S.A., shallots must be planted late enough in autumn to ensure exposure to short days and low temperatures during the growing period.

FLOWER BULBS

The introduction to the symposium at the 14th International Horticultural Congress, 1955, on 'The influence of artificially created climatic conditions in horticulture', was by E. van Slogteren of the Laboratory for Bulb Research, Lisse, Netherlands. The speaker paid a tribute to the bulb grower Nicolaas Dames, who about 50 years ago laid the foundation of the preparation of bulbs for early forcing and introduced the application of an artificial climate to improve the growth and flowering capacities of flower bulbs. All the later work by Blaauw and others was founded on his insight.

The aim of growers is to lengthen the season during which their flowers will be available to the public, and especially to accelerate blooming. The periodicity of the plants was first changed by growing them in a milder climate, such as the South of France, but better and more remunerative results are now obtained by lifting the bulbs prematurely and storing them in an artificial climate. It is now possible to make hyacinths, daffodils and irises bloom practically throughout the year. Tulips are more difficult to cope with, but they can be retarded for about 6 months or advanced by a few months, thus giving a flowering period of about 8 to 9 months. In deciding on the appropriate conditions of storage, primarily temperature, it is necessary to know when the bulbs are expected to flower or to which part of the world they are to be shipped. Stuart, Gould and Gill (1955) reported to the same Congress on the forcing of Easter lilies, bulbous iris and tulips. Taking tulips alone, it was found that stem length of forced plants is related to temperature and length of storage of the bulbs prior to forcing. Precooling bulbs of some varieties at temperatures lower than 9° or 10°C for 6 weeks in September and October followed by planting and storage for 6 weeks at 10°C results in the production of longer stems and in earlier flowering in the greenhouse than storage at 10°C for 12 weeks. Similar results were obtained in a field test in Georgia when bulbs of certain varieties were stored for 6 weeks at 4°C and then for 6 weeks at 10°C (or *vice versa*) before planting. These treatments can also be applied successfully to tulips forced in the greenhouse at 15°C. Storage of the bulbs for less time, or above 10°C, results in production of short stems or in delayed blooming. Modification

I*   265

of these treatments is necessary for some varieties. This technique differs considerably from that adopted in the Netherlands.

In British Columbia, a degeneration to a 'papery' texture occurs in early-forced tulips of the William Pitt variety (MacArthur and Chan, 1956). The abnormality decreases with increase of flower bud development at the time the bulbs are stored at 48°F. Delaying cool storage until carpels are formed in the flower bud practically eliminates loss from this factor. Increased weight of the cut flowers and shortening of the harvest period are associated with more advanced bud development when the bulbs are stored at 48°F. Bulb dissection shows that when the rooted bulbs are benched all flowers are morphologically normal. Degeneration of the flower bud occurs just before, and frequently after, the flower stem emerges from the encircling leaves.

By applying the following method of preparing daffodil bulbs (Beijer, 1955), it is possible in the Netherlands to have flowers from the end of November until April. After lifting the bulbs on about 15 July, they are stored at 34°C for only 4 days. Hereafter a two weeks' treatment at 17° is recommended. After this 17° treatment the bulbs are stored at 9°C till planting time. The best time for boxing the bulbs is the first part of October, the temperature of the soil then being low enough. Late in November the forcing can be started at about 15·5°C. If, however, still earlier flowering is needed, late in November or early in December, the bulbs have to be lifted prematurely, preferably in the middle of June. After a two weeks' heat treatment at 30°C followed by 2 to 4 weeks at 17°C, the bulbs can be cooled at 9°C. The best time for boxing these bulbs is late in September or early in October. Special treatment is necessary when the bulbs are to be shipped to the Southern Hemisphere.

Although the total light requirement for adequate photosynthesis is high in most plants and cannot be economically supplied by artificial means, flower bulbs may be forced successfully since their requirements are favourable for the economic utilization of artificial light (Stoughton and Vince, 1957). In the tulip, hyacinth and daffodil, the carbohydrate reserves within the bulb are adequate for the production of a bloom of good quality, and light is required only for normal stem extension, flower expansion and greening of leaves. Furthermore, these bulbs are forced during the winter, when the fuel consumption to maintain an adequate temperature in a glasshouse is extremely high. Consequently they may economically be grown in a well-insulated building under low-intensity artificial light; fuel economy is further improved by complete utilization of the total heated volume of the structure by placing the boxes of bulbs, one above the other, in tiers, each layer having its own row of lamps. The lighting is by tungsten-filament or white fluorescent lamps, installed at the rate of 10 watts/sq. ft of planted area. Tulips may be successfully forced in this way when irradiated for 10 hours daily; the irradiation period is usually extended to 12 hours for daffodils and iris. The quality of bloom is claimed to be as high as from bulbs forced in glasshouses, while the saving in fuel costs is very considerable.

Chapter XV

FLORIST CROPS

It is probably in the field of horticulture that there are most possibilities for the practical application of the principles of growth and reproduction. Horticulturists are best able to control the environment, and their economic success frequently depends on early or out-of-season crops. In the first edition, Table 34 from Bulletin 787 of Cornell University (Post, 1942) quoted recommendations for the practical treatment of some 67 florist crops at the latitude of Ithaca, New York, under the heads of: night temperature for growing or for budding, when to use artificial light, effects of long days, when to darken, and effects of short days. The author of this Bulletin stated that Garner and Allard's classification into one or other of the main daylength groups is inadequate unless the other conditions essential to flowering are clearly stated and understood. Daylength and temperature are the decisive (primary) factors, while other incidental (secondary) factors include time of propagation, supply of moisture and nutrients in the soil, humidity of the air, amount of sunshine, and supply of carbon dioxide in the air. The interaction of light and temperature is also important. Some plants do not form flower buds until the temperature is below 65°F (stocks, *Calceolaria*, *Cineraria*, *Genista*); others such as *Chrysanthemum* fail to form flower buds when the night temperature is below 60°F.

In reviewing the horticultural application of the results of photoperiodic experiments before the 14th International Horticultural Congress, Doorenbos (1955) stated that one had to consider:

(*a*) the intricate nature of the photoperiodic reaction, caused by interactions between the photoperiod and other factors such as temperature and light intensity, and the phase of development of the plant,

(*b*) the fact that photoperiodic reactions are genetically controlled, and often show considerable variation within a species, making it possible to select cultivars which are better adapted to a given set of daylength conditions, and

268

(c) the practical possibilities arising from the fact that in some species the photoperiod affects processes other than flowering, e.g. tuber formation and the onset and termination of the dormant period.

P. Chaumier on the same occasion reviewed the techniques adopted for control of light and photoperiods by horticulturists in France; J. Wasscher (Netherlands) described methods of spreading the flowering time of forced shrubs by cold treatment. A glance through the programme of the 15th International Horticultural Congress, 1958, indicates the wide interest in the subject. Two general lectures are: R. Bouillenne, Belgium, on 'Hormone végétale, organogénèse, sexualisation et floraison', and S. J. Wellensiek, Netherlands, on 'Theoretical backgrounds of flowering'. The chrysanthemum is popular for environmental studies. Reports were presented on the pattern of growth as a response to changing seasonal environment (D. T. Mason and D. Vince, U.K.), internode extension in rosetted plants (S. N. Mitra, India, and D. Vince, U.K.), and the effect of low temperatures on photoperiodic response (Y. Samman, U.S.A.). A new photoperiodic response has been noted in *Petunia hybrida*; it is considered incorrect to regard this as a long-day plant, since it flowers 3 weeks earlier if exposed to 6 hours morning light, apparently short-day treatment (T. C. N. Singh, India). The perpetual-flowering carnation is a facultative long-day plant in which the photoperiodic response is affected by temperature, but so far little information has been available about the relative effects during the light and dark periods; the rate of formation of leaf initials is largely dependent on the temperature of the light period, but the number of leaves laid down before the initiation of flower primordia is determined by the temperature during the dark period; the number of leaves laid down before flower initiation is reduced and the mean internode length increases when the temperature is lowered during the dark period; the development of flower buds from initiation to anthesis is greatly retarded by low temperature during the dark period, and this is not compensated for by a high temperature during the light period (J. Blake and R. Spencer, U.K.).

A review of the literature on the application of artificial illumination in horticulture was published in Dutch by de Zeeuw (1952), with a bibliography of 372 references. This review also contains a summary of the practical recommendations extracted from this literature in tabular form, with the headings: crop, year, treatment, light source, distance of lamp from soil, light intensity in lux or capacity in watts installed per unit area, duration of daily illumination, season of illumination, period of illumination (day), purpose, and literature reference. This table contains about 60 species of florist crops and vegetables.

Naturally, florist crops have been among those on which gibberellin has been tested. S. H. Wittwer and his associates in the Department of Horticulture in Michigan State University found that 20 micrograms of gibberellin applied to stem apices or a foliar spray of 10 to 100 p.p.m. hasten flowering 10 days to 4 weeks in stocks, petunia, larkspur, English daisy, China aster, and gerbera when grown in the greenhouse during autumn and winter, without affecting market quality. Treated plants of pansy and forget-me-not flower while controls remain vegetative. Size and duration of inflorescence are increased in *Pelargonium hortorum* (the geranium), the size because of increase in petal size and in length of pedicel.

Examples are given below of results obtained with some florist crops, without claiming in any way to be exhaustive. The production of flower crops from bulbs has been discussed in Chapter XIV.

Aechmea fasciata

This ornamental, belonging to the Bromeliaceae, represents the principal source of revenue of many horticultural establishments around Ghent (van Onsem, 1955). The original period from sowing to flowering extends over 3 years. The plant responds strongly to light, and may be induced to flower in winter by daily application of 8 hours of artificial lighting, for 4 to 5 weeks. Temperature is also important; below 20°C the results are unreliable, and below 16°C flowering does not generally take place, especially with 2-year-old plants. By efficient combinations of irradiation it is possible to reduce the culture period by a few months, a result of substantial financial advantage.

ASTER

Earlier flowering of asters may be obtained by darkening the plants at any time after they are 4 or more inches high. The earlier the darkening is started, with respect to size of plant, the earlier will the plants flower, the shorter will be the stems, and the smaller the flowers. Darkening hastens the development of lateral buds if done when the terminal bud shows colour. A grower can darken without greatly reducing the quality of the flowers, and can obtain the maximum cut in a 10-day period. This method is particularly applicable for the short-day treatment of asters, especially Royal and late varieties. Plate 29a shows the aster variety, Ball's Late White, grown in a cloth house. The plant at the left received short-day treatment beginning 20 June, that on the right was in normal day (photo, 28 July).

BEGONIA

On varieties of begonia such as Melior, Lady Mac, and Marjorie Gibbs, flower buds are started between 10 and 20 October. Longer days from 1 October do not delay flowering, probably owing to the low light intensity. Darkening before 10 October hastens flowering in proportion to the time when treatment begins before 10 October. Leaf cuttings produce small crowns and fail to develop a top rapidly until after March, probably because of the short-day period. The plants might develop much more rapidly if propagation were delayed until April, and time and greenhouse space might be saved thereby. Plate 29b shows the effect of daylight on young *Begonia* plants of the variety Lady Mac. Left: leaves treated with 4 hours of artificial light in sand and after potting; centre: plant grown in normal day (New York State); right: plant grown in normal day, but 2 months older. Photos taken on 27 March.

In the Netherlands, the normal season for the propagation of the short-day winter-flowering begonia is from December to February; at this time the plants are flowering freely and suitable material for cuttings is scarce. Neon or tungsten-filament lamps, installed at the rate of about 1 watt/sq. ft, are used to prevent flowering of the stock plants and to increase the quantity of material for propagation. The long-day treatment is frequently continued after the cuttings have rooted so as to encourage vigorous vegetative growth and to prevent the young plants from flowering; lighting is discontinued in spring, when the days become naturally long enough to suppress flowering.

CARNATION

The perpetual flowering carnation has hitherto been classified as insensitive to photoperiod, but recent experiments have shown that flower initiation is delayed by short days; the delay has been measured in terms of increase in number of nodes before flower initiation. The response is more marked at low nitrogen levels. There is no apparent interaction between daylength and temperature. A consistent increase in internode lengths is associated with an increase in daylength (Blake,

1955). A period of low temperature is necessary to induce *Dianthus barbatus* to flower. Low temperature does not promote flowering unless given to plants of a certain minimum size, reached about 12 weeks after sowing when growth conditions are favourable. The effect of low temperature is indirect; the actual formation of flower primordia proceeds afterwards at higher temperatures. A period of 35°C given immediately after the low temperature treatment may nullify its effect, but only when the low temperature has not lasted very long. The effect of daylength on flowering is very slight and apparent only when low temperature has been just sufficient for flowering (Waterschoot, 1957). Nitrogen has a marked effect as a modifying factor on the growth and flowering response of carnations to radiation. When plant height is reduced due to inhibition of internode elongation, nitrogen produces plants not distinguishable from the controls; earlier flowering of treated plants is eliminated again by nitrogen (Sagawa, 1957).

CHINA ASTER

Generally speaking, fewer applications of light have been developed for long-day than for short-day plants. However, in the United States the China aster, *Callistephus chinensis*, has been successfully treated; accelerated flowering results when plants are irradiated from sunset to 10 p.m. from the seedling stage until they are about 2 ft tall. Lighting is unnecessary between May and September.

CHRYSANTHEMUM

This plant has been studied from the scientific and practical points of view. The factors controlling flowering have been the subject of six articles by Schwabe, the two last (1955, 1957) dealing with devernalization in relation to high temperatures and low light intensities, and devernalization by low light intensity in relation to temperature and carbohydrate supply.

Factors other than short photoperiod affect the initiation and differentiation of flower buds. Chrysanthemums are so heterozygous that responses to daylength can vary and many garden varieties can reach anthesis under long day if temperature is not limiting. Temperature has a cumulative effect on flower bud initiation and development. The response is variable; for sensitive varieties temperatures of 53° and 48°F during the growth of stock plants can delay flowering considerably,

(a) ASTER (BALL'S LATE WHITE)

(b) BEGONIA (LADY MAC)

29. Effect of daylength and temperature on florist crops (see p. 271). Photos: Cornell
University Agricultural Experiment Station

(*a*) CINERARIA

(*b*) CHRYSANTHEMUM

30. Effect of daylength and temperature on florist crops (see p. 275). Photos: Cornell University Agricultural Experiment Station

DIDISCUS

GENISTA

31. Effect of daylength and temperature on florist crops. Photos: Cornell University Agricultural Experiment Station. The plants of *Didiscus* were grown at 60° F (*left*) and 50° F (*right*) respectively

even though plants propagated from this stock are subsequently grown at optimal photoperiod and temperature. In the varieties studied by Chan (1955), some had a minimum temperature requirement, some a maximum, others were indeterminate, and still others had both a minimum and a maximum limit beyond which anthesis was delayed. Plants with a hard woody growth do not initiate flowers more readily than succulent vegetative plants. Very low levels of mineral nutrients will delay flowering in some varieties, while some are affected by excess nitrogen. The locus of maximum response to photoinduction is the upper third of the plants. Cathey (1954) studied responses to temperature, especially thermal induction of stock plants of C. morifolium, thermal modifications of photoperiods previous to and after flower bud initiation, and the effect of night, day and mean temperatures on flowering (Plate 27).

After Borthwick, Hendricks and Parker (1952) had discovered that far-red radiant energy (7,000 Å to 8,000 Å) 'repromoted' floral initiation in plants that had been inhibited by red, Cathey and Borthwick (1957) studied the possible practical application of this reaction to the production of chrysanthemum. It was thought that far red might possibly be used as a substitute for shading during periods of the year when the natural dark periods were too short to promote floral initiation. The belief that this might prove true depended on the apparent similarity between the action of far red and the action of several hours of darkness. In both cases the plants change from being unresponsive to a brief irradiation with red light to becoming responsive to it. Might this change from a red-insensitive to a red-sensitive condition during darkness be the time-requiring step that defines the critical duration of darkness for flowering of a particular kind of plant? If this were true, would not a far-red treatment at the beginning of darkness bring about this change immediately and thus reduce the duration of darkness required for completion of any remaining light-sensitive biochemical steps leading to floral initiation (Cathey and Borthwick, 1957)?

The study was made on greenhouse plants grown from rooted cuttings and transferred to plant-growth rooms. The 8-day radiation treatments were preceded and followed by non-inductive photoperiodic conditions. In most experiments, the treatments consisted of brief irradiations with red or far red or both near the middle of the dark period, and the plants were dissected 2 weeks later to observe the flowering condition. Floral initiation was markedly reduced by 1 minute of filtered red light from an eighteen-tube fluorescent light source, and in most experiments was completely inhibited by 16 to 27 minutes. Floral initiation was repromoted in many varieties by a few minutes of far-red radiant energy from incandescent lamps equipped with appropriate filters. Repeated alternations of red and far red resulted in repeated inhibition and repromotion.

If the far-red treatment is separated from the red by a dark interval, repromotion becomes less with increasing duration of darkness. The loss of reversibility was first noted by Downs (1956) in *Xanthium* and soybean, and is thought to be possibly of general occurrence in short-day plants. Far red alone or following a brief red treatment inhibits flowering if the duration of far red is about 81 minutes. In chrysanthemums the use of far red at the beginning of a dark period of subcritical length is not likely to increase its flower-inducing effectiveness. In this respect, chrysanthemums differ from *Xanthium* (Downs, 1956), in which the minimum duration of darkness at which floral initiation occurs is as much as an hour less for plants that received far red at the beginning of the dark period than for those that did not.

The glasshouse chrysanthemum normally sets its buds in the latitude of U.S.A. or Great Britain between September and April; by a suitable control of daylength, it is possible to produce flowers throughout the year, and this is done extensively in U.S.A. Artificial light is used during the winter months to prevent budding until a sufficient length of stem has been made, and black covers are drawn over the beds daily during the summer to shorten the day sufficiently for bud initiation and development. Detailed schedules of times of planting, lighting and/or shading have been determined for American varieties, and several different systems of growing, such as spray, standards, short-disbuds and pot chrysanthemums, are employed; three to four crops are normally obtained in a single year. No one variety is entirely suitable for flowering all through the year; in general the later varieties (normally requiring 13 to 14 weeks to flower from the beginning of short days) are more suitable for flowering in winter than the earlier varieties (usually requiring 10 to 11 weeks to flower from the beginning of the short-day treatment); the latter are more suitable for spring and autumn crops. Yellow and white varieties are more often grown in the summer, as pink and bronze colours tend to become pale when grown at high temperatures. The American system of flowering chrysanthemums throughout the year is now being developed by a number of growers in Britain (Stoughton and Vince, 1957).

Flower-bud formation of *Chrysanthemum morifolium* (*hortorum*) is prevented or greatly retarded when the night temperature is 50°F or lower. The night temperature should be kept above 60°F in the autumn until the flower buds are well developed, to obtain the maximum number of buds per stem and to prevent blindness of the vegetative shoots. High temperature reduces the intensity of colour in pink and bronze varieties. This colour intensity appears to be determined before the bud actually shows colour and is associated with the carbohydrate supply to the developing buds. High night temperatures or low light intensity produces a decrease in the reserve food and a paler colour. Plate 30b illustrates the relation between temperature and blindness in *Chrysanthemum*. The plant on left was grown at a night temperature of 50°F, that on right at a night temperature of 80°F.

A demonstration has been carried out by the Horticultural Department of Nottingham University for 3 years on the controlled timing of chrysanthemum flowering. Well-known mid-season and November-flowering varieties were grown, representing a number of types which included Exhibition incurved, reflexed and incurving decoratives and singles (Dullforce, 1957). The plants were irradiated by 40-watt tungsten-filament lamps suspended 4 ft apart and 3 ft above the plants, which stood in double rows. Lights were switched on from 12 midnight to 2 a.m. each night. A time switch for turning on the lights in order to break the dark period was more effective and convenient than giving the additional light at the beginning or end of the day.

Cineraria and *Calceolaria*

Both genera form flower buds from December to April but only at temperatures below 60°F. After buds are formed, the flowers develop faster when the days are longer than from December to April. Temperatures above 60°F delay flowering if given before buds are visible. Additional light during January hastens flowering, but the long stems raise the flowers far above the foliage, a condition undesirable economically. If lights are used, they need to be discontinued when the first flowers show colour. The temperature can be at 60°F after the buds have formed, to hasten flowering. The bronze, red and pink pigments in the flowers of *Cineraria* develop very poorly under the low light intensities and high temperatures of an ordinary home. The plant on the left in Plate 30a was grown at 50°F, that on the right at 60°F.

Euphorbia

Daylength regulation has been employed to control flowering time in both the species which are grown as glasshouse flower crops (Stoughton

275

and Vince, 1957). In the Netherlands, a technique for inducing flowering of *Euphorbia fulgens* twice in one season has been demonstrated. The plants are exposed to artificial short days in the late summer—i.e. in advance of the natural season—and, after the resultant early crop of bloom has been cut, artificial long days are given to stimulate vegetative growth; the long-day treatment is stopped in late winter and the natural short days occurring at this time induce a second crop of flowers. In the United States the poinsettia, *E. pulcherrima*, is traditionally associated with the Christmas season, but in many parts of the country it flowers a little too early; the plants may be successfully delayed until Christmas by lighting at about 10 lumens/sq. ft for 2 hours each night from 25 September to 10 October. More uniform flowering is also claimed, since all buds start to initiate together when the lights are switched off. Workers at Beltsville have studied the photoperiodic responses of poinsettia for several years. As anthesis occurs 65 to 75 days after the beginning of short photoperiods, treatments should start about the end of the first week of October to have the plants in proper condition at Christmas. Increase of photoperiods to 12 hours sharply delays flowering and to 13 hours inhibits it. Under natural conditions at Beltsville, the days in the second half of September are just short enough to be conducive to flowering, but within a month the photoperiod has become much more effective. Growers attempt to reduce the seasonal variability found under natural conditions by adjusting other factors such as temperature. More uniform results will be obtained if the plants are kept vegetative until late September or early October by the use of additional light and are then abruptly transferred to photoperiods of 8 to 9 hours for a few weeks. If the period from the time a cutting is made until the photoperiodic treatment is started is short, the number of days after the beginning of a particular photoperiodic treatment is usually high, possibly because active growth may not yet have been resumed when the treatments are started. The failure of growers to recognize the requirement of these plants for long uninterrupted dark periods (accidental switching on of lights, or dim illumination by street lamps) is probably the chief cause of failure to flower in the home. Red wave lengths are most effective in inhibiting flowering, and 80 per cent of the invisible radiation from ordinary incandescent filament lamps is in this region of the spectrum.

Forsythia

Nurserymen in the Netherlands would like to be able to spread flowering beyond the usual period of 1 February to 1 April, not only to avoid a drop in prices due to peaks in supply, but also to bring parts of the spring work into the late winter. As the initiation of flower buds starts in June and is completed by early August, it might be expected that cold treatment would accelerate flowering. Depending upon the winter, the plant should have obtained its cold requirement by about 15 January, by which time it will have been exposed to a temperature of +5°C or lower for about 4 weeks. The cold can be provided by placing cut branches in a refrigerator at −2°C for 4 to 5 weeks, under certain specific conditions, at any time after 1 October (Broertjes, 1955).

Genista

Plants flower in March from buds laid down in November or December. Buds are formed when the temperature is kept between 50° and 60°F. Plants in full flower placed at a minimum temperature of 65° drop their buds and flowers within 3 to 6 days (Plate 31b). Plants kept at high temperatures during February, in order to cause buds to drop, form a second crop of buds and flower in May when placed in the lower temperature immediately after the first crop of buds has dropped. Growers having difficulty in holding genista back for Easter or later may be able to do so by keeping the night temperature above 60°F until 4 to 4·5 months before flowers are desired and then reducing the temperature to 50°F.

Hydrangea

The varieties of *H. macrophylla* used for forcing have a rest period following immediately after the period of floral initiation; a relatively cool temperature is necessary for its termination, e.g. storage in unheated greenhouses, cold frames, etc. A storage temperature of 40°F is as effective in reducing forcing time and producing long stems as 34°F. Nitrogen applied before cold storage reduces the number of days required for forcing (Link and Shanks, 1954). Plants initiate and develop flower parts sooner in an 8-hour day than in a natural or 16-hour day. Flower buds may ultimately be initiated on plants in all photoperiods at a minimum temperature of 21°C. Plants grown in natural photoperiods and forced in 10-hour days are shorter and have smaller flowers than those in natural photoperiods, or in natural ones supplemented near the middle of the night with 1 or 4 hours of low-intensity artificial light (Stuart, Piringer and Borthwick, 1955).

Salvia

The growth of *S. splendens* is seriously inhibited at a root temperature of 50°F. Five definite stages of bud development can be identified (Fig. 50 from Cooper and Watson, 1954). The rate of flower bud development is less rapid at 50° than at 70°F root temperature, but there is only slight difference in the time of flower bud initiation in the earliest stages.

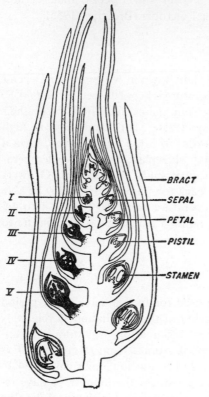

Fig. 50. Flower-bud development in *Salvia*. Cameralucida drawing of a flower bud, showing five arbitrary stages (Cooper and Watson, 1954).

Later, bud development is accelerated at the higher root temperature. A reduction in light intensity does not affect the time of flower bud initiation or the rate of development of the flower bud.

Weigela

W. florida is very sensitive to photoperiods. Downs and Borthwick (1956 b) tested the plant under 8-, 12-, 14- and 16-hour photoperiods and found the following mean increases at the four treatments during a 2-month period:

number of nodes	5·6	7·6	12·8	16·1
stem length (mm)	21·2	71·2	254·1	478·2

Control of growth by regulation of daylength would appear to be economically practicable in the propagation of *W. florida*. Its responsiveness might be used to increase the amount of growth suitable for making cuttings. Controlled photoperiods might also be used to induce the plant to make growth at seasons when propagation of cuttings might be desirable but impracticable under natural conditions because of inadequate growth to provide the cutting material. Photoperiod can also be regulated to promote or retard growth of the rooted cuttings according to the preference of the grower.

Chapter XVI

FRUIT VEGETABLES

Tomato

The history of the tomato (Whyte, 1958) is rather remarkable, since it originates from Latin America, was then introduced and greatly developed in Europe, and recrossed the Atlantic to the United States of America where hitherto it had been regarded as a toxic ornamental. Now the annual value of the crop, whether grown in the field or in greenhouses, must reach astronomical figures. The science of reproductive physiology is making a great contribution to the efficiency of this industry. There are indications that the cultivated tomato now differs in certain respects from its wild prototypes. New material introduced from the wild vegetation of the Galápagos Islands is highly self-pollinated, setting fruit even in the greenhouse without the aid so often required in horticultural production. Some lines grown at Davis, California, however, grow poorly and set very few fruits in the field, perhaps because on the Galápagos the sky is often overcast and temperatures are generally mild (Rick, 1956). In Indonesia, the lack of growth and of flowering has been found to be due to the absence of trace elements in the soil.

The natural environment has an important effect on the proportion of cultivation in the greenhouse and in the field in any particular country. For example, in New Zealand there are about 1,000 commercial producers of tomatoes under glass, operating some 2,200 glasshouses of 5·5 million sq. ft with an annual production of £700,000. These glasshouses cannot be operated economically for more than 7 months in the year, because outdoor crops compete from January onwards and reduce the price to an uneconomic level (Hockey, 1955).

Tomatoes have been the guinea pigs in many academic studies on the factors governing growth and reproduction, while many other workers have been primarily concerned with the control of the environment for economic production. It was in the tomato that Went observed thermo-periodicity (see Went, 1957, for full review of work on this crop at the Earhart Plant Research Laboratory, Pasadena). The plant is photo-periodically indifferent since, under properly controlled temperatures (air-conditioning), the daily length of illumination has practically no effect on its development. For best growth and fruit set, the day tempera-ture should be 26°C and the night 15° to 18°C (thermoperiodicity). The cool period for optimal development is effective only in darkness or at least in greatly reduced light. Since no fruit set is possible above 22°C and below 10°C night temperature, tomatoes do not bear fruit in winter or spring nor during hot spells in summer, even though day temperatures are within the rather wide range of possible growth (15° to 35°C). Each day sugar production by assimilation in tomato leaves con-tinues only until early afternoon, when a maximum sugar content is reached.

In Southern California, winter and early spring night temperatures are usually below 10°, but the afternoon temperatures range between 15° and 20°C, optimal for growth and fruit set. Therefore, if part of the after-noon were changed into a functional night, by daily covering tomatoes from 3 p.m. onwards, no loss of photosynthesis would occur, and an optimal night temperature would exist for a few hours. To discover whether by these means tomato plants growing outside could be made to produce fruits out of season, some were planted in the field in the middle of November 1943. Each afternoon at 3 p.m., half the plants were covered with tar paper, and uncovered next morning between 7 and 8 a.m. The first ripe fruits were harvested from the covered plants on 1 April 1944, and from then onwards they continued to produce. The non-covered plants did not produce any fruits.

It appears that the development of tomato plants is not limited by photosynthesis, but that the use of the photosynthates is regulated by processes occurring in darkness at temperatures between 15° and 20°C. This is not true for all plants, since the covering of beets produces only a slight and insignificant increase in weight. Under certain conditions by proper treatment, the apparent efficiency of photosynthesis can be increased considerably in tomatoes. The effects of the covering are not due to photoperiodicity, but to thermoperiodicity (simulating photo-periodicity).

A gradual varietal shift in optimal night temperatures has been noted, from 30°C in small plants to 18°C for the San José Canner and 13°C for the Illinois T 19 in the early fruiting stage. A similar response has been found in fourteen other varieties, but they each have slightly different temperature characteristics. In general, the English and Greenhouse varieties grow fastest and have the lowest optimal night temperatures. Western American varieties have the highest optimal night temperatures; Eastern varieties are intermediate as far as night temperature is concerned, but have the lowest absolute growth rates. When tomatoes are grown in full sunlight, their optimal night temperature is higher than on cloudy days, provided they are shaded by other plants. Incidence of virus diseases is greatly modified by both day and night temperatures.

In other experiments at the Earhart Laboratory, tomatoes were grown in various cycles of alternating light and dark periods of equal length (each period 2, 4, 6, 9·6 or 12 hours in length) for 17 days (Bonde, 1955). It appeared that rhythms other than diurnal ones are operative in growth. When even shorter cycles were used (6 seconds, 1, 5, 30 and 60 minutes), the young plants grew best in the 6-second cycle, also well in 5-minute cycles, but poor and quite poor growth was made in 30 and 60-minute cycles. Chlorophyll deficiencies were noted in 5 and 30-minute cycles (Bonde, 1956). These effects are difficult to explain on the assumption that a daily rhythm exists in plant processes concerned with growth (Highkin and Hanson, 1954), as Bünning has suggested with responses to environmental factors (see p. 32). Exposure of plants to continuous illumination at constant temperatures results in leaf injury symptoms characteristic of the temperature used, but only in leaves exposed from an early stage in development (Hillman, 1956).

The work of W. J. C. Lawrence and his associates at the John Innes Horticultural Institution on the factors, particularly temperature, governing flowering can be found in the Annual Reports of that centre. It has been shown that the progress of the young plant is punctuated by thermophases during which the temperature of the environment determines the subsequent development of the plant. It is now known that from germination onwards the tomato passes through successive thermophases and photophases. The knowledge of the existence of thermophases and the ability to control temperatures accurately in glasshouses could make the commercial production of the tomato more profitable (Calvert, 1955).

The first thermophase affects the differentiation to the 'rogue' character, an off-type which has segregated for many generations in certain varieties and is characterized by short internodes, small leaves and a lack of apical dominance. The problem of this character is essentially genetical, but environmental conditions can cause a transformation to the rogue character in the seed or seedling. A high temperature applied to the germinating seed and extending to several days beyond cotyledon expansion will increase the percentage of rogue plants in a rogue-producing variety. The onset and duration of the sensitive period may vary according to the particular temperature levels under which the seed is germinated. Differentiation to the rogue character may also occur as a result of a high temperature during a period covering pollination and fertilization. Immediately after the germination process is complete, as indicated by the expansion of the cotyledons, the plant enters a second thermophase during which the number of leaves between the cotyledons and the first inflorescence is determined. Calvert considers this to be a vernalizing effect since ripeness-to-flower is pre-determined by the number of leaves before the first inflorescence. The number of leaves is at a minimum if the temperatures are low during this thermophase, and at a maximum if they are high. The number of flowers, or the degree of branching on the inflorescences is determined by temperature during sensitive periods. It would appear that for each inflorescence there is a sensitive period during which temperature determines flower number, low temperature increasing flower production. This thermophase follows immediately after the second or vernalization phase.

As an outcome of this earlier work, a full analysis of the factors affecting early growth and development has been started at the John Innes Horticultural Institution to fill the gap in the knowledge of the physiology and culture of the tomato (1957 Report). G. Hussey has examined the growing point by micro-dissection and, in collaboration with L. S. Clarke, photographed the apex at all stages from the early vegetative to the initiation of the first inflorescence, noting variation in the plastochrone (time interval between the initiation of successive primordia), development of the axillary bud, etc., as influenced by environmental conditions. A. Calvert has repeated the experiment on the influence of light and temperature on leaf number to the first inflorescence and has obtained additional data by periodic dissections. The rate of production of the leaf primordia is enhanced both by increase in temperature and light intensity. Therefore for a particular combination of light and temperature the actual time of flower initiation is an expression of the rate of leaf production and the final number of leaves to flowering.

Further, it has already been shown that, at a given temperature, the number of leaves to flowering decreases as light intensity increases: now Calvert has found that the plastochrone also decreases with increase in light intensity. Again, at a given light intensity it was shown that the number of leaves to flowering increases with increase in temperature: now it is found that the plastochrone decreases with increase in temperature.

With the improved facilities provided by the new growth rooms, it will be possible to assess in detail the action and interaction of light and temperature on the growth and development of tomato and to extend the scope of the work.

Since leaf number to flowering is influenced by light and temperature from the time the cotyledons emerge, it seemed pertinent to inquire whether these organs play a part in determining leaf number. The evidence from Calvert's experiments is as follows. First, leaf number is increased by reducing the area of the cotyledons immediately after expansion. Secondly, the area and dry weight of the cotyledons decrease as the temperature is increased above 60°F and/or if the light intensity is reduced. It appears that little growth of the cotyledons occurs after the initiation of the first inflorescence. These findings emphasize the importance in tomato propagation of producing large, undamaged cotyledons, first, by adequately covering the seed when sowing and employing a temperature of 65 to 70°F to ensure rapid germination and the easy withdrawal of the cotyledons from the testa, secondly, by reducing the temperature to 60°F after pricking out and, in winter time, giving the seedlings as much light as possible.

The effect of temperature in association with light has been studied at the Earhart Laboratory (Verkerk, 1954), again using contrasting day and night thermoperiods (23°C day and 22°, 17° and 11°C night); at the lower night temperatures, stem growth is less, root weight high, clusters longer and heavier, and fruit yield later but larger. Reduction of light intensity has greatest influence on the cluster; if the light is poor, temperature has to be low, or the clusters will not show any growth.

In the Department of Horticulture of Michigan State University, tomato seedlings were subjected to night temperatures of 10° to 13°C for 2 to 3 weeks after the expansion of the cotyledonary leaves (Wittwer and Teubner, 1957). These plants, in contrast to those grown at 18° to 21°C, produce flowers when the plant has fewer leaves (nodes) and produce significantly more flowers in the first cluster. Cold exposure at very early stages of growth (seed vernalization) has no effect, while cold treatment of older seedlings will increase the number of flowers in later-formed clusters. Plants subjected to 10° to 13°C for 3 or more weeks after cotyledon expansion often produce compound clusters with two or three times the number of flowers. In solution culture, high (440 p.p.m.)

in contrast to low (55 p.p.m.) levels of nitrogen favour earlier and increased flower formation. Optimal temperature patterns for tomato plants at various stages of development are not fully defined since many interacting factors appear to control flower formation as well as being involved in the subsequent expression of the cold temperature effects.

The following economic advantages accrue from chilling for 2 to 3 weeks at 50° to 55°F (night temperature), beginning after the cotyledons have unfolded (Wittwer and Teubner, 1956):

(1) there are one or two leaves fewer before the first cluster, i.e. plants flower nearer the ground level;

(2) the plants are sturdier, have thicker stems and recover rapidly after transplanting;

(3) numbers of flowers on the first and second clusters may be doubled, 15 to 25 flowers on branched (compound) clusters being common; and

(4) fruit clusters are correspondingly larger and early yields are increased.

American growers have been recommended to try the following treatment, based on more than 50 plantings over a 3-year period seeded from October to March, under commercial as well as experimental greenhouse conditions. Growers may combine chilling with the use of chemical treatment (N-m-tolylphthalamic acid) and appropriate fertilization.

(1) Germinate the seed at a temperature of 75° to 80°F in the usual manner using sterilized flats of soil, sand, vermiculite, or a mixture of the three.

(2) When the first true leaf begins to show, either before or after transplanting, grow the young plants for three weeks at a night temperature of 50° to 55°F. The temperature in the plant house may be lowered or the plants transferred to a cooler area. If necessary, transplanting or pricking-off from seedling flats may be done during the cold treatment. Daytime temperatures higher than 50° to 55°F often cannot be avoided, and they do not nullify the effects of the cold treatment if night temperatures are kept cool. Expose to as much sunlight as possible.

(3) After 3 weeks of cold, raise the night temperature and maintain it thereafter at 58° to 65°F, depending on the season of the year, the amount of light, and the variety grown.

(4) Give seed tomatoes the cold treatment 10 days to 2 weeks earlier than normal. They will grow very slowly during the cold treatment.

Steam-sterilized soil should be used; otherwise, more than the normal loss of plants may result from 'damping-off'.

(5) The cold treatment does not affect early fruit set, even though it results in many more flowers. Ensure fruit set by regular (daily) vibration of the flowers with an electric or battery-operated pollinating device.

Although it is uneconomic to irradiate a growing crop of tomatoes or cucumbers, it may frequently be advantageous to use supplementary sources of light for massed seedlings (Stoughton and Vince, 1957). Using 400-watt HPMV lamps, these are suspended 3 ft above the seedlings on the propagating bench and, in multiple-lamp systems, at 4 ft apart. Each lamp will illuminate an area about 3 ft 6 in. × 4 ft. In commercial practice it is usual to mount the lamps on curtain rails, and to use them alternatively on two batches of plants for 12 hours each. Tomato plants must have at least 6 hours of darkness so that on this 'double-batch' system, the lights are moved at 10 a.m. and 10 p.m. (though noon and midnight would be more nearly ideal); it is necessary to ensure that stray light from the batch which is being irradiated does not reach the batch which is intended to be in darkness. Irradiation begins as soon as the seedlings have germinated and is continued for 3 weeks, when it is essential that the temperature of the house remains between 55° and 60°F. Because of the heat from the lamp, the internal temperature of the plant is likely to be 5° to 8°F. higher than that of the ambient air; if the temperature is too high, the early trusses of fruit will be damaged (later formation of truss and reduction in number of flowers on the truss). If irradiated plants are subsequently well managed, they yield earlier and heavier crops during the first harvesting months.

Reports have indicated that tomatoes grown in the greenhouse are often markedly lower in ascorbic acid than those that mature out of doors, because the short wave region (2,900 Å to 3,800 Å) of the radiant energy is absorbed by the glass. In an experiment planned to clarify this point, it was not found possible to distinguish between the influence of light intensity and light duration on ascorbic acid synthesis, nor was any consistent increase in ascorbic acid concentration found in irradiated plants (Frazier et al., 1954).

The vegetative and flowering responses induced by gibberellin vary with variety. With early determinate varieties such as Fireball, the increase in node numbers to and the reduction of flower numbers in the first clusters, combined with greatly accelerated growth and flowering, may be of practical significance. The increased earliness is of little advantage in early or late indeterminate types, and the excessive elongation and abnormalities in vegetative growth would be objectionable (Bukovac, Wittwer and Teubner, 1957). Gibberellin has a marked effect in breaking 'summer dormancy', the condition characterized by considerable reduction of growth of both vegetative and reproductive structures (Liverman and Johnson, 1957).

Gibberellin profoundly affects the reproductive development of Earlypak tomatoes (Rappaport, 1957). While flowering is accelerated only slightly (3 to 6 days), this and other work suggests the need for further studies. Rappaport emphasizes especially the value of leaf numbers preceding the appearance of flower parts as an index of accelerated flowering. Gibberellin did not influence the number of nodes preceding the appearance of flowers in his experiments. 'This indicates the need for careful consideration of the plant material when leaf numbers are used as an index of flowering. The implication is that in some plants Ga may accelerate maturation of vegetative parts preceding flowering.'

Under certain conditions, the coastal regions of southern California, for instance, tomatoes that come into bearing during the colder portions of the spring and autumn may fail to set commercially significant numbers of fruits when grown under cultural practices that give an abundant set during the warmer months. The procedure of applying synthetic auxin sprays to individual blossoms or to whole plants during the first 6 weeks of the blossoming period has become so widespread that some 50 per cent of the acreage in San Diego County is treated in this way (Wedding *et al.*, 1956). There is some evidence that hormone-treated fruits are physiologically more mature at the time of harvest than untreated ones.

In this connection it is pertinent to attempt to define 'unfruitfulness', if one is to understand how growth regulators may reverse the causes for it and hence increase fruit set (Johnson, 1956). As in other plants, certain physiological balances exist which are capable of limiting fruitfulness during periods of unfavourable temperatures and light intensities. The visible signs of these balances are to be found in the abscission of flowers due to excessive vegetative vigour, pollen sterility, retarded pollen tube growth, style exsertion, and in the dormancy of ovules which may or may not be fertilized. The role of growth regulators is to reverse these physiological limitations effectively, so that fruit set is increased. The growth regulators may function as an auxin-type hormone or antiauxin hormone or both. The fruit set by growth regulators may vary in seed content from entirely parthenocarpic to fully seeded fruits.

FRUIT VEGETABLES

Cucumber and Muskmelon

With reference to cucumbers, Wittwer and Bukovac (1958) obtained stimulation of vegetative growth by the application of 10 to 100 p.p.m. of gibberellin to the foliage during early growth. The delayed fruiting may be useful for mechanical harvesting of pickling types, but deleterious in slicing types. In muskmelons, the vegetative growth was again stimulated; there was some delay in fruiting and reduction in crown set of fruit.

Chapter XVII

FRUIT-BEARING TREES
AND SHRUBS

L ittle work has been done on the relationships between environment and the growth and reproductive development of fruits, with the exception of the strawberry (dealt with in Chapter XVIII). With the increasing availability of equipment for studies on large perennial plants, progress is now to be expected.

'An old bit of research, which still lays a heavy and controlling hand upon much horticultural thinking and practice is the so-called carbohydrate-nitrogen relationship . . . though it may represent an oversimplification or only a partial statement of the truth, it nevertheless is a good example of the synthesis of research into a working hypothesis. . . . The general idea is that the ability of a plant to fruit is indicated by the relationship between carbohydrates and nitrogen in the plant' (Tukey, 1957) (see, however, pp. 20 and 34). With the following four classes in mind, much can be done to control the behaviour of a tree by pruning, ringing, girdling, bringing out of the shade, applying nitrogenous fertilizer, and so on:

(1) plants with abundant nitrogen but deficient in accumulated carbohydrates, thin-wooded, spindly, weak trees growing in the shade;

(2) adolescent plants with abundant nitrogen and carbohydrates, which continue to grow exuberantly, with large dark-green foliage, but no fruits;

(3) highly productive individuals, with accumulations of sufficient reserve carbohydrates to provide for fruit-bud formation and fruiting;

(4) senescent plants, in which carbohydrates have accumulated to such an extent that the foliage is yellowish in colour, the tree biennial in bearing, and the characteristics of age appear.

The fact that fruit trees undergo a series of growth phases from seedling to senile tree is not generally appreciated (Blair *et al.*, 1956). These phases are of a physiological nature; although the fundamental causes are not fully understood, they have marked external features which can be referred to as juvenile, transitional, mature and senile. These are of great importance to workers engaged in fruit tree research, particularly the propagator and breeder. Most of the work on growth stages has been done in Europe, particularly Germany. Various authors have found differences between juvenile and mature forms, in respect of growth form, morphology, anatomy and chemical composition. The duration of these phases is a controversial subject. It is reported that the juvenile stage of apricot resembles the wild tree, and the mature form more closely resembles the cultivated types. The thorny juvenile and smooth mature types of branch growth in the pear are shown in Plate 13.

An example of a recent recruit to horticultural research is represented by Kenya, where work began in about 1947 (Jackson, 1955). The reactions to temperature at different altitudes have been obtained for citrus, pineapple, litchi, olives and deciduous fruits. It has been proved that the hop is a long-day plant and therefore unsuitable for Kenya.

Before turning to the individual species of fruit-bearing trees and shrubs, passing reference should be made to the use of growth regulators. These may be used to control pre-harvest drop, to increase size and to hasten maturity. Bradley and Crane (1957) have studied the effects of auxins on development of apricot seeds and seedlings, and the stimulation of cambial activity in stems of apricot spur shoots by treatment with gibberellin. Reports to the 15th International Horticultural Congress also dealt with the effect of gibberellin on the apricot (J. C. Crane and M. V. Bradley, U.S.A.), and on the growth of physiologically dwarf seedlings of peaches, cherries and plums (P. Remy, France).

Plant regulators are now entering the field of grape production (Weaver, 1956). The compound 4-chlorophenoxyacetic acid (4-CPA), for example, induces a good set of large berries in Black Corinth and is being used commercially to replace the girdling operation. (This compound is also known as para-chlorophenoxyacetic acid or PCPA). It is also beginning to replace or supplement girdling to produce a larger berry in Thompson seedless raised for table grapes. Another experimental compound, benzothiazol-2-oxyacetic acid (BOA), markedly delays maturity in seeded and seedless raisins. A grower may thus control rate of maturation, delaying the process in part of his vineyard to facilitate picking, or he may use it to carry his grapes into later and more lucrative markets. Experimental results are available concerning the use in California of both 4-CPA and BOA.

Plant regulators such as alpha-naphthaleneacetic acid (NAA) are also being used experimentally to thin grapes and to root cuttings. Their use for weed control is still experimental, but the success so far achieved with 2,4-D and other compounds indicates that eventually this will be another acceptable use for plant regulators.

We will now take the individual fruit-bearing trees and shrubs in alphabetical order, rather doubtfully including pineapple among woody species.

APPLE

Gorter (1955) 'in this age of photoperiodism' tested the reaction of young apple trees (grafts of Yellow Transparent and Jonathan on Malling IX) to different daily periods of light and darkness, and found no response. Hoyle (1955) had the same negative result with tests at Reading on Cox's Orange Pippin and Worcester Pearmain. It is possible that night temperature may be involved.

Before a young apple tree raised by budding or grafting from an existing variety begins to flower, it repeats the pattern of growth already established, but when it begins to crop there is a change in its metabolism leading to the production of flowers, fruits and seeds. This process appears to be different from that in an annual or biennial plant, which has a juvenile stage before the mature flowering stage. The young apple tree is in the mature condition, and the seedling stage of non-flowering has already been passed through before the tree was propagated. In a given locality there is a close relationship between the proportion of trees flowering and the mean number of inflorescences per tree, suggesting that the factors initiating flowering also operate in the subsequent production of flowers (Maggs, 1955). The rate of increase in number of inflorescences per tree is greater than the rate of increase in the number of trees coming into flower, indicating that the inception of the flowering condition has more stringent requirements than the production of flowers once this condition has been reached.

At the 15th International Horticultural Congress, the biological and physiological bases of fertility in the apple were reviewed by P. K. Oursoulenko (U.S.S.R.), while J. Pandele (Rumania) described the use

291

of the chlorophyll content of the leaves as a standard to establish pheno-phases during active growth of fruit trees. Experiments to control biennial bearing of apples by chemical sprays were reported by A. Pieniazek (Poland), while J. Pieniazek discussed the effect of photo-period and temperature on winter dormancy in apple seedlings.

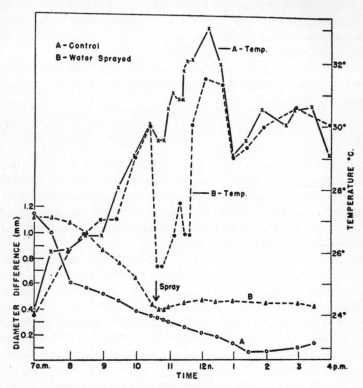

Fig. 51. Avocado fruit diameter as affected by water spray on tree (Schroeder and Wieland, 1956).

AVOCADO

The avocado has two flowering periods at Mvuazi in the Belgian Congo, one at the end of the long dry season in September and October and the other during the short drought in February. The first is the more important, the second being limited to certain varieties and not occurring every year. The varieties have been classified by Philippe (1957) as follows:

292

FRUIT TREES AND SHRUBS

Group A: Female stage in the morning, male stage in the afternoon.

Variety	Type
Collinson	Hybrid
Family	West Indian
Gottfried	Mexican
Lula	Hybrid
Simmonds	West Indian
Taylor	Guatemalan
Waldin	West Indian

Group B: Female stage in the afternoon, male stage in the morning.

Variety	Type
Eagle Rock	Guatemalan
Fuerte	Hybrid
Linda	Guatemalan
Mvuazi	West Indian
Pollock	West Indian
Winslowson	Hybrid
Winter Mexican	Mexican

As similar characteristics have been observed in California and Florida, it seems that the behaviour of the flower is independent of latitude. No overlapping of stages has been observed in the Belgian Congo and isolated trees remain unproductive. Mixed plantations are therefore necessary to obtain a yield; the current practice is to establish homogeneous plantations of one variety and to surround it with polyvarietal borders. The fruits of the avocado show diurnal fluctuations in size due to competition for moisture with other plant parts during periods of active transpiration around noon (Schroeder and Wieland, 1956; see Fig. 51).

CHERRY

The classification of American cherry varieties (*Prunus avium*) adopted by H. B. Tukey (early, midseason and late) has been found to apply equally well to Dutch varieties (Braak, 1955). Between full bloom and fruit maturity, three successive developmental stages may be distinguished: I—rapid growth of the pericarp; II—reduced pericarp growth and accelerated growth of nucellus, endosperm and embryo; III—renewed growth of the pericarp. The difference between an early and a late variety lies mainly in the duration of stage II. The average age at which a cherry seedling flowers and bears fruit for the first time is 6 years. To breeders a reduction of this juvenile period would mean a saving of space and time. By growing excised embryos in artificial culture, it is possible to save a year. The method has also been applied to peaches.

As a number of cherry plants grown in this way show dwarfed growth, observations have been made on the effect of photoperiods and temperature on the seedlings (Smeets, 1956, 1957). First- and second-year seedlings respond differently to the photoperiod as regards termination of shoot growth. In first-year seedlings, many plants under 8- and 16-hour photoperiods cease growth at the same time; however, some of the 8-hour group cease growth much earlier, some of the 16-hour group considerably later. In the second year, growth ceases at about the same time in 8-, 16- and 24-hour photoperiods. Different day and night temperatures were also tested under natural days. After termination of growth, significant differences occurring simultaneously in shoot length and leaf number between the temperature treatments are due mainly to the effect of the day or night temperature on the duration of growth.

In controlled experiments, branches of trees may be enclosed in cooled or heated chambers to discover if that type of plant would be adapted to different climatic conditions (Tukey, 1957). It is found, for example, that some cherry fruits grow rapidly at high night temperatures for a period immediately following full bloom, but that they develop slowly, with poor quality and colour, if the night temperatures are high late in the season, when the fruit is maturing. The sour cherry industry in the United States is confined largely to Michigan, Wisconsin and New York, where early summer temperatures are relatively high, and night temperatures prior to harvest relatively low.

CITRUS

The problem of small-sized fruit has caused concern to California orange growers for many years, and is one of the most serious troubles now facing the industry. In one year it may require 20 per cent more fruit to fill a box (Harding *et al.*, 1954). A sudden and simultaneous decrease of fruit sizes in all the major Californian citrus areas save one from 1945 to 1949 is found to have been due primarily to some climatic circumstance or combination of circumstances. There are no simple correlations between temperature or rainfall and fruit size. Because unusual and undefined climatic conditions are recurrent, research under controlled environmental conditions is necessary to find the relative importance of various diurnal, seasonal and annual climatic conditions which affect fruit size and the extent to which these may be overcome by soil modifications (nutrition, reduction in salinity, irrigation, fumigation, and improvement in structure).

Studies on grapefruit in California (Furr and Armstrong, 1956) suggest that the procedure of ringing and defoliating branches at intervals offers a means of determining the percentage of buds in which floral induction has occurred by the date of treatment. The treatment was made at intervals of 2 to 3 weeks from early August through December; the number of floral shoots that had appeared in the treated branches in the following February was recorded. On trees with a normal crop, floral induction had started by 1 September and progressed at a slightly increasing rate through December. On trees from which the fruit was removed in June, induction had started by early August and the percentage of buds that produced flowering shoots increased markedly during autumn and early winter. Girdling the trunks of uncropped trees in August or September greatly increased the rate of floral induction in early autumn and winter.

COFFEE

An early study of the effect of photoperiodism on floral initiation was made at the Instituto do Café at São Paulo, Brazil. One lot of three trees was exposed to natural daylight plus 4 hours artificial light, another lot to natural daylight reduced by 4 hours by shading between 2 p.m. and the evening, and a third lot to normal daylight. It was concluded that coffee appears to belong to the short-day group. Piringer and Borthwick (1954) made experiments at Beltsville, Maryland, on young plants grown from seed obtained from El Salvador and Brazil. It was found possible to control, by photoperiodic adjustment, floral induction and vegetative growth of *arabica* coffee aged 12 or 18 months. In these experiments, the critical photoperiod lay between 13 and 14 hours; floral initiation occurred under days of 13 hours or less, not under days of 14 hours or more. The formation of flower buds took place earlier in 8-hour than in 12-hour photoperiods. Lateral branches were larger under long day than under short day.

However, the literature on the seasonal flowering of coffee shows that variable and apparently conflicting observations have been made in different parts of the world (Mes, 1957). In general one may conclude that in tropical regions with no well-defined alternations of wet and dry seasons, the coffee trees may flower at odd intervals throughout the year. In tropical areas where wet and dry seasons alternate, flowering appears to take place only at certain fixed periods which may occur only once or sometimes twice a year, when large areas may flower simultaneously. Flowering seems to be determined by various climatic factors. Although many varieties are typical short-day plants, *semperflorens* produces flower buds in 18- and 16-hour days. The actual opening of the flower appears to be closely related to rainfall. Mes (*loc. cit.*) has studied the influence of temperature on the initiation, number and development of flower buds. Rain has a positive influence in breaking the dormancy of flower buds, which is due to a water deficit in the buds while a plentiful supply of water is still available to the roots. A lowering of the temperature plays no part. A striking characteristic of the peduncles is the presence of a well-developed phloem cylinder and the relatively small number and very small size of the water-conducting elements.

The most recent review of the physiological bases of coffee production (with 50 literature references) has been presented by Paulo de T. Alvim of the Interamerican Institute of Agricultural Sciences, Lima, Peru, in *Coffee and Tea Industries* for November 1958. Further research on physiological responses to light intensity is apparently necessary in order to reconcile the conflicting opinions regarding the role of shade in coffee growth. It appears that coffee does not behave as a shade-loving species in so far as its reaction to light is concerned. Although shade may be desirable for economic reasons, most evidence available indicates that, by intensifying cultural practices such as use of fertilizers or weed control, coffee can be grown successfully without shade in any producing area.

CURRANT

Black currants (Amos Black, Boskoop Giant) are strongly photoperiodic with regard to vegetative growth (Hoyle, 1955). If measured by extension growth and leaf number, growth increases with increase in daylength and corresponding decrease in darkness over the range of photoperiod used; growth ceases progressively earlier as the photoperiod is reduced. Interruption of the dark period also affects the growth response.

LITCHI

Litchi chinensis resembles pineapple in that floral initiation has been successfully induced with growth regulators (Nakata, 1955). Blossoming in Hawaii is favoured by a dry autumn followed by substantial rain from

December to February. Sodium naphthaleneacetate inhibits vegetative growth and therefore promotes blossoming only when there has been heavy rainfall during October and November and when adequate water is available from December to February.

MANGO

Indian workers in Uttar Pradesh find that not all shoots in *Mangifera indica* produce only terminal inflorescences under normal conditions (Singh and Singh, 1956), and that the inhibiting effect of the terminal bud may not be universal in nature. They conclude that there is some substance (hormone) which is largely responsible for changing a leaf bud into a fruit bud, but that it is effective only when leaves are present. The optimal amount required for axillary fruit bud formation may be a varietal characteristic.

OLIVE

In the University of California, Davis, it has been shown that *Olea europaea* requires winter chilling to induce flower-bud differentiation, which in California occurs about mid-March, followed by blooming in May. Vegetative growth proceeds without chilling (Hartmann and Porlingis, 1957). This situation is quite different from that in most deciduous fruit trees, where flower-bud differentiation takes place the previous summer, and the winter-chilling period serves only to overcome the rest period of the buds. Unlike the olive, too, vegetative buds in deciduous species require a chilling period to resume growth in spring.

On the basis of these findings, a further investigation was undertaken to determine whether differences in chilling requirement for flower formation exist among olive varieties, and to examine the possibility of using those with a low chilling requirement in areas with relatively warm winters. Eight varieties were tested; when kept in a warm greenhouse throughout the winter, trees of each failed to produce a single inflorescence. The number of flowers per inflorescence or the percentage of perfect flowers were not affected by the amount of winter chilling. Two varieties required the maximum amount of winter chilling (1657 hours below 45°F), four were intermediate, while two were able to produce substantial numbers of inflorescences under the minimum amount of chilling given (613 hours below 45°F), indicating that they might be adapted to regions of relatively high winter temperatures.

A state of practically unlimited juvenility can be experimentally induced in the olive tree and the normal correlation between growth and

K*

reproductive development can, according to Vieira Natividade (1957) be altered at will (see Plate 14). In the grossly overgrazed wild trees of the Mediterranean region, the systematic clipping of the twigs by grazing animals determines the dwarf condition of the plants, as well as the retention of the juvenile growth habit for periods of more than 50 years (Plate 15).

Papaya

Physiologists studying environmental relationships consider the sexes not as fundamentally distinct characters governed by the operation of internal genic mechanisms, but as inter-grading physiological states responding to variations in the environment. *Carica papaya* is a dioecious plant, with male and female inflorescences borne by different individuals. Sometimes plants bear female flowers and fruits in one season and male flowers in the next. It may be possible to predict sex in papaya by physiological investigations of the balance between carbohydrate and nitrogen accumulations in leaves and flowers and related biochemical characteristics, and ultimately to control sex expression through physiological adjustments (Choudhri, Garg and Borah, 1957).

Peach

Considerable economic losses have occurred in the Southern United States through delayed and scattered foliation and blossoming in some seasons. Varieties differ in their requirement of hours of chilling; those adapted to the long chilling of northern winters do not break dormancy in southern regions. Catalogues of fruit trees for the South now indicate the amount of chilling required to break dormancy. Breeders have produced varieties of peaches adapted to southern California and other southern regions, and have made possible the extension of peach production southward even into Florida. December and January temperatures are the principal influence in breaking dormancy in peach buds (Weinberger, 1956). The physiological dwarfing that occurs in seedling peach may be due to an inhibitor that is removed or to a stimulating substance formed when the seeds are chilled for 2 to 3 months in a moist medium at 5°C or when the seedlings are exposed to 5°C for 6 to 8 weeks (Flemion, 1956). Studies have been made to discover whether an inhibitor is present in the unchilled cotyledons and whether an inhibiting substance disappears during after-ripening. The changes at 5°C are cumulative since dormant seeds produce dwarfs, partially after-ripened seeds produce semi-dwarfs, and fully after-ripened seeds produce normal plants.

PINEAPPLE

The use of the sodium salt of naphthaleneacetic acid (SNA) to induce flowering in *Ananas comosus*, a day-neutral plant under Hawaiian conditions, has been a commercial practice for some years in Hawaii, but the role of this chemical in stimulating flowering has not been fully understood. We have seen in Chapter IV that the level of auxin may influence the morphogenesis of stems, roots and vegetative buds, and that the concentration of auxin which stimulates one may inhibit another. Leopold and Thimann (1949) showed that flowering may be primarily a response to effective auxin level; it has also been suggested that, in inducing flowering in the pineapple, naphthaleneacetic acid and 2,4-dichlorophenoxyacetic acid may be acting as antiauxins rather than as auxins, i.e. antagonistic to the native auxin in the plant.

Gowing (1956) has presented evidence to support his working hypothesis regarding the role of SNA in the induction of flowering in the pineapple. The hypothesis is that SNA acts by competitively lowering the effective native auxin level in the stem tip, that the time of appearance of the inflorescence can be controlled by the amount and frequency of SNA applications (i.e. by the length of time the effective native auxin level is kept low), that the number of flowers produced is governed by the rate of SNA application, and that earliness of flowering is directly related to the effectiveness of flower induction. It appears that indoleacetic acid is the native auxin of importance in flowering in the pineapple.

RASPBERRY

The red raspberry (*Rubus idaeus*) has a perennial root system but normally fruits upon biennial shoots. A demonstration at the Nottingham Easter School, 1956, showed a series of plants of the variety Malling Promise, all of the same age and propagated from root cuttings on 1 November 1955. By moving the plants through a series of growth rooms, it was possible to contract the entire biennial growth cycle into a period of 6 months and to arrest or maintain some plants in successively earlier stages of development. These stages included the primary rosette, vegetative elongation, flower initiation, winter dormancy, axillary bud development, flowering and fruiting. The environmental factors which have the most important effects are daylength and temperature (Williams and Hudson, 1956).

299

Chapter XVIII

HERBACEOUS FRUITS

STRAWBERRY

The strawberry, the only economic plant in this class, has for some time been the object of intensive study in the United Kingdom, the Netherlands, Belgium and the United States, with respect both to vegetative growth and reproduction (for review of earlier literature see Kronenberg *et al.*, 1949). Growth aspects have been investigated by Arney of University College, Cardiff, and published in a series of eight articles (most recent reference in series on leaf growth, Arney, 1956 a) on factors affecting the rate of leaf production in Royal Sovereign strawberry, the initiation, growth and emergence of leaf primordia, the growth of leaves and shoot, the characteristics of winter and spring growth, the effect of photoperiod and temperature on leaf size, and the effect of defoliation on leaf initiation and growth.

Winter dormancy in leaf growth involves a physiological change resulting in a lower level of activity rather than a complete cessation of activity. Leaf emergence and expansion, on the other hand, are completely stopped during the winter, due not primarily to the fall in temperature but to the photoperiod, which plays the dominant role in bringing about the reduction in leaf size and in the number of cells in the shortening days of autumn. Plants in various physiological conditions all respond similarly by prolonging the period of cell division in expanding leaves in response to long-day treatment, and by curtailing the period of cell division in short days. At the lowest temperatures within the normal range for active growth there is a reduction in leaf size and in cell size, and a less marked reduction in cell number. The effect of artificial illumination depends on the duration of the daily light period, and not on the total daily dose of light. Light intensity has no effect on leaf growth over the ranges used by Arney, either from fluorescent lamps or from high pressure mercury vapour lamps.

A method of determining the date of floral initiation which does not require dissection has been used by Arney (1956 b) to find the mean date of floral initiation for the M.48 clone of Royal Sovereign strawberry over a number of seasons, and under different conditions at various latitudes. The natural shortening of the photoperiod in autumn is the factor primarily responsible for floral induction, with night temperatures playing only a secondary role, even at high latitudes. Confirmatory experiments were made using supplemental illumination of plants growing in the open, and red light irradiation during short photoperiods, together with a series of experiments to determine the upper critical night temperature at which floral initiation is independent of photoperiod. Low night temperatures were obtained by moving plants into a refrigerated chamber for 12 hours each night.

Reduced yields and unfruitfulness following severe winters have frequently been observed in the United States, but these conditions have not usually been associated with low winter temperatures. Many growers have believed that unfruitfulness has been largely due to late spring frosts killing the blossoms. Plants do not harden in the absence of light (Campbell and Lingle, 1954); maximum hardiness is reached in 7 days when plants are exposed to a 12-hour day and alternating temperatures of 32° and 55°F. Flower buds may be killed or damaged in several different ways: complete killing of the whole primordia, differential killing of the flowers in the bud, killing of the opened flower parts, or injury to part of the vascular tissue of the peduncle. The danger point of mortality of plants hardened at the above alternating temperatures is probably 18°F.

Regulation of flowering and of expression of several vegetative responses (length of petiole, area of leaf, number of runners) has been found by Borthwick and Parker (1952) to result from interruption of the dark period with relatively low energies of artificial light. Regulation of the vegetative responses depends on the length of the dark period.

In the Netherlands (Jonkers, 1958), a combination of seed- and plant treatment for shortening of the life cycle was applied to seeds and resulting seedlings of the varieties Climax, Jucunda and Deutsch Evern. Treatment of seed for 16 days at 3° to 5°C produces bad germination; treatment with 96 per cent sulphuric acid gives more rapid and abundant germination. Seedlings with three trifoliate leaves cannot be induced to flower by short-day treatment. In Deutsch Evern at least five and in Climax and Jucunda at least seven trifoliate leaves should be formed before treatment. The freshly harvested seed from seedlings forced to rapid flowering has normal germination power. Through a combination of sulphuric acid treatment of the seed and short-day treatment of the seedlings as soon as the latter have become sensitive, the life cycle can be shortened from 18 to 24 months to 8 or 9 months. The earliest date of flowering in Jonkers' experiments was reached 158 days after sowing. Some seedlings of Deutsch Evern that had five trifoliate leaves at the beginning of the short-day treatment were involved. The plants brought to rapid flowering in this way are not of commercial importance. The method is primarily helpful for repeated backcrossing.

Plants can be induced to flower in Scotland at any season of the year by subjecting them to a period of short-day treatment (Guttridge, 1958). The season for runner production can be prolonged, especially in the glasshouse, by extending the daylength with artificial light. Fruit may be obtained at any time of the year (even from summer-fruiting varieties) by suitable combinations of chilling, short-day treatment and the use of artificial light. The best source of artificial light for winter fruit production appears still to be the HPMV lamp, but there are economic drawbacks to fruit production at this time of year. The Dutch method of autumn cropping is more likely to be a success; plants forced in Dutch lights in spring, for early cropping, are given short-day treatment by covering them with cane mats from 6 p.m. to 7 a.m. daily for a period of 6 weeks, starting in May. Fruit may be picked in September.

The chief value of understanding the seasonal cycle of the growth and behaviour of strawberry plants is in assessing new cultural techniques (such as out-of-season planting of runners from cold storage), in the revaluation of old techniques (such as post-harvest defoliation), and in developing new methods of controlling plant growth and behaviour by the use of chemicals.

The analysis of the responses of the perpetual-flowering strawberry (*Fragaria vesca* var. *semperflorens*) to relative length of day and night and to temperature has shown that the behaviour of the plant changes in the course of its development (Sironval, 1957). The morphological changes from the seedling to flowering are merely an outward expression of profound physiological transformations involving the functions of the plant. These transformations are linked with three main physiological stages:

(*a*) the vegetative stage from germination to the 15th to 17th leaf, during which the plant has little specific requirement for temperature and photoperiod;

(*b*) a physiological photophase from the 15th to 17th leaf to flowering, with greatly increased sensitivity to photoperiod and less obviously to temperature; development is immediately arrested by short days, and resumed in the long days which are essential for the completion of this phase;

(c) the 'reproductive' stage begins after first flowering and continues throughout the life of the plant. Sensitivity to photoperiod and temperature persists, but in a modified way, short days causing a slight reduction in number of flowers and affecting the shape of their stems.

The physiological functions of the photophase are most important for flowering. Sironval finds that the photophase is without doubt the period of very specific modifications which prepare the plant for flowering. The completion of the photophase in long days inevitably leads to flower formation and this to the beginning of reproductive life, which continues regardless of environmental conditions.

The chlorophyll content of the petioles varies according to certain laws closely connected with the stage of development and with environmental conditions, in particular, the relative length of day and night. In certain cases these variations may be large and rapid, even within a single day, a proof that chlorophyll is constantly metabolized in the leaf. The changes in chlorophyll metabolism during development are especially marked in the photophase. Previously the quantities of these pigments had increased from leaf to leaf under long days, but towards the end of the vegetative stage the metabolism becomes of a reproductive type. The characteristics of the chlorophyll content have been noted under varying daylengths and temperatures, and a clear connection has been found to exist between chlorophyll metabolism, environmental conditions (especially daylength) and flowering.

By using cuttings separated from the flowering mother plant, a sufficiently sensitive test of the flower-promoting activity of any particular substance can be made. It has thus been possible to show the effect on flowering of the non-saponifiable crude extract of leaves of flowering strawberries (active elements include vitamin E and the sterol fraction). When this extract reaches certain meristems, it induces the formation of floral organs.

Sironval concludes that the relative length of days and nights affects the transition from the vegetative to the reproductive stage by controlling the chlorophyll metabolism, particularly during the photophase, thus governing the availability of vitamin E and possibly some other flower-promoting substances.

Considerable attention has been directed recently in the Department of Plant Breeding (Watkin Williams) of the John Innes Horticultural Institution to the possibility of developing varieties of perpetual or ever-bearing strawberries (1957 Report). These differ from the June bearing forms in that they continue fruiting throughout the summer and produce a flush of fruit in September. Thus, they tend to be day-neutral in their photoperiodic response. The everbearers arose independently in France and the United States and are probably the result of selection from the ordinary varieties, some of which occasionally fruit during the autumn. The varieties of perpetuals at present available in Great Britain from other countries are very inferior to the summer bearers, and over the last 4 years H. Williams has been pursuing a programme of hybridization and selection with a view to their improvement. Crosses involving the varieties Sans Rivale and Evermore and, more recently, Red Rich, have yielded promising selections. Even the best of these, however, tend to fruit too late in the season; they also lack vigour and are poor in the production of runners. The most promising segregates have been derived from crossing everbearers with the ordinary varieties and a further two generations of breeding should result in substantial improvements in fruit quality and cropping.

The new variety, Merton Princess, together with recent selections, has been tested in yield trials using Huxley, Royal Sovereign and Talisman as control. Expressed as a percentage of Huxley, the relative yields were: Merton Princess = 187, J.I. 663 = 156 and Talisman = 142. The very high relative yield of some of the selections suggests that a much higher commercial yield can be expected in future from improved varieties, and that present-day varieties are substantially below the ceiling yield of the crop.

Chapter XIX

SEED FIBRES

COTTON

Acomprehensive review of the literature on the physiology of this plant (with 126 references) has been published by Eaton (1955), who opens his statement with the following paragraph:

'A measure of distinction is attached to the physiology of the cotton plant by reason of the dimorphism of its branches, its indeterminate growth habit, and the shedding of small floral buds and small bolls. According to environmental conditions, the branches produced by the cotton plant may be either vegetative or fruiting; the Upland cottons of the Southern States produce variable proportions of the two. Customarily, one or more vegetative branches are developed from the lower sixth to ninth main-stalk nodes after which fruiting branches appear at the successively higher nodes. The interval between the appearance of new fruiting branches is about three days and between the successive nodes of the fruiting branches (each with a floral bud) there is an interval of about six days. Flowering is thus progressive and for a time it becomes more rapid as the plant grows. After flowering and boll setting have continued for a number of weeks, however, both the growth of the plant and the production of flowers are checked and may stop. Also, many, if not most, of the floral buds abort before anthesis. The flowering and fruiting behaviour of American Upland cotton, *Gossypium hirsutum* L., is day-length neutral; however, there are short-day cottons which develop only vegetative branches during long days. Without the advantage of suitably high temperatures, the day-length neutral cottons behave like short-day cottons under long days and produce only vegetative branches.'

In areas of highly variable climate such as west-central Texas, it is difficult if not impossible to predict climate even for short periods. Moldenhauer and Keating (1958) have studied the relationships between climatic factors and yields of cotton and sorghums on sandy soils in the Southern high plains, where winters are very dry, May and June have the highest rainfall, July is usually dry and is followed by a period of rainfall in late August and early September. Successful crop production must fit this climatic pattern and the crops grown must withstand long periods of summer drought. Detailed statistical analyses were made as a basis for adapting land use and cropping practices to the climatic conditions, with reference to correlations between climatic factors and yields, relationships between pre-seasonal precipitation and soil moisture, and between precipitation and yield.

'Year to year variations have been observed in cotton fibre properties, as well as yield and gin turn-out (Hanson *et al.*, 1956). Often the differences in cotton properties within a variety from year to year are greater than between two varieties at the same location in the same year. In general, it has been observed that in years of high temperatures and low rainfall cotton fibres tend to be shorter and stronger and yields higher than during cooler, wetter seasons. However, there are few data on the direct effect of measured environmental factors on the fibre properties, lint percentage, or yield. One of the principal reasons for the lack of such data is the fact that only in recent years have instruments been developed for measuring fibre properties. The many factors which have made the effect of environment on other crops difficult to study are also common to cotton. In addition, the progressive fruiting habit of cotton exposes it to environmental changes within a single season, making the study of climatic effects on cotton more difficult than for the crop plants with terminal inflorescences.

'The possible benefits from a greater knowledge of the effects of environment on cotton are unlimited. There has been an increasing demand by the textile mills for cotton fibre with specific or minimum requirements of strength, length and fineness. With added information concerning the effect of environment on the cotton grown in a given area, the risk in buying cotton to meet certain specifications should be reduced.

'Many irregularities in experimental results can be attributed to varying climatic factors. In cotton research more knowledge of the effect of environment would aid in drawing conclusions from field experiments. It may also reduce the number of years an experiment must be conducted before definite conclusions can be reached' (Moldenhauer and Keating, *loc. cit.*).

These workers summarize the results of their study of the effect of environmental factors on fibre properties and yield of the cotton variety, Deltapine 15, grown and tested for 11 years under natural conditions at

Scott, Mississippi. As already stated, during warm, dry, sunny years, this variety tends in general to have shorter, stronger fibre and higher yield than in cooler, wetter growing seasons. Fibre strength is significantly correlated with all climatic factors studied except minimum temperature for the period 6 July to 13 September of the years 1945 to 1955. Fibre length is correlated significantly with maximum minus minimum temperature and rainfall for the period 6 July to 23 August. Lint percentage is not highly correlated with any of the factors. The average yield of the cottons tested is negatively associated with rainfall in June. A stress-index based on the difference between maximum and minimum temperature and rainfall is proposed.

Plants suitable for experiments on boll set can be grown under completely artificial conditions with an illumination of 2,200 to 2,400 foot-candles from a combination of fluorescent and incandescent lamps, if the light period and temperature are adjusted appropriately (light period 18 hours, day temperature 80°F, night temperature 72°F) (Sowell and Rouse, 1956).

Chapter XX

OIL CROPS

FLAX

In oil flax (linseed) it is possible in Sweden to improve the seed setting per capsule, and to increase the mean weight of seeds and the seed weight per capsule by changing the environmental conditions (dates of sowing, distance between plants, and plant nutrients, especially potassium, nitrogen and copper). The same three characters are greatly dependent on the length of time between flowering and ripeness; the longer the period the greater the mean seed weight, seed weight per capsule and number of seeds per capsule. The seed weight per capsule may also depend on the length of the branch on which it is borne, but Manner (1956) does not believe that time in itself nor position of capsules is the deciding factor, rather the quantity of nutrients available to the capsules, which seems to be affected by these factors.

In West Bengal the best vegetative growth in linseed is found in November sowings. There is little photoperiodic response although flowering is slightly promoted by long days. In 14-hour day, flowering takes place after 56 days, 5 days earlier than normal and 6 days earlier than in a 10-hour day. There is practically no induction effect in 14 and 28 days and no effect of treatment at the ages of 30 and 45 days (Sen Gupta, 1955).

GROUNDNUT

A remarkable cyclic periodicity of flower formation has been observed by Smith (1954), who presents an evaluation of reproductive efficiency in the Virginia variety, measured by comparing the numbers of seeds produced with the total numbers of flowers and fruits. Plants usually flower profusely but a relatively small proportion of the ovaries become mature fruits. Approximately two-fifths of the flowers in Smith's trial failed to begin fruit development; an additional two-fifths produced immature pegs which aborted before pod enlargement occurred; only

13·5 per cent of the original flowers produced mature pods. Calcium deficiency inhibits seed development but does not influence the disparity between fruiting potential and number of mature pods produced. Flowering follows a normal frequency distribution with its mode in the third month of the growing season. Day-to-day flower frequencies, not correlated with environmental factors nor influenced by fruit development, fluctuate cyclically over periods of 2 to 5 days with marked maxima and minima.

A new system of classification of groundnuts is based on two different patterns of branching (Bunting, 1955): form A, the alternate branching type in which vegetative and reproductive secondary branches alternate, usually in pairs, on the primary branches, and form B, the sequential branching type in which a continuous sequence of nodes on the primary branches bear reproductive branches and later nodes are sterile. The first type corresponds to the Virginia types of U.S.A.; these consist of true runners and spreading-bunch forms, all long-season forms of a somewhat indeterminate growth period subject to environmental restrictions, and sometimes even weakly perennial. The second type corresponds to the Spanish and Valencia types, all short-season annuals.

Work has been done in Wageningen on the influence of calcium and other elements on the fructification of the groundnut, in connection with the absorbing capacity of its gynophores, and in Japan on the effects of defloration on flowering and fruiting. In West Bengal the best vegetative growth is found in sowings in July, August and September, followed by June, May and April, and the lowest growth is found in November sowings (Sen Gupta, 1955). The flowering time is the longest in the sowings of November, December and January. The variety used (AH 25 spreading) is, however, completely day-neutral or indeterminate and there is no effect of induction or age.

MUSTARD

The early studies of Indian workers on mustard were reviewed in the first edition. Apart from the fact that this plant has been used in the laboratory for plant physiology research at Wageningen for studies of the photoperiodic and formative effects of various wavelength regions (Stolwijk, 1952), most of the new work originates from India. Sen Gupta (1955) refers to his finding that under similar photoperiods greater shortening of the vegetative period takes place under an increased temperature range. These reactions have been regarded by Sircar (see

Murneek and Whyte, 1948) as contradictory, as it was overlooked that 'in the first case a shortening of vegetative period with low temperature is an absolute value and in the second case a greater shortening of the vegetative period due to photoperiodic treatments with increased temperature range is a relative one, indicating the difference in the flowering time between the photoperiods at two temperatures'. Sen Gupta also reports recent results with varieties P 72 and P 74, and on effect of time of sowing and photoperiod on yellow sarson.

POPPY

Any general statement that all opium poppies are long-day plants should, according to Mika (1955), be accepted with caution. Since hybridization in nature and by man has probably occurred over many centuries, it is thought conceivable that the entire spectrum of photoperiodism is involved. On the other hand, the strong possibility exists that, if all sub-species of *Papaver somniferum* are long-day plants, the geographical distribution of the cultivated poppies might be determined by differences in photoperiodic sensitivity, by loss of that sensitivity with increased physiological age, and by the effect of temperature on photoperiodic response. It seems that either a relationship exists between the effects of temperature and photoperiod, or that maximum and minimum temperatures exist beyond which floral induction will not occur. The growth and development of the opium poppy in the greenhouse throughout the year, and perhaps also in the U.S.S.R., are apparently controlled by a complex interaction between photoperiod and number of leaves, and between night temperature and dry weight.

RAPE

The interest in *Brassica napus* in Germany has been in the vernalization of the seed (Kurth, 1955), in the Netherlands in the relationship between light (wavelength and time of irradiation) and formative and photoperiodic reactions (Wassink, Stolwijk and Beemster, 1951), in France in the relation between the duration of the flowering period and susceptibility to pests (Rives, 1957) and in Japan on the influence of photoperiodic treatment on the distribution of phosphorus absorbed in young rape. Some of these studies refer to practical aspects, others to rape as a convenient experimental plant. In the United Kingdom an extension of winter rape production has been recommended because of its superiority to spring rape in oil production.

OIL CROPS

The varieties of rape at the Station Centrale de Génétique et de l'Amélioration des Plantes at Versailles can be divided into four groups:

those from maritime climates where there is little frost,

types such as Lembke and its derivatives, which begin to flower and continue growth fairly late,

types from central and eastern Europe liable to suffer from late frosts in France, and

those originating in south-east France.

The Lembke group is evolving towards the third group in Poland; it is obvious that, in the contrasting climates of eastern and south-eastern Europe natural selection does not eliminate early types. These types, although less productive, have the advantage of more rapid growth. For present cropping systems, necessitating the harvesting of rape before the earliest cereals, late-maturing types are also undesirable (Rives, 1957). The objective in breeding should be to shorten the flowering period so as to reduce the period of exposure to insect attack and the difference in time of seed maturity, a factor in seed shattering.

SESAME

Sesamum indicum is one of the most important and ancient crops in India where one-fourth of the world's crop is produced from 30 varieties cultivated in both the rabi and kharif seasons. Sesame is a short-day plant flowering in 10-hour day in 43 days (Sen Gupta, 1955). When two varieties (I.P. 7 and I.P. 29) were sown in January, April, July and October, it was found that the season has a marked effect on the photoperiodic reaction. In both varieties leaf form is greatly influenced by photoperiod as expressed by a leaf heteromorphism index (see also Ghosh, 1955).

Observations were made on the growth phenomena and photoperiodic behaviour of sesame at the Central Rainlands Research Station (Tozi Research Farm) in the Sudan in the 1952 and subsequent cropping seasons. The maturation period is regarded as the vegetative phase (from planting to the opening of the first flower) and the reproductive phase (from that time to the dehiscence of the lowest capsule). The varieties tested fall into four distinct groups in respect of length of the vegetative phase, and this is associated with yield. The two lowest-yielding groups have vegetative phases of 29 to 31 days, and of 63 to 65 days respectively. The early flowering group is composed of varieties introduced from America, the late flowering group of varieties from Tanganyika and Venezuela. Those in the latter group produce unfilled and immature seed. The vegetative phase in the two intermediate groups varies from 44 to 46 days and 53 to 55 days respectively; these groups contain local varieties and varieties from India. The four groups therefore represent four different types of response to daylength in relation to latitude. The duration of the reproductive phase does not fall into such distinct groups, but the majority of the varieties fall into two groups, 42 to 57 days and 64 to 74 days in length respectively. Higher yield is not associated with either group.

The cultivators in the eastern rainlands recognize three main types of sesame of varying season length, known as heavy (branched and late), medium, and light (few branches and early). In order to discover whether these agronomic differences are related to differences in photoperiodic adaptation, the three types were planted in the field on the same date and each was subjected after emergence to three durations (15, 30 and 45 days) of three daylengths (normal, normal minus 1 hour, and normal minus 2 hours). These durations and photoperiods were selected to cover the lengths of the vegetative periods of the varieties and to exceed the natural range of daylengths in the region respectively. Data were collected on date of opening of first flower, date of dehiscence of lower capsule, and number of branches at maturity. In view of the small differences in daylength at the latitude of Tozi during the planting season, the daylength responses demonstrated (earlier flowering and fewer branches in shortened days) do not account for the agronomic differences between the varieties; they may, however, be one of the factors influencing native agricultural practices.

In breeding experiments in the Sudan, the objective in crossing a dwarf, unbranched, early-flowering American variety, K 10, with four local varieties was to retain the large branched habit of the local type while increasing the number of capsules by selecting for shorter nodes and the three-capsule character. Selections were also made for a date of flowering intermediate between the two parents. In order to discover whether such intermediate flowering types might be available, studies were made on the nature of the inheritance of the date of flowering. It appears that this character is dependent on a minor gene complex and that selections from types with the desired time of flowering should therefore be successful.

SUNFLOWER

This plant has been used in experiments on the analysis of the plant environment by Blackman and his colleagues, for example, adaptive changes in the growth and development induced by an alteration in light level (Blackman and Wilson, 1954), and an analysis of the effect of seasonal variations in daylight and temperature on growth in the vegetative phase (Blackman, Black and Kemp, 1955). In West Germany Schuster (1956) has found that the vegetative phase is shortened by later sowing, an effect of temperature rather than of photoperiod. The best time of sowing for fodder is mid-June, for seed towards the end of April.

Chapter XXI

GRAIN LEGUMES AND PULSES

The information available for this group of crops is more of an academic than a practical nature, since peas, the two types of beans and soybeans represent suitable material for experiments on the more fundamental aspects of growth and reproductive development. It will, therefore, be necessary to omit reference to many papers the practical significance of which is not, at the moment, apparent.

BEANS (*Phaseolus*)

Academic studies include observations on the influence of light on the loss of labelled phosphorus from leaves, absorption of cobalt by leaves in the dark and the photoreversibility of leaf and hypocotyl elongation under normal conditions and in the dark. Treatments have been recommended for the application of gibberellin to seed (Wittwer and Bukovac 1958), and gibberellin A_1 has been isolated from the seeds of runner bean. Activity increases with increase in seed size and decreases only after seeds have approached their final size (Ritzel, 1957).

The elongation of stems in Kentucky Wonder beans under different regimes is shown in Fig. 52 (from Viglierchio and Went, 1957). Night temperature is the most critical factor influencing developmental processes. This variety is day-neutral, although long photoperiod greatly improves both growth and fruit production. The Red Mexican variety of dry bean is one of the principal crops on new land in the Columbia Basin Project in the U.S.A. The predominance of coarse-textured soils and the nature of the plant's root system have made frequent irrigation necessary to avoid injury (Robins and Domingo, 1956). Reductions in yield of 20 per cent under visible moisture stress are due to reductions in number of pods before blooming, in number of pods and number of beans per pod during blooming and in bean weight during the maturing process. Plant development is retarded by stress before blooming and hastened during blooming and maturing. Irrigation before visible

314

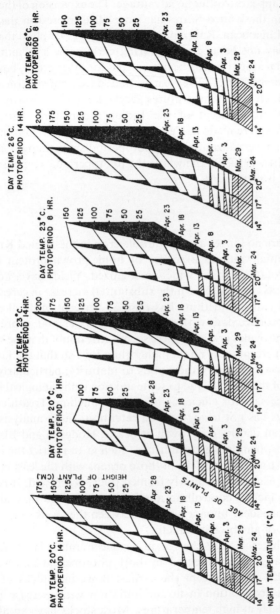

Fig. 52. Stem elongation of Kentucky wonder rust-resistant beans in regimes differing in photoperiod, day temperature and night temperature (Viglierchio and Went, 1957).

moisture stress appears to offer no advantage. The expansion of the frozen food industry in the United States has intensified interest in the erratic fruiting of the Lima bean. Rappaport and Carolus (1956) find that night temperature may not be as critical during early growth in influencing production and maturity as has been reported for other crops, but nevertheless cool temperatures after early bud development consistently delay whereas high night temperatures accelerate green maturity.

Under a research project of the Indian Council of Agricultural Research, studies were made in Calcutta (Sen Gupta, 1955) on the effect of time of sowing, vernalization and photoperiodism in mung (*Phaseolus aureus*) from 1947–1950. On the whole the photoperiodic response of the varieties tested is very feeble.

BEANS (*Vicia*)

Field beans are no longer a major arable crop in the United Kingdom but their potential value as a source of home-grown protein feeding stuff and as a rotation crop is widely recognized. Yields have, however, remained static as compared with the substantial increase in cereal yields for the past 50 years. Something less than 25 per cent of the flowers in normal crops produce pods with only three seeds per pod, representing 50 per cent of the ovules present. There seems little doubt that the successful pollination percentage is much higher than this, so that the failure of the fertilized flowers to carry their pods to maturity, particularly in the upper regions of the plant, is due to some unknown physiological factors. Tripping is necessary for efficiency of pod production. Treatment with hormone sprays has not increased pod retention. In an analysis of the influence of plant density on growth of beans, Hodgson and Blackman (1957) find that when the light gradient is such as to restrict the internal supplies of substrates, the growth of those organs with the least competitive ability, for example, the newly formed pods, is arrested. It is at this phase that the factors controlling abscission come into play and that abscission is dependent upon a balance between the levels of auxin and the production of an abscission factor.

There is a heteroblastic change in leaflet number in *Vicia faba*, the rate of change being affected by both photoperiod and temperature (Evans 1958 c). All except the earliest flowering stocks of broad beans show an acceleration in flower initiation with increase in daylength, particularly at high temperatures. Most stocks have an absolute requirement for long days for full floral development. Flower initiation

316

may also be accelerated in all except the earliest stocks by brief exposures to temperatures below 14°C. The low temperature reactions appear to proceed more rapidly at 10°C than at 4°C. Their effects increase with increasing plant age, but may nevertheless be apparent even during embryo development. At temperatures above 14°C, and particularly above 23°C, a reaction is probably restricted to the diurnal dark periods, but is operative at all stages of the life cycle, including embryo development. Its inhibitory effects may be overcome by subsequent cold treatment, and when the low temperature processes have reached saturation subsequent high temperatures are no longer inhibitory.

In Sicily, vernalization at 2° to 4°C for 32 to 35 days causes plants to flower 20 to 29 days earlier than the controls when sown in autumn but not when sown at the end of winter.

Peas

Peas hold an important place as experimental plants in physiological research, being used in studies on light action, on the photoinductive alteration of auxin metabolism, on the spectral sensitivities for leaf and stem growth of etiolated seedlings and their similarity to action spectra for photoperiodism, on the effects of gibberellic acid on shoot growth and on the complementary action of gibberellic acid and auxins (Brian and Hemming, 1955, 1958).

Although it is true that the pea has long been a classical subject for work in both genetics and physiology, research in either field has been carried out with little reference to results from the other. The few exceptions concern studies on the physiological activity of genes controlling growth in length of the internodes. Summarizing results since Wellensiek (1925) reviewed the genetics of *Pisum*, Paton and Barber (1955) describe their studies on the genetics of the wide differences in flowering behaviour which occur in commercial varieties of peas. In their combined physiological and genetical study, the two extreme varieties, William Massey (early dwarf), and Telephone (late tall), were used in grafting experiments. As previously stated (p. 98), the grafting of Massey on Telephone leads to flowering at a higher node; in reciprocal grafts, the scions of the late variety flower at the earlier (lower) node. Grafting scions to stocks of the same variety has no effect with Massey scions, but leads to earlier flowering in Telephone. It is assumed that flowering behaviour is mainly determined by the production of a flowering inhibitor in the cotyledons of late varieties which is then

317

transported to the plumule. There is some evidence that the cotyledons of Massey may also contain a substance promoting flowering. A review of the literature makes it inadvisable to exclude the possibility that an auxin activity is responsible for most of the flower inhibition transmitted across a graft, but Paton and Barber consider it is more likely that the inhibitor formed by genetically late peas is not the natural auxin IAA. Later Sprent and Barber (1957) reported on the leaching of a flower inhibitor from young cuttings of late varieties of peas.

Highkin (1955), showed experimentally that a diffusate from pea seeds contains a factor which can promote flowering in plants grown from other pea seeds, and that it can be used to replace vernalization, its effect again being to reduce the number of nodes before formation of the first flower. The pea (var. Alaska) has also been used by Leopold and Guernsey (1954) to show that treatment of seeds or seedlings with various chemical materials plus low temperatures (the 'chemical vernalization' to which other workers have since given attention) appears to be promotive of flowering.

It has been found that two late varieties, Unica and Zelka from the Netherlands, are normally vernalizable by cold treatment with respect to both flower formation and vegetative development and that these two phenomena can be separated (Highkin, 1956). A pre-treatment during germination at 20° or 26°C for up to 5 days before the optimal cold treatment results in a progressive loss of ability to be vernalized. Highkin concludes that his experiments seem to delimit the period in development which is most critical in studies of vernalization and indicate developmental stages which should be used in studies of the biochemical changes occurring during vernalization. The fact that the above pre-treatment makes the plant insensitive to cold with respect to flowering, although it remains sensitive to a cold treatment with respect to vegetative development, suggests that the effect of cold treatment can be separated into (a) a vegetative effect and (b) a reproductive effect. In subsequent work, Highkin induced variability in two homozygous strains of peas; when seeds grown at any of six constant temperatures were returned to the normal control environment, they behaved as though they were still in the constant temperatures. The seeds formed on these plants when grown in the normal control environment reverted to a normal type, but when grown in the original constant temperature reacted as though they had never been removed. Again, when two varieties differing in many genetic characters were reciprocally crossed, the F_1 population could be separated into distinct groups, depending on the temperature at which the pollen was formed (Highkin, 1957). The thermoperiodicity described by Went for vegetative growth is very important in controlling flowering behaviour in peas (Paton, 1957).

Investigations of great importance to pea-growing farmers as well as to the canning industry have been made in South Sweden on 'the growth and maturation of canning peas in an attempt to elucidate qualitative and quantitative changes in the peas during maturation. In addition, the so-called heat-unit system was studied to test its applicability under South-Swedish conditions. Factors capable of influencing the reliability of the system were also investigated (Ottosson, 1958). According to the heat-unit system, the development of a plant is determined by the sum of daily mean temperatures above a certain base temperature. In the present investigation the base temperature was taken as 5°C, and the air temperatures were used in the calculations.

'In germination trials a good correlation was found between 8° and 28°C; below 8°C the development was more rapid than might have been expected at such a low temperature. It was found that the more rapid development at low temperatures is often compensated by the fact that at higher temperatures the temperature of the soil is higher in relation to that of the air, which results in a more rapid development during the earlier stage. The greatest advantage of the heat-unit system is that it permits a more reliable planning and realisation of a sowing schedule and thereby a more even supply of raw material to the factories. The heat requirements of a pea plant vary with the light factor. In the south of Sweden the amount of light available during the middle of the summer appears to be in excess, but during the latter part of summer the amount of light available decreases because of the shortening of the days and increased cloudiness. Therefore, late varieties, if they are sown late, have greater heat requirements. Shading trials showed that in cloudy weather the light factor is often minimal, and irrigation trials that the increased requirements of the heat units during late summer is due only to a small extent to the increased moisture of the soil, but mainly to decreased availability of light. All peas except for the very late varieties are day-neutral. The late varieties are long-day plants. However, the length of the day in the south of Sweden during the actual growing season must be regarded as too long for the daylength to impede development. Analysis of the amount of light the peas are exposed to during the last 30 days before harvesting showed a very close correlation between the heat requirements and the amount of light in the years 1954, 1955 and 1956.

'The heat requirements appear to vary with the type of soil. The reason is, however, that because of varying heat capacity and heat conductibility, the temperature of a given soil varies with its type. A careful analysis of the micro-climate in different regions should often be able to even out these variations. However, the supply of nutrients, above all the availability of nitrogen, might also possibly influence the requirements of heat units. A good supply of nutrients with consequent luxurious growth sometimes increased the heat requirements. On the other hand, extreme malnutrition results in poor growth and increased rate of maturation.'

A practical measure of the heat requirements of wrinkled peas during four stages of development is as follows:

		Heat units
(1)	From sowing to visible germination	20
(2)	From visible germination to full development of the fifth node	100
(3)	From full development of the fifth node to full development of the first flowering node, *per node development*	40
(4)	From full development of the first flowering node to normal harvest time	310

Ottosson (*loc. cit.*) classifies different methods for determining the degree of maturity under four headings:

(1) Mechanical apparatuses which measure the hardiness of the peas.
(2) Chemical methods, which are based on the chemical composition of the peas, as determined by chemical and physiological processes.
(3) Methods based on the determination of the specific weight of the peas, either by the sink test in brine or by weighing and measuring the volume.
(4) Morphological methods which are based on the weight or size of the seeds or from ratios between the pea plant and certain parts of it.

As an outcome of his study on the measurement of time-to-flowering in peas (see p. 35), Hänsel (1954 a) attempts to explain the apparently obligate daylength neutrality of early-flowering varieties with a small number of sterile nodes by the very early differentiation of the first flower primordium (5th day from germination, as found by Haupt in 1952 (see Haupt, 1957) in the early-flowering variety, Kleine Rheinländerin). Later maturing varieties which differentiate their first flower primordium at a higher node are more sensitive to daylength because in this case the length of day is one of the factors which determine the node at which the first flower will appear. Daylength causes the number of sterile nodes in later flowering varieties merely to vary, since in these varieties an increase of photoperiod from 10 to 16 hours increases the number of sterile nodes by only 2 to 3. Hänsel therefore doubts that it is possible to breed late-flowering varieties with many sterile nodes which are daylength-neutral.

Hänsel (1954 b) also used peas to study the hereditary character of the relation between number of nodes and time-to-flowering under long days. It was shown that selection by number of nodes can be used to distinguish between groups differing in their time-to-flowering, although types deviating from the average relation may be overlooked. On the average, a genotypical delay of 2 days in flowering time corresponds to an increase of one sterile node.

In experiments at the University of Pretoria, it was found that pea plants flower under both 16- and 12-hour photoperiods, but more rapidly with the former. A longer photoperiod and a 27°C day temperature reduced and a 21°C night temperature increased the percentage of nitrogen. A full day's sunlight with an 18°C day temperature and a 15°C or natural night temperature results in the highest dry weight and total nitrogen content.

PIGEON PEA

Trials have been made in Calcutta on the response to variable sowing dates and photoperiods of three varieties of arhar (*Cajanus cajan*). The photoperiodic response is feeble but all three show short-day characteristics, flowering slightly earlier in a 10-hour day than in a 12-hour or 14-hour day (Sen Gupta, 1955).

SOYBEAN

Frequent references were made in the early chapters to the use of the soybean, and most frequently the Biloxi variety, as a botanical guinea-pig in some of the outstanding studies on growth and reproduction, for example, the work of K. C. Hamner and his associates, and studies on light (Borthwick and Parker, 1952), the promotion of floral initiation by auxin (De Zeeuw and Leopold, 1956), the interaction of auxin and temperature (Leopold and Guernsey, 1953 a and b), the photoreversibility of flower initiation (Downs, 1956) and the influence of daylength on nodule formation (Bonnier and Sironval, 1956), to mention only a few. Here we shall discuss some investigations not already dealt with.

There has been much discussion among growers, agronomists and others in the United States of America concerned with the production and quality of soybeans as to the effect of high and low temperatures

GRAIN LEGUMES

during critical periods of plant growth. A number of investigators have found temperature to be one of the major environmental factors affecting the growth of the soybean plant and the oil content of the seed. R. W. Howell and J. L. Cartter, of the U.S. Regional Soybean Laboratory studied the relation between the oil content of the soybean seed and the maximum temperatures for 10-day periods beginning 50 days before pod maturity. They found that, in the north, high temperatures exert greater influence than low temperatures, temperature 20 to 30 days before maturity being more closely associated with oil level than temperatures earlier or later; in the south, minimum temperatures exert more influence on oil level than do high temperatures.

In controlled growth chambers, day temperatures exert a major effect on plant height, night temperatures have little effect. When three chambers with constant controlled day and night temperatures were used it was found that day temperatures during the pod filling period exert a marked effect on oil content. Increasing day temperature from 70° to 85°F results in substantial increase in oil content. On the other hand, temperatures exert very little influence on protein content or non-protein nitrogen content of the seed. Under controlled environments, temperatures also exert a major influence on the type of oil as well as the quantity of oil. Extremely high temperatures of 98°, 110° and 120°F for a 2-week period cause reduction in the growth rate. Optimal temperature for seed set is between 80° and 90°F, with a rapid decline in the number of pods set and a rapid increase in the number of flowers aborted as the temperatures rise to 105°F. In these growth chamber studies, moisture was always adequate and the temperature of the growth solution uniform during day and night. High temperatures occurring in fields during drought may give different results.

Figure 53 is from the article by Blaney and Hamner (1957) on certain interrelations between effects of temperature, photoperiod and dark period on floral initiation of Biloxi soybean. The authors discuss the possible nature of the endogenous rhythm which they observed and its relationship to the photoperiodic results; they present alternative hypotheses to explain the results obtained with cycles of different durations at both normal and low temperatures. K. K. Nanda and K. C. Hamner reported on similar work to the Seminar on 'Modern Developments in Plant Physiology' at the University of Delhi in April, 1957. They consider that the rhythmical process which they observe is inhibitory in nature, with phases of increasing and decreasing ability

322

to inhibit the flowering stimulus. It does not, however, appear to be related to diurnal fluctuations in either auxin concentrations or in metabolism; these fluctuations appear to be the result rather than the cause of this endogenous rhythm.

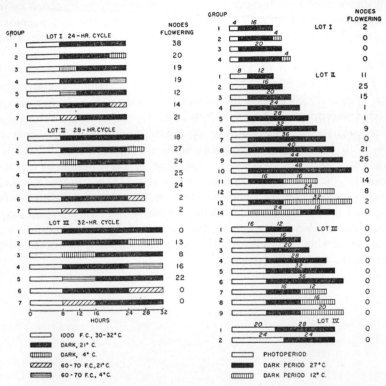

Fig. 53. Floral initiation in Biloxi soybean. Interrelations between effects of temperature, photoperiod and dark period. (*Left*) Experiment 4. Cycles employing 8-hour photoperiod and dark periods of several durations with variable conditions of temperature and light intensity interposed between photoperiod and dark period, and flowering response to each. (*Right*) Experiment 5: Cycles employing photoperiod of constant duration and dark periods of various durations with low temperatures intercalated into dark periods for various durations, and flowering responses to each. Numerals above various areas represent duration of exposure to conditions shown in the legend at bottom of figure (Blaney and Hamner, 1957).

Work concerned with the antagonistic reactions between vegetative growth and sexual development and arising out of the chance discovery that soybeans can be forced into flowering with nicotine sulphate, has reviewed the interaction of variety, photoperiod, size of plant and auxins and antiauxins in the flowering of this short-day species (Fisher, 1955). Results support the hypothesis that flowering is conditioned by a balance between auxin produced in young tissues and a flower-forming substance produced in older leaves. Flowering may be hastened by (*a*) short days, (*b*) a high ratio of mature to immature leaves, (*c*) removal of the young leaves, or (*d*) spraying the plants, particularly the young leaves, with nicotine sulphate. Although the greatest proportion of soybean literature is of American origin, studies have also been made in Europe including the U.S.S.R., and in India, Indonesia and Japan. Sen Gupta (1955) studied the effects of varied sowing times and controlled photoperiods. Keleny (1959) in his report to the Government of Indonesia on the Development of Leguminous Crops has observed the relative sensitivity of soybean varieties in Indonesia and finds that American varieties grown for some time in the Philippines are less sensitive than varieties imported from the U.S.A. direct. Japanese studies include that by Tadao Koyama on the effects of high temperature and short-day treatments applied in the young stage on plant shape and date of blooming of three varieties in Hokkaido. Response was most noticeable in middle and late-maturing varieties, not in the early maturing variety, Okuhara No. 1.

Chapter XXII

CEREALS

The group of plants which includes such basic world food crops as wheat, rice, maize and the sorghums and millets deserves much more attention than can be given in the last chapter of an already overcrowded review. These are among the first crop plants which should be the subject of the reviews suggested in Chapter I, describing the present state of scientific and practical knowledge of the nature of their responses to the primary and secondary factors of the environment, and indicating the main gaps in that knowledge and the type of research, national or international, which might be undertaken. Within the limited space available here, reference will be made only to certain data which relate to the distribution of these crops, to a greater understanding of their morphology, behaviour and responses, and to the manipulation of the processes of growth and reproduction for economic purposes.

A major contribution to our knowledge of the vernalization of cereals has been made in the long series of articles of F. G. Gregory, O. N. Purvis and their associates at the Research Institute of Plant Physiology in the Imperial College of Science and Technology, London (see bibliography under Gregory, Purvis, Gott, Hussey). There is also the work of Cooper (1957) on the developmental analysis of populations of cereals and herbage grasses based on their response to low-temperature vernalization. A close correlation was found between the climatic or agronomic origin of each population and its response to low temperature; response to low temperature was found only in one ecological group of wheats, namely, the winter varieties from western Europe.

Nuttonson (1953) has studied the relationships of wheat and climate on the basis of data from stations in North America and from some thermally analogous areas in the Soviet Union and Finland, and has used phenological stages—sowing, emergence, heading and ripening—in ascertaining the thermal and photothermal requirements of this

325

crop. The summations of day-degrees were calculated from monthly mean temperatures and involved the following steps:

(1) subtracting the 40°F base temperature from each of the pertinent monthly means,

(2) multiplying the remainder for each month by the number of those days of the month which are included in the time interval under consideration, the product thus obtained being the total effective day-degree summation in that month, and

(3) adding the products (effective day-degrees) of all the months within the time interval under consideration to obtain the day-degree summation for the required developmental stage of wheat.

Fig. 54 reproduced from Nuttonson presents an average growth/ development curve showing the mean summation of photothermal units required by Thatcher spring wheat throughout the greater part of the various climatic, latitudinal and altitudinal areas of the spring wheat belt of North America. The length of day of the average emergence time of wheat at various latitudes in the Soviet Union has been recorded as follows (see Fig. 55):

47° N.	15 April	13·5 hours
52° N.	1 May	15·0 hours
57° N.	12 May	16·3 hours
62° N.	22 May	18·2 hours

Other general works include Pohjakallio's review (1957) on the relation between light climate and crop growth in Finland. Cereals do not ripen in North Lapland, the effect of the continuous day being insufficient to permit the extension northward of the limit of cultivation. Winter rye and early barley varieties are cultivated a little north of the 67th parallel; the northern limit of spring wheat and oats is roughly the 66th parallel. The importance of the interaction between genotype and night temperature in the cereal producing areas of the United States is stressed and measured by Grafius (1956). A phenoclimogram has been evolved for spring barley in the south-western clay district of the Netherlands by W. Wilten of the National Committee for Malting Barley (1956).

An important general consideration with regard to cereal cultivation and utilization is the effect of defoliation either under experimental conditions (see section on oats) or in the field by the grazing animal or the cutter knife on the subsequent yield of grain. Holliday (1956) has

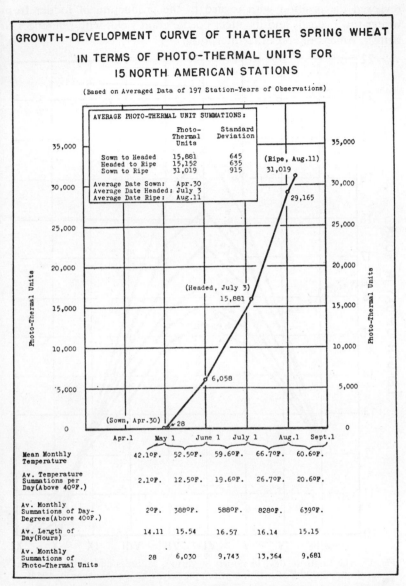

Fig. 54. Growth-development curve of Thatcher spring wheat in terms of photo-thermal units for 15 North American stations (Nuttonson, 1955).

327

reviewed the position with regard to the production of fodder from winter-sown cereals and its effect on the grain yield, with references to British, American and other literature.

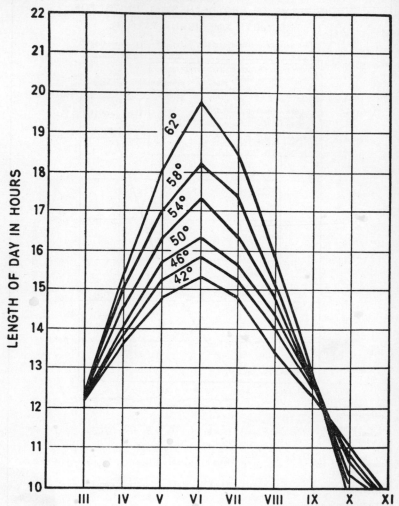

Fig. 55. The length of day, in hours, at various latitudes and during different months (on the 20th of each month) in the Soviet Union (Nuttonson, 1955).

Investigations have been made at the University of Geneva on the course of reproductive development in cereals, with special reference to the photophase, vegetative hybridization and 'Michurinism' (Stroun,

328

1956). Mathon, working at the University of Poitiers, has published a series of articles and scientific notes on the developmental physiology of the cereals, wheat, barley, oats, rye and *Aegilops* (most recent reference, Mathon, 1955). He has also studied the ecology of development of *Triticum turgidum compositum* (Mathon, 1956), 'grafting' of embryos in the Gramineae (Mathon, 1957), and the influence of very long wave radiation on the formation of the ear (Fustec-Mathon and Mathon, 1958). Mathon (1959) reviews his experiments on the rhythm of development, vernalization and photoperiodism, and their relation to phytogeography.

BARLEY

British physiologists and farmers are interested in subjects such as the physiological causes of differences in grain yield between varieties and in the seasonal variations which occur in the nitrogen content of the grain, a matter of great importance in the malting industry.

In a field experiment at Rothamsted, with the high mean yield of 49 cwt of grain per acre, Watson, Thorne and French (1958) found that the varieties Proctor and Herta produced 10 to 15 per cent more grain than Plumage-Archer on plots that received no nitrogenous fertilizer. When nitrogen was applied the difference was increased to about 30 per cent, because the higher nitrogen supply caused the Plumage-Archer crop to lodge and did not increase its yield, while Proctor and Herta remained standing. The three varieties did not differ in leaf-area index nor in net assimilation rate before ear emergence, so that all had the same total dry weight. After ear emergence, the leaf area indices of Proctor and Plumage-Archer were nearly equal, but that of Herta was smaller. Assuming that the photosynthetic efficiency of the leaves continued to be the same in all varieties, the higher grain yields of Proctor and Herta cannot be attributed to greater production of dry matter by the leaves, either before or after ear emergence. A pot experiment on plants with shaded ears confirmed that the dry matter contributed to grain yield by unit leaf area was nearly equal in all the varieties.

The general conclusion is that the source of the higher grain yield is additional photosynthesis in the ears. The evidence for this is indirect and inconclusive, depending mainly on elimination of the other possibilities. Direct evidence will be difficult to obtain, because the

L*

relative performance of the varieties in pot culture appears to differ from that in the field; it will be necessary to devise a technique for measuring total photosynthesis by the ears of cereals that is practicable on a field scale. There is some evidence that the additional photosynthesis by the ears of Proctor and Herta was associated with a greater weight of ears at the time when they emerged and a larger surface area of ears per unit area of land, but whether it is wholly attributable to an increased amount of photosynthetic tissue in the ears, or whether increased photosynthetic efficiency of the ears, especially of Herta, is also involved, is not known.

There may perhaps be some connection between these results and the observations made in Japan by Kinebuchi and others (1957), who recorded that the number of sterile spikelets in the lower part of a barley ear increases with early sowing, and under environmental factors such as high temperature, shade, long day, drought and high soil moisture. A top-dressing of nitrogen 15 to 7 days before heading favours normal development of the spikelets.

Humphries (1958) has also used the variety Herta for studies on the effect of removal of part of the root system on the subsequent growth of root and shoot and on the production of ears. Removal of part or the whole of the root in barley (and rye) leads to a differential effect on the growth rate of shoot and root. The growth rate of the shoot decreases with increasing amount of root removal, due apparently to the supply of nutrients to the shoot being retarded while the supply to the root is still adequate. A possible explanation of variability in the top/root ratio is that the roots and shoots are in competition for nutrients absorbed by the root and carbohydrates manufactured by the shoot. When the mineral supply is limiting, the root will grow relatively more than the shoot, while a reduction of photosynthetic products will have an immediate effect on root growth. If the roots of plants grown in water culture are completely removed before they have attained their maximum shoot number, there is a significant increase in number of ears at harvest. If the roots are removed when shoot number is beginning to fall, the number of ears is reduced. This may be due to a temporary diversion of carbohydrate to the shoots when the roots are excised (Humphries, *loc. cit.*).

An unusually large proportion of the barley grown in Britain in 1957 was very high in nitrogen, thus rendering the grain unsuitable for malting for brewery purposes. More nitrogen means more protein, and hence a lower content of the carbohydrate which yields valuable extract for the brewer. Certain conditions and practices may increase the nitrogen content of the grain, for example:

late cultivation,
late sowing,
dry weather during the late spring months, especially April and May, growing the barley on soils rich in organic nitrogen,
soil acidity,
giving late top-dressings of nitrogenous fertilizer, and
increasing beyond a certain point the total supply of nitrogenous fertilizer.

Late cultivation and late sowing were both dictated by weather conditions in 1957, but the dry weather in late spring of that year is regarded as the main factor in producing the high nitrogen content.

Reference is now made to several papers which deal with temperature relationships, vernalization and winter resistance of barley varieties. In a study on root morphology of germinating seeds, Hänsel (1952) found that vernalization had the following effects:

The lateral spread of the first three roots of partially germinated seeds decreased after cold treatment; the reduction is probably accentuated by a longer duration of the treatment.

The degree of reduction of root spread is determined by the growth stage of the germinal roots and/or humidity during cold treatment. The lateral spread of roots which had not been visible at the end of cold treatment is greater than of those already 5 mm long. The reduction of lateral spread after cold treatment occurs in both winter and spring varieties, indicating that it is not an effect of vernalization *in sensu stricto* (= increase of the ripeness-to-flower), but rather of the method of cold treatment (= exposure of germinated seeds to low temperature).

A number of germinal roots are killed by rapid thawing of vernalized seeds, while all are preserved, even in summer barley and after very long chilling, if the seeds are thawed and moistened carefully. The reduction in root spread occurs also when all roots remain intact. This point is of practical importance in transplanting vernalized seed.

Interruption of the cold treatment by room temperature causes a strikingly different degree of damage in the germinal roots of a cold-resistant and a cold-susceptible variety, although there is no difference in the reaction of the shoot. This is important in testing and selection for cold resistance.

CEREALS

Following on a study concerning the influence of vernalization on lamina length of the first and second leaves of spring and winter barley (Hänsel, 1953), it was later found that both winter and spring varieties react markedly to vernalization by a reduction in length of lamina of the first leaf. It is therefore assumed that this reaction is an effect of the treatment (= cold exposure of germinated seed) which is independent of the vernalization process itself.

In a study of the changes in the condition known as ripeness-to-flower (Blühreife) which occur in winter barley during the winter season in Austria, Hänsel (1949) found that optimal ripeness-to-flower is reached by different varieties at different times from early December to late February. Continued exposure to cold does not appear to affect optimal ripeness-to-flower once this has been attained. The number of initiated spikelets per ear then declines, but differentiation of initiated spikelets, growth of the apex and shooting increase. With increasing ripeness-to-flower the intensity of initiation of primordia is greater than that of extension growth, but beyond a certain stage of differentiation this relation is reversed. The first visible reproductive processes, namely, initiation and differentiation of ears, occur even in 12-hour days once the cold requirement has been met. A maximum rate of development due to optimal overall conditions for reproductive development probably leads to the initiation of fewer spikelets per ear than a development hampered by lack of ripeness-to-flower or short days. Temperatures of $0°$ to $10°C$, and even of $-4°C$ have a vernalizing effect, both on partially germinated seed and on dormant seedlings from autumn sowings. Reproductive development thus apparently starts at a lower temperature than growth.

An example of a Soviet study based on the concept of phasic development is that by Skripčinskiĭ (1956) on barley varieties differing in their winter resistance and phasic development, namely:

winter-hardy types, Krasnyĭ Dar and Stavropoljskiĭ 7,
non-hardy spring variety Kruglik 0188/49, and
indeterminate types usually considered as winter forms, Pallidum 17 and Kruglik 021.

There is evidence that Krasnyĭ Dar and Stavropoljskiĭ 7 (biologically winter types) do not react to change in daylength. Kruglik 0188/49 reacts under continuous day to the extent of initiating anthers in the florets and under 8-hour day ear differentiation with flower initials is observed. Kruglik 021 and Pallidum 17 also react to changes in daylength.

Under continuous light they achieve the same stage of development as the spring type Kruglik 0188/49, but under an 8-hour day they behave as winter types. This confirms that the three types, Kruglik 0188/49, Kruglik 021 and Pallidum 17 are biologically spring forms, the difference between them being in their reaction to daylength. Kruglik 0188/49 is more a short-day type than are Kruglik 021 or Pallidum 17.

The data from observations on the extent to which winter resistance is affected by daylength confirm that in different barley varieties two forms are evolved in regard to overwintering. One form acquires a winter character by which it is possible to complete the vernalization phase during autumn. This prevents further development until chilling enhances frost resistance. The same result may be achieved by spring forms which cannot pass the photophase in the short days of autumn. The adaptation to hibernation in annual plants may arise not only by their acquiring a long vernalization stage but also by being grown under the particular conditions for passing the light stage of development. In a population comprising spring varieties and forms able to pass the light phase in short autumn photoperiods, there may be specimens which can pass this phase only in longer day. When sown in autumn, the former would inevitably perish during the winter but the latter would be preserved. As a result of such selection, the constitution of the population would be changed and in the second autumn sowing, seed of the unaffected plants would produce winter-hardy types. In the absence of such preliminary knowledge, this would give the impression of 'transformation', i.e. the converting of biologically spring types to biologically winter types.

The action spectrum for the photoperiodic control of flowering in short-day plants indicates that all visible light is active, with two regions of maximum effectiveness, one in the red and the other in the blue-violet (Borthwick, Hendricks and Parker, 1956). With these data available, a comparison with the action spectrum for a long-day plant would show any points of similarity or difference between the initial reactions controlling flowering of the two types of plants. For this purpose, Borthwick, Hendricks and Parker (1948) used Wintex barley, a facultative winter type, one that flowers and fruits readily without special low temperature treatments. It was already known that barley could be induced to flower by interrupting a dark period that would normally keep the plants vegetative. It would thus be possible to examine critically the quality of light most effective in promoting flowering.

The action spectrum for the production of spikes of barley is very similar to those preventing floral initiation in soybeans and *Xanthium*. The long-wave-length cut-off beyond 7,200 Å, the positions of maximum effectiveness between 6,000 and 6,600 Å, and the region from 5,000 to 5,600 Å in which effectiveness changes rapidly with small changes in wave-lengths, coincide very closely. Minimum effectiveness seems to be near 4,800 Å for all three plants. This indicates that essentially the same pigment is involved in transferring energy to the photoperiodic reaction both in long- and short-day plants. A possible working hypothesis is that flowering in both types is controlled by the same substance and that effectiveness is due to optimal concentration.

Barley was also the experimental plant used by Hussey and Gregory (1954) to study the effect of auxin on flowering behaviour; these workers suggest that the earlier results of Leopold and Thimann (1949) may be evidence of a post-initiation effect of auxin on the developing ear, and in this sense may be said to promote or inhibit flowering, but there is no proof that auxin has any determinable effect on flower initiation. Passing reference should be made to the observation by Johnson and Obolensky (1954) that treatment with ultrasonic vibrations gave in every replicate appreciably earlier heading in Olli (early) and Montcalm (medium) varieties, suggesting that the breeder's earliest varieties, for which further genetic improvement may be difficult to attain, might be profitably treated with vibrations.

BUCKWHEAT

This crop must be included here, although not a member of the Gramineae. It has been considered as photoperiodically indeterminate, since it will produce flowers over a wide range of photoperiods, but these do influence time and rate of flowering as well as habit of growth. Skok and Scully (1955) found that short photoperiods promote floral development, fruiting and lateral shoot production, but depress elongation of the main axis. Long photoperiods favour growth of the main axis and an increase in total plant weight, but depress growth of lateral shoots, floral development and fruit production. Although both floral and vegetative development is photoperiodically controlled, this control operates through separate mechanisms, as indicated by results of experiments involving interruption of the dark or light period. Floral development is chiefly associated with a dark-dependent mechanism, which appears to be similar to that controlling floral initiation in a typical short-day plant. Elongation of the main axis is chiefly associated with a light-dependent mechanism.

334

CEREALS

Maize

This is one of the major world crops which would merit a special study at an early date, starting with a consideration of its possible wild ancestors and centres of origin, the present distribution of the crop, whether grown for grain or green matter, the characteristics of growth and reproduction of the crop and its relatives and ancestors, and the possibility of extending its cultivation into new zones where existing or new genotypes would be exposed to primary and secondary factors of the environment outside the present range of distribution. In a review of the problems involved in the extension of maize cultivation into northern temperate regions, Harper (1955 a) has noted the remarkable spread of the crop northwards in U.S.A. and Canada, into regions of lower temperature and shorter growing season than are characteristic of the Corn Belt of U.S.A.

In Europe, the cultivation of maize for grain is important in parts of the Danube basin, U.S.S.R., Italy and Spain, all of which (apart from Spain) lie further north than the American Corn Belt. The main European maize-growing areas and the Corn Belt have summer temperatures of 70°F or above and winter mean temperatures of above 50°F. The approximate climatic requirements for high yields of the crop are summer temperatures of 75°F with night temperatures of 58°F and a growing season of 140 days. However, strains exist which grow 20 ft tall and require 300 days to mature, as well as dwarf strains reaching 2 ft in height which will mature in 60 to 70 days. European breeders have been conducting trials with American hybrids which range from Wisconsin 1600, which requires 70 days to reach maturity, to Dixie 11, which requires about 150 days. (These 'maturity classes' refer to the performance of varieties in Minnesota, and these values should be doubled to give reasonable expectations for Northern Europe.) In general, the height, number of tillers produced, and weight and number of leaves are correlated with the length of the growing season required for maturity. The growing season is usually determined as the interval between the last killing frost of spring and the first killing frost of autumn. Varieties differ in frost resistance, and so the potential growing season for maize in one area may differ markedly from one strain to another.

Harper discusses a number of important factors in maize cultivation and adaptation, such as date of planting, disease resistance, cold germination, seed pre-treatment with fungicides and rainfall. The length of day is another factor which influences the rate of development and ripening of

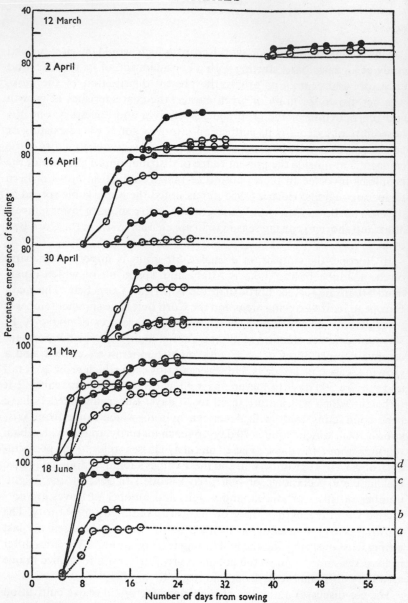

Fig. 56. Time curves for the emergence of four varieties of maize from six sowing dates in Oxford in the spring of 1952. *a*, Nodak 301; *b*, Wisconsin 275; *c*, White Horsetooth; *d*, Country Gentleman (Harper, Landragin and Ludwig, 1955).

maize. Over a long period of maize cultivation, races have been evolved which are adjusted to the daylength characteristic of particular latitudes. In general, the shortening of daylength from that to which a variety is adapted results in earlier flowering and decreased leaf area. This feature is made use of when choosing varieties of maize for use as fodder crops, for varieties from the southern U.S.A. will have flowering delayed by the long days of northern temperate regions and will produce excess leafage. For this reason, Virginian White Horsetooth maize became a popular green fodder and silage maize in Great Britain, although it is now being replaced by hybrids.

Studies relating to the effects of seed pre-treatment or of environmental conditions in the field during cultivation include Andrew and others (1956) on maturation and yield as influenced by climate and technique of production, Henkelj and others (1955) on the effect on development and ripening of subjecting the seed to fluctuating temperatures, Mihalovskiĭ and Meljnik (1956) on hastening development and ripening by vernalization of seed, Genter and others (1956) on the effects of location, hybrid, fertilizer and rate of planting on the oil and protein contents of grain, Lana (1956) on the effects of plant population and seasons on the performance of sweet varieties for canning, Inselberg (1956) on the effect of increase in sowing rate or prevention of pollination of one or two earshoots on the development of earshoots in dent varieties, Jones (1956) on growth and development of three population intensities of hybrid maize under irrigated or natural conditions, Stacy and others (1957) on the joint effects of maximum temperatures and rainfall on yields, and Petinov and Ivanov (1957) on the effect of short day during the sprouting period on the water regime and acceleration of development. Harper and his associates in the Department of Agriculture, Oxford, have published a series of papers on the influence of the environment on seed and seedling mortality (most recent reference Harper, 1955 b).

Nuttonson (see Murneek and Whyte, 1948) demonstrated that in considering a certain period of development of a wheat variety, for example, over a number of years, the product of the average daily temperature and daylength is a much more constant factor than the number of days. Workers in the Netherlands have found that this thermal unit accumulation also applies to maize (Dijkhuis, 1956). In 1955, complete synchronization of flowering was obtained by sowing the experimental varieties with the interval indicated by the difference in the heat unit accumulations from sowing to flowering in 1954. The computation of these was made on the basis of both air and soil temperatures. It appears that air temperatures alone are adequate, provided that sowing is done on the same type of soil as in the previous year. A more accurate heat unit accumulation can be computed from the addition of the heat unit accumulation from sowing to emergence (soil temperatures) and that from emergence to flowering (air temperatures).

MILLETS

Millets belonging to a number of genera of the Gramineae are very important food crops of the tropics and subtropics. Nanda, Grover and Chinoy (1957 b) have used Indian varieties of the following species in their studies at the Botany Department of the University of Delhi on the relation between growth and reproductive development: *Panicum miliaceum, Setaria italica, Echinochloa frumentacea, Eleusine coracana* and *Paspalum scrobiculatum*. Seeds were sown at five different dates at intervals of 35 days between 5 April and 24 August. Methods of growth analysis developed by F. G. Gregory were used.

The vegetative period is reduced by a delay in time of sowing. The regular differences observed in the vegetative periods of main shoots in progressively later sowings are thought to indicate that reproductive development is influenced by environment. Under natural conditions, the vegetative period of each of these millets appears to determine the pattern of stem elongation. Apparently stem growth does not take place until the growing points have changed from a vegetative to a reproductive condition. With earlier sowings and thus longer vegetative periods, increase in height before the change in the growing point is probably due to elongation of leaf sheath; similar observations had already been made for wheat (Chinoy, 1950; Chinoy and Nanda, 1951). Dry matter production in *Panicum miliaceum* and *Setaria italica* is a function of the vegetative period (Nanda, Grover and Chinoy, 1957 a). Tillering is also determined by the length of the vegetative period, being suppressed by the acceleration in flowering caused by late sowing (Fig. 57). The length of the vegetative period therefore also affects other components of growth besides stem growth, a subject with which the Delhi school will deal later. It is considered that the interaction of endogenous auxin and other nutrients affects the synthesis or stabilization of the nuclear material as a result of which morphogenetic changes take place which lead the meristem towards reproduction. The basipetal succession in the initiation and flowering of lateral branches is considered to be brought about by the inhibition caused by the developing branch above and its release after its ear emergence. The alternative inhibition and its release are probably due to the differential effects of endogenous auxin concentrations on DNA/RNA ratio in the meristem.

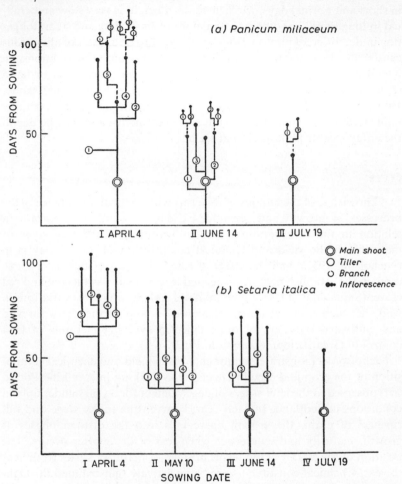

Fig. 57 (a) *Panicum miliaceum*. Diagrammatic representation of plants under different sowings showing the number of tillers and branches as well as the lengths of vegetative periods (in days) of main shoots, tillers and branches.
 (b) *Setaria italica*. Diagrammatic representation of plants under different sowings showing the numbers of tillers and their vegetative periods (Nanda, Grover and Chinoy, 1957 a).

Nanda (1958) continued the studies on *Panicum miliaceum* by observing the effect of short day, normal day and long day on stem elongation.

flowering, tillering, and branching of plants. Flowering occurred only in short days and normal days. Stem elongation is very much accelerated in short and normal days, while increase in height is very slow and gradual in long days. The differences in mode of branching and stem elongation under different photoperiods are thought to be a result of alterations caused by these treatments in flowering behaviour. Observations on lateral bud development have also been made on pearl millet or bajra (*Pennisetum typhoideum*), in relation to its flowering (Nanda and Chinoy, 1958). Pollen sterility in axillary spikes is common, is considerably influenced by differential photoinductive treatments, and may be due to the unfavourable photoperiod at Delhi.

Oats

A knowledge of the biology of this crop, with particular reference to the processes of growth and reproductive development, is important in relation to the distribution of oat cultivation, the effect of stage of maturity on the yield and chemical composition of an oat hay crop (Nicholson, 1957), and the effect of rate of sowing of oats as a nurse crop on the establishment of associated legumes such as lucerne and red clover (Smith *et al.*, 1954). Morphological and physiological variations in wild oats such as *Avena fatua*, *A. ludoviciana* and hybrids between wild and cultivated oats, are of importance in evolving methods of field control in Great Britain (Thurston, 1957).

Nicholson demonstrated major changes in yield and chemical composition of the crop and certain effects of haymaking in Ayr Line Potato oats observed in the later stages of development for 3 years under upland conditions in Scotland. In each year, between the milky stage and full ripeness of grain, the growth curve falls into the distinct phases of growth, maturity and senescence when loss of dry matter occurs. The position of the peak yield in terms of stage of maturity varies from year to year. Chemical constituents are being actively redistributed throughout the plant during the experimental period; with the exception of crude fibre and calcium, all constituents tend to be concentrated in the grain with advancing maturity. The tentative conclusion is that, in the high rainfall areas, cutting between the late milky and late cheesy stages should give optimal results. Pestalozzi (1956) studied the effect of temperature and rainfall upon the length of time taken for oats to reach the yellow-ripe stage from sowing, in trials over 6 years within the latitudes 65 to 69° N., the economic limit for the growing of oats in Norway.

Wiggans (1956) also finds that seasonal temperature is the primary factor affecting maturity in oats sown at different dates. A delay of 3 to 4 days in seeding in April or early May in Iowa represents a delay of one day in maturity.

Several studies have been made on the characteristics of tillering, sometimes in relation to photoperiod. The undisturbed main stem does not appear to be affected by tillers, although translocation of nutrients can take place under certain conditions, for example, when blades are removed from the main stem or tillers, and when panicles are removed and blades remain intact (Labanauskas and Dungan, 1956). Various combinations of defoliation, defloration and removal of tillers of field-grown plants were tested just before anthesis, when stem and leaf growth was nearly complete, and it would be likely that elaborated carbohydrates and protein would be used largely in the maturation of the grain. Main stems yield much more than undivided tillers; the yield of these declines from the first one formed to the last. Main stems with leaf blades intact give grain yields 70 to 108 per cent greater than those from defoliated main stems. The performance of any stem appears to be influenced by the favourableness of conditions surrounding other stems on the same plant.

In trials at Bangor, North Wales, spring and winter defoliation of S.147 oats significantly reduced the number of productive tillers, grain yields (particularly after winter defoliation) and straw yields. Nitrogen has no effect on tiller numbers, but increases grain yields of non-defoliated and spring-defoliated plants, and straw yields under all treatments (Davies, 1956).

When over 100 varieties from the World Oat Collection were sown at Ames, Iowa, it was found that the average number of fertile tillers per plant was lower for spring than for winter varieties, although certain spring varieties produce nearly as many as the highest-tillering winter varieties. The tillering capacities are relatively constant from year to year, and there is little relationship between the heading date of spring varieties and their tillering capacity (Frey and Wiggans, 1957). Highly significant differences are noted in the production of tillers when varieties are grown under different temperatures and photoperiods (Wiggans and Frey, 1957). With sowing at weekly intervals from early April, the number of head-producing tillers per plant increases for the first five sowing dates and then decreases. There is, however, no marked decrease in the photosynthetic surface area nor in the total dry weight of top growth unless the sowing has been delayed until after the first week of

May. Sowings in that week produce the maximum number of head-producing culms per plant. Increasing the seeding rate tends to reduce the number of tillers per plant. No variety grown in a 9- or 12-hour photoperiod produces heads within 90 days after sowing, but if the 9-hour photoperiod is supplemented with one hour of light at midnight, head-producing tillers are formed. Plants grown at 58°F need 4 to 9 days longer to produce heads than those grown at 70°F. The shortest period from sowing to heading in all varieties occurred under 18- and 24-hour photoperiods.

RICE

In spite of the great amount of scientific data and practical experience which have been obtained on this major world crop, frequently so highly sensitive to slight changes in daylength, in Japan (Morinaga, 1954, for review of 39 Japanese papers on photoperiodism), India (Ghose *et al.*, 1956), the countries of South-east Asia, the United States of America and elsewhere, it cannot be claimed that the relationship between the developmental physiology, the primary factors of the environment and the geographical distribution and introduction of the innumerable varieties is in any way clear. There does again appear to be a need for a global review of the present state of knowledge and experience by a fully qualified agricultural physiologist; this would obviously bring out gaps in our knowledge or inexplicable experimental results and crop behaviours, particularly in relation to latitudinal distribution, which should then be the subject of a new series of planned experiments under the auspices of the appropriate Working Party of the International Rice Commission. Morinaga and Kuriyama (1954) reported on an earlier series of co-operative studies on photoperiodism, and on the photoperiodic responses of Javanese and Indian varieties. In the meantime, reference will be made to some recent studies in order to indicate the current trends of research (see review of literature on photoperiodism in rice by the Dutch worker, Best, 1959).

As far as temperature is concerned, workers at the National Institute of Agricultural Science in Tokyo are analyzing the developmental factors which determine yield and yield prediction, with particular reference to the mechanism of ripening. Recent work has been concerned with the effects of temperatures and light intensities and their combined actions, and with the effects of the range of daily temperature, both at different stages of growth, on the ripening of rice plants. Workers further north at the Aomori Agricultural Experiment Station find that the optimal temperature for flowering under natural conditions seems to lie between a daily maximum of 29·5° to 32·5°C and a daily minimum of 19·5 to 22·5°C. Further research at Tokyo shows that plants subjected to normal night temperatures and high night temperatures (7°C above normal) throughout their life do not differ in times of heading, but that high night temperatures at the young seedling or tillering stages inhibit growth.

In trials in Rio Grande do Sul, Bernardes (1956) sowed fourteen varieties at 15-day intervals from 15 September to 15 December. Days from germination to flowering decrease in later sowings, but the varieties differ in this respect, as also in days from flowering to maturation; for all varieties this latter period is shortest with sowings between 15 October and 15 November. The effects of a sequence of pre-sowing hardening treatments, namely

soaking seed in water for a certain period,
keeping the seed in air in a wet condition for a certain period, and
air-drying the seed until completely dry,

have been observed by Ariyanayagam (1953) in Ceylon. Gangulee (1955) reports on experiments in Arkansas and Texas in U.S.A. and at the Presidency College, Calcutta, on the relation between sowing time and date of ear emergence. Gangulee confirmed the earlier finding of Beachell (1945) that the variety Caloro is strongly sensitive to short day while the varieties Nira and Fortuna are less sensitive. Aman varieties tend to flower mainly in the autumn and rarely in the spring, while non-aman varieties flower evenly throughout the year when sown at different dates. Gangulee suggests that all aman varieties are to be regarded as short-day plants, but that the others do not form a homogeneous group, and queries whether there may not be some correlation between plant height, grain size and sensitivity to daylength.

Most of the literature on rice naturally deals with the photoperiodic response, relative sensitivity of varieties, and reaction to different light intensities. Coolhas and Wormer (1953) of the Laboratory for Tropical Crop Husbandry, Wageningen, refer to earlier reviews of photoperiodism in rice by Wagenaar and Wormer. Though some of the data are contradictory, they believe that the following conclusions are justified:

(1) rice flowers earlier when grown in short rather than in long photoperiods;

(2) in Japan, China, India and Ceylon, late varieties are said to be sensitive to the length of the photoperiod, while varieties with a short growth period are said to be more or less indifferent; in Indonesia, awned varieties are regarded as indifferent, awnless as sensitive;

(3) even sensitive varieties do not react to the length of the photoperiod in the first 4 to 6 weeks of their growth cycle;

(4) treatment of short duration with a short photoperiod can have a strong influence on plant behaviour;

(5) even in the tropics, where variations in daylength are small, the sowing date may have a marked effect on the length of the growing period;

(6) treatment with a short photoperiod in the nursery bed where no tillers are formed, after the insensitive period mentioned in point (3), results in early earing of the main shoot, followed by normal or delayed earing of the tillers.

Research on photoperiodism in rice has so far produced only limited results because of:

(1) the failure to dissect plants carefully during growth and reproductive development,

(2) the use of normal or natural daylengths as control, when these are in fact not controls, and

(3) the fact that no distinction is made between the photoperiodic and photosynthetic action of light (Coolhas and Wormer, *loc. cit.*).

The Malayan Department of Agriculture in its Annual Report for the year 1955 states that, in the variety Siam 29, the period of ripening of the grain (flowering to maturity) is constant, regardless of the natural daylength conditions, being approximately 35 days. Experimental treatments using long days showed that, during the first 4 weeks of growth, the rice plant is not photoperiodically sensitive, since, whether in continuous short days or in 4 weeks of long days, the plants behave alike; but thereafter each subsequent increase of 2 weeks in long days gives a constant increase in time-to-flowering. Examination of the apices of plants grown in natural daylength showed that the flowering primordia are formed when the daylength is between 12 hr 12 min 30 sec and 12 hr 10 min 42 sec, and that visible exsertions of flowers take place about 24 days later.

Morinaga and others (1955) tested the response of twenty varieties from eight countries to 10·5- 11·5- and 12·5-hour photoperiods and the natural daylength of Tokyo. Vegetative growth periods under the optimal daylength were 40 to 60 days for Japanese varieties, 40 to 70 days for Burmese varieties, 50 to 80 days for Indian varieties and 70 to 150 days for Indonesian varieties. Experiments in the Philippines show that the Elon-elon variety is a short-day plant capable of flowering only from November to March under natural conditions, regardless of the month of planting. Ripeness-to-flower appears to be reached in about 15 days; the older the plant, the fewer short-day cycles are needed to initiate flower buds. The optimal daylength for the initiation and subsequent development of flower buds is 8 to 10 hours (Velasco and Manuel, 1955). Curves relating the inflorescence emergence to the photoperiod have been constructed by Chandraratna (1954) for eight pure lines from Burma, Ceylon, Indonesia and India. The pure lines vary widely in sensitivity, but variation in minimum heading duration and optimal photoperiod is less marked. In one pure line, apart from a striking influence of photoperiod on initiation of inflorescence primordia, the photoperiod exercises a small but significant effect on their further development.

Recent work in India includes the long series of studies by G. Misra (most recent reference 1956) dealing, for example, with the photoperiodic response of two early varieties, the effect of short photoperiod on varieties of early winter rice, and response of an early variety to long photoperiod. When 24-hour photoperiods were given to 10-, 20- and 30-day-old seedlings for one month in pot cultures, there was a significant delaying effect in ear emergence of the main shoot. The grain yield is higher in the 10-day-old group, not different in the 20-day-old group, but considerably depressed in the 30-day-old group as compared with controls. The higher grain yield is due to a marked increase in total number of spikelets and grains per panicle. Other Indian work includes Roy and Subramanyam (1955) on the response of twenty-five early (aus) varieties in Bihar to an 8-hour day, which showed that these varieties can be grouped as short-day, long-day or day-neutral; and Samantarai and Misra (1956) on the behaviour of a Philippine variety.

Aus (summer) and aman (winter) are the two types cultivated in West Bengal; most aus varieties are photo-indifferent (period-bound), while all aman varieties are short-day (season-bound). Both types are sown in May/June before the monsoon rains; the summer varieties flower in about 90 days, but the winter types do not flower until daylength is less than 11·5 hours, in October/November. The F_1 plants with all combinations of crosses are intermediate in photoperiodic reaction (Sen and Mitra, 1958); the F_1 plants display hybrid vigour in respect of growth characters, such as height, tiller number and yield.

Chandraratna (1953) has noted a gene for sensitivity to photoperiod linked with apiculus colour. Crosses made in Malaya between the non-photosensitive indica, Radin Kling, and photosensitive indicas have shown no sign of flowering within 120 days of planting in March; it appears that non-sensitivity is recessive in crosses between local indica parents. This is in contrast to dominant non-photosensitivity in crosses between photosensitive indica × non-photosensitive japonica from which the F_1 is 100 per cent non-photosensitive.

Misra and Sahu (1957) have studied the effect of various growth substances on flowering of four varieties, and noted a differential behaviour of these substances on varieties normally of different flowering duration; one particular substance causes a delay in early and early-winter varieties, has no effect in the midwinter varieties, but causes significant earliness in a late-winter variety. This earliness is of no agricultural importance, a result in sharp contrast with the conspicuous earliness obtained by Sircar and Kundu (1955) in the late midwinter variety, Rupsail, of Bengal.

M. Okuhiro at the University of Hiroshima in Japan has studied the effects of nitrogenous fertilizers on the photoperiodic responses, especially on the C/N ratio of dry tissue powder and on the osmotic pressure, specific electric conductivity and relative viscosity of the expressed sap. Misra and Samantarai (1955) found that the number of days to ear emergence is little affected by treatment in pots with different levels of nitrogen. The full rate induces marked increases in tillering, leaf production and stem elongation, particularly after the third application. S. M. Sircar of Calcutta University reported to the Seminar on 'Modern Developments in Plant Physiology' at the University of Delhi in April 1957 on the auxin relations of the rice plant. The endosperm contains auxin which gradually disappears at normal germination temperatures. At low vernalizing temperatures, consumption of auxin is markedly inhibited. In young leaves the high auxin level observed appears to be destroyed or inactivated at maturity. The quantity found in the developing ear rapidly increases with size and weight. Before floral initiation a considerable amount accumulates in the crown, but with extension growth both the total quantity and concentration decrease. Young nodes contain much higher concentrations than the internodes. It appears that auxin concentration regulates extension growth.

RYE

Petkus winter rye is one of the outstanding varieties used in research on growth and reproductive development, particularly in the studies of vernalization, devernalization and related matters made at South Kensington by F. G. Gregory, O. N. Purvis, D. J. C. Friend, G. Hussey and M. B. Gott. The Austrian physiologist, H. Hänsel, followed his earlier studies on the effect of short days on time of shooting and spikelet number per ear in Petkus winter rye with an investigation at the Plant Breeding Institute, Cambridge, on vernalization of the same variety by negative temperatures, and the influence of vernalization on lamina length of the first and second leaf (Hänsel, 1953). Finch and Carr (1956) at the University of Melbourne have recorded the nucleic acid content of Petkus rye embryos in relation to vernalization and devernalization. Laube (1956) observed the effects of temperature and light on the morphological and physiological characteristics which distinguish diploid and tetraploid Petkus winter rye. Jungfer (1955) describes the use in rye breeding of clones which have been subjected to short-day treatment. Apart from these academic studies, there appears to be little relevant information on the ecology and agronomy of rye as a crop.

SORGHUM

Indian juar is a short-day plant with a strong photoperiodic response (Sen Gupta, 1955). When seeds were sown at monthly intervals from 15 February in one year or 4 March in another, the flowering time in days and the height at flowering decreases with increased lateness of sowings. For widely different sowing dates over a range of 180 days, flowering took place within 10 days in one year and 16 days in the other, indicating that the environmental conditions at the end of October/ early November are very favourable for flower initiation, and that the plants are very sharp in their flowering response. Vernalization has no effect on earliness or lateness. The differential response to varying photoperiods is apparently due to the combined effect of temperature and photoperiod. Observations on seasonal behaviour of kharif (monsoon) and rabi (winter) types have been made at Poona by Chavan and Kajjari (1956). Rabi types sown in the kharif season are mainly vegetative, take 3 weeks longer to flower, yield less grain, are nearly twice as tall, and yield up to three times the fodder produced in the rabi season. Kharif types sown in the rabi season flower 2 weeks earlier, tiller more, give double the grain yield, but only a third of the fodder yield, and are less tall than in the kharif season.

CEREALS

Borthwick, Hendricks and Parker (1956) refer to work on inheritance of photoperiodic response. This is controlled by a single gene Ma, which is modified in its expression by two others, Ma_2 and Ma_3 (Quinby and Karper, 1945), which are dependent for their expression on the presence of the dominant Ma. In the F_2 progeny of the cross, intermediate maturing SA 5484 Dwarf Yellow milo × earlier maturing Sooner milo, 46 of 192 progeny are earlier maturing. Early maturing corresponds to flowering in short nights and is an indeterminate expression for sorghum. Single gene control of inheritance is also found in crosses between long-night teosinte and maize, which is only weakly responsive to long nights.

WHEAT

The histogenesis of the inflorescence and flower of two standard varieties of *Triticum aestivum* (Victor and Yeoman), three speltoid mutants, and the variety Federation has been studied by Barnard (1955). One of the speltoid mutants and Federation are spring wheats in that they do not require vernalization; the others are winter varieties and need vernalization for early development of the inflorescence. The apical meristem of the spike and spikelets is similar to that of the vegetative axis: a two-layered tunica encloses a central corpus. Leaf primordia arise by the periclinal division of cells of the tunica. Spikelet primordia are initiated in periclinal divisions of cells of the outer layer of the corpus (sub-hypodermis). Their mode of origin is comparable with that of vegetative buds. The glumes and lemmas arise in the same manner as the foliage leaf; the flower primordia by divisions in the sub-hypodermis like the spikelets. The early histogenesis of the palea, lodicules, and carpel is also essentially the same as that of the foliage leaf, while the stamens arise as cauline structures like the spikelets and flower primordia. The ovule is derived directly from the apex of the flower primordium and the integuments originate in the manner of foliar structures (see Plate 6).

Trials have been made at the University of Padua on tillering of Italian wheats in relation to variety, sowing date and manuring (Toniolo, 1956). Tillering is much lower in a year when the January/February temperatures are very low (1952/3) than when they are higher (1953/4). The mortality of the principal stems is lower, and that of the secondary stems higher in the first than in the second year. The density of secondary stems per unit area was greater in the first year. Excessive tillering results in shoots which remain green or do not form ripe ears.

Cooper (1956, 1957) has analyzed the ecological differences between

348

populations of wheat (*T. aegilopoides, T. monococcum, T. vulgare*—Punjab IX, April Bearded and Yeoman) in terms of one important developmental system, the timing of inflorescence development on the shoot apex and its corollary, the partition of energy between seed production and continued vegetative growth. Hänsel (1955 b) conducted spring-sowing trials in order to study the varietal characteristics in terms of developmental physiology of Austrian and other winter wheat varieties. Gassner (1953) made similar observations for the physiological characterization of German varieties. J. J. Chinoy and his colleagues in the University of Delhi undertook a project on behalf of the Indian Council of Agricultural Research in 1952 'to study the physiology of growth and development of wheat with a view to elucidating their relationship with the yield of wheat and also with a view to evolving a simple index by which high-yielding varieties may be selected for cultivation in the different regions of India'. Geslin's Heliothermic Index has been used by Pascale and Damario (1954) to classify thirty-seven Argentinian varieties into four groups, each with well-differentiated temperature and photoperiodic requirements. Chinoy (1956) has evolved a photothermic quantum, being the product of the photo quantum $= P =$ total number of light hours, and the thermic quantum $= T =$ the sum of degrees of mean diurnal temperatures of vegetative periods (number of days from germination or transplantation to anthesis). The difference between the photothermic quanta of non-vernalized and vernalized plants has been called the vernalization quantum. In wheat varieties these quanta increase progressively with the length of their vegetative period. The relation between the photothermic quantum (E), the length of the vegetative period (F), the mean temperature (t) during the vegetative period, and the mean photoperiod (p) is expressed by the following equation:

$$E = PT = ptF^2$$

$$\text{and} \quad \therefore \quad F = \sqrt{\frac{E}{pt}}$$

Nuttonson (1955) assembled phenological data to show the possibility of combining these with meterological and daylength records in order to disclose the thermal and photothermal requirements of winter and spring wheat under uncontrolled field conditions, to provide a means for a physiological-thermal classification or indexing of varieties, and to develop criteria for predicting dates of heading and maturity.

CEREALS

Taiwan is unique as a subtropical island suitable for growing hard spring wheat as a winter catch crop from November to mid-February, after harvesting two crops of rice per annum (Shen and King, 1958). It is interesting to compare the period of heading to maturity of wheat in Taiwan with that in the spring wheat region of North China. The latter region includes the provinces of Suiyuan, Chahar, the North-east (Manchuria), and parts of Kansu and Chinghai provinces. Wheat is planted from late March to the middle of April and harvested from July to the middle of August. It is grown under semi-arid conditions. The temperatures of the wheat growth period in North China are different from those in Taichung, Taiwan. Kweisui, Suiyuan Province, an important centre of spring wheat production, can be taken as representative of the North China region. It is located at northern latitude 40° 48', eastern longitude 111° 38', altitude 1,035 m. Taichung is at 24° 09' N., 120° 41' E., and at an altitude of 77 m. From planting to heading, November and December, temperatures at Taichung are higher than those in April, May and early June at Kweisui, while temperatures from heading to maturity, late December to the middle of February, at Taichung are lower than those at Kweisui from the middle of June to July. The low temperature from December to February accounts for the longer heading-to-maturity period at Taichung than at Kweisui.

Many experiments have been made on the response of wheat varieties at various stages of their vegetative period to temperature and light alone or in different combinations and sequences. Only a few representative studies are to be mentioned.

The literature on pre-treatment of seed with low temperature has been dealt with adequately in the First Edition and elsewhere. Spring cereals differ from winter varieties in their ability to initiate ears immediately under a favourable daylength, without cold treatment of the seed. Unvernalized winter cereals will eventually initiate ears but not before 6 to 8 weeks after planting (Gott, Gregory and Purvis, 1955). Vernalization of sprouted seed will eliminate this period of delay. Although field studies have suggested that the growing plant is also capable of responding to cold treatment during this early period of growth, direct evidence of the response of the green plant of a winter variety to cold treatment was not available until Gott (1957) showed in Australia that the winter wheat, Winter Minflor, is capable of being vernalized at any stage from the seed which has just germinated up to a 6-week-old plant with 6 to 7 leaves on the main shoot, even though earlier growth had taken place above vernalizing temperatures. Gott's interpretation is that in the unvernalized control plants the substance B produced by the vernalization reactions (Purvis and Gregory, 1952, see pp. 89 and 91)

$$A \rightleftharpoons A' \rightarrow B$$

is slowly accumulating even under high temperatures, and that in his experiment it reached a level comparable with the fully vernalized plant at about 90 days after planting. Therefore it appears likely that the older the plant the shorter the period of cold treatment necessary for complete vernalization.

At the National Institute of Agricultural Science in Tokyo, Nakayama and Sawamura (1955) found that high night temperatures 6°C above normal promote growth particularly in spring wheat, and in winter wheat only when the vernalization process is complete. In spring wheat, high night temperatures before spike initiation increase leaf numbers; if commenced after spike initiation, plant height and tiller numbers are increased. The trends are not so clear in winter wheat.

Cooper (1957) has compared the response to low-temperature vernalization in populations of wheats from a range of climatic and agronomic regions. The main climatic factors limiting the length of the growing season are temperature and soil moisture. In northern continental climates low winter temperatures are limiting and spring sowing is essential. In Mediterranean climates, summer drought is the limiting factor, the crop is sown with the winter rains and must mature before the water supply is exhausted. In Western Europe, spring sowing may be necessary because of unsuitable soil conditions, or because the land is not available until the spring. Varieties from regions with a short growing season, due to climatic or agronomic limitations, and without a period of moderate cold show no response to low temperature vernalization, as measured by leaf number before heading, and produce heads rapidly after 5 to 8 leaves on the main shoot.

Workers in Argentina have attempted to increase the resistance to drought of wheat varieties by exposing moistened germinating seed to 18°C for 24 hours, and then to 25°C until the seed had again become completely dry (Michajlikov and others, 1954). Increases in yield from the subsequent crop were 30 and 66·5 per cent in two trials.

Much of the literature on the relation between vernalization or completion of the thermo-phase and winter-hardiness was reviewed in the First Edition. Examples of recent studies include that by Hänsel (1954 c) on winter-hardiness and methods of controlling it in cereals, and by

Schmalz (1958 b) on reproductive development in winter wheat varieties with differing winter-hardiness, when spring-sown after vernalization with temperatures above and below freezing point.

Fedorov (1956) has studied the effect of sowing dates of vernalized and unvernalized seed on reproductive development in winter, spring and interchangeable varieties. Compared with spring wheat, the passing of the photo-phase is retarded in interchangeable and winter wheats under autumn conditions; there is evidence that this retardation is greater in the more winter-resistant varieties. Stroun (1955) noted that Fylgia, unlike other spring wheats, survived the winter frosts in France in

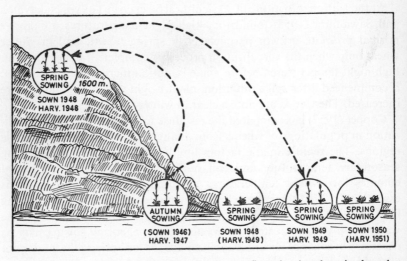

Fig. 58. Effect of altitude of seed production on flowering in wheat in the subsequent season (Lona, 1954 b).

1953/4 when sown in early November, and concludes that this variety should be regarded as interchangeable in the sense of Fedorov. J. C. Frazier of Kansas State College has over a 10-year period observed the temperatures which are lethal to flowers of hard red winter wheat. The floral organ (pistil or stamen) most susceptible to cold damage has been determined.

The length of the ripening period (the mean period between date of anthesis and date of full ripeness) is dependent on the mean maximum temperature during that period. This period is shifted to a lower range of temperature because of earliness in flowering in long-day plants, and the ripening period is longer, *vice versa* in short-day plants (Nanda and

Chinoy, 1957). High temperature (above 90°F) during the last 15 days before harvest of wheat leads generally but not always to subnormal volumes in the loaf made from the grain (Finney and Fryer, 1958). The association is only partially (51 to 84 per cent, depending on variety) accounted for in terms of amount of high temperature, percentage of protein in wheat, and the quality of protein as reflected by the mixing time of the dough. The physical and chemical condition of the soil appears to be an important factor in regulating the extent of injury from a given amount of high temperature during the last 15 days of the fruiting period. In the absence of high temperatures during the last 2 weeks before harvest, other environmental factors such as rainfall and the chemical and physical composition of the soil appear to have relatively minor effects on protein quality. Protein content accounts for about 95 per cent of the variations in loaf volume if temperature during the fruiting period was not a limiting factor. Varieties with longer mixing times are more tolerant or resistant to the detrimental effects of high temperature during fruiting than those with shorter mixing times.

Many studies have been made on the photoperiodic response of wheat varieties, generally in relation to associated temperature. Chinoy and Nanda have published a series of articles on the effect of vernalization and photoperiodic treatments on growth and development (most recent paper 1952), dealing respectively with varietal differences in flowering and correlation with length of spike (Chinoy and Nanda, 1951), varietal differences in stem elongation and tillering and their correlation with flowering, the rate of dry matter production, net assimilation rate and water content, and the uptake of nitrogen, phosphorus and potassium, all under varying photoinductive and post-photoinductive treatments. More recently, these workers (Nanda and Chinoy, 1957) have studied the effect of photoperiodic treatments on yield of grain and straw, and with particular reference to the temperature of the ripening period.

In experiments by the Science Service in Ottawa on Marquis spring wheat, it has been found that, although floral initiation is little affected by temperature or light intensity, the later growth of the flower primordia is affected by both; the time to anthesis is 12 days shorter at 30° C than at 20°C and 4 days shorter under 2,400 foot-candles than under 1,000 foot-candles of light. The mean times to floral initiation and anthesis for all treatments is 15 and 46 days respectively from time of sowing.

Schmalz (1958 a) subjected plants of spring wheat (four varieties with different critical daylengths) to a regular alternation of short-day and permanent daylight in two experiments (May/June and July/August/

M   353

CEREALS

September 1957) from emergence (opening of the first leaf) to the end of the sixth week of growth. The regular alternation was arranged in daily, 3-day and 7-day cycles. There were two variants of the last cycle, one starting with short day, the other with permanent daylight. Controls were exposed to permanent daylight, normal daylength and short days. The time of ear emergence and the length of the apical meristem, or the ear, at a given moment were taken as indicators of development.

In both experiments, plants exposed to a daily alternation show least reproductive development, those exposed to 3-day alternation more, and those with 7-day alternation most. The two variants of the 7-day cycle, however, are markedly different in both trials. In the first trial the variant starting with short-day treatment shows greater reproductive development, in the second trial that starting with permanent daylight, due to the different periods at which the experiments were carried out (change in natural daylength and temperature). These results may be due to the different intensity or degree of inhibition of the production of a flowering hormone under the different treatments.

The varieties, Chinese and White Federation 38, were studied in Indiana by J. A. Riddell and others, under 8-, 12-, 16- and 20-hour photoperiods at 15·5, 21·1 and 26·7°C. Short daylengths and high temperature retard pre-inductive development as indicated by the number of differentiated vegetative nodes and the time for induction to occur. As the daylength increases, the delaying effect of high temperature on induction becomes less marked. High temperature favours rapid post-inductive development with the result that flowering of White Federation 38 under long photoperiods is promoted. Chinese is relatively insensitive to photoperiod and temperature, so that it is earlier than White Federation 38 under short days with low temperature and later under long days with high temperature.

Having obtained a preliminary indication that a dark period is important for maximum efficiency in the utilization of light by spring wheats grown under controlled conditions of temperature and photoperiod, G. A. Gries and others in Indiana found that spring wheat flowers earlier when the daily light-dark cycle is divided into several cycles without altering the ratio of light to dark. This earliness is ascribed to shortening of the dark period since brief night interruptions reduce the time-to-flowering whereas day interruptions do not. Shortening of the dark period causes differentiation of few vegetative nodes before induction and thereby hastens post-inductive development.

Numerous workers have studied the optimal time for applications of fertilizers, particularly nitrogen, in relation to the growth, reproduction and ultimate yield of wheat. For example, Thorne and Watson (1955) have investigated the effect on yield and leaf area of applying nitrogen as a top-dressing in April or in sprays to the soil or to the leaves at or about the period of maximum leaf area, before or during ear emergence. All three methods of application cause similar increases in yield and nitrogen content of the grain. April nitrogen gives a greater yield of straw than the later dressings. Chinoy and Nanda (1950) find that the nitrogen uptake and distribution under different light treatments can be made to resemble that occurring in early and late varieties, and suggest that the regulatory mechanism which puts an early check on tiller production and dry weight increase in leaves of long-day plants and in early-flowering varieties also controls the nitrogen uptake and its early translocation to the stem. The 1955 Report of the Uttar Pradesh Department of Agriculture and Animal Husbandry refers to trials on the effect on respiration and photosynthesis of fertilizers applied at different growth stages.

Working at Quimper in France, Jolivet (1956) compared the effect of different nitrogenous fertilizers applied at tillering on the stand, and at tillering and shooting on the yield. The utilization by Cappelle and Progress wheats of nitrogen applied at shooting was also compared. Holmes and Tahir (1956) found that time of application affects growth and development but not grain yield. Late applications produce less straw and a higher nitrogen content in the grain.

With the object of establishing basic rules for dates of application of fertilizers and irrigation water, Hänsel (1955 a) sowed winter wheat and winter rye in the open in autumn and examined the course of development of the yield-determining organs, namely, shoot axis, spike, spikelet and flower, at 10- to 20-day intervals beginning at the end of the following March. Four periods in the development of these organs are recognized: (1) the laying down of the organs; (2) maximum number of organs (of one kind); (3) reduction in number of organs; (4) final number of organs and their maturity. The timing of these stages for each of these organs reveals a pattern of regular, developmental relationships within the development of the whole organism. For each of these organs, there are stages of development before which the addition of nutrients influences the crop yield and after which this is no longer possible. Such 'limiting stages' can be recognized by external features of the plant. Hänsel (1955 c) also observed the post-winter development of winter wheat with special reference to the influence of spacing and nutrients on the number of each yield-determining organ (on each plant). It is stated to be possible to predict the effect on yield-determining organs of the application of nutrients at any given date.

Finally, there are the questions relating to the occurrence and movement of active substances within plants, and the effect of synthetic substances on growth and general behaviour. Simpson (1958) reports evidence that gibberellin-like materials occur naturally within the tissues of seedlings, a highly significant activity having been found in the extract obtained from the basal region of seedlings, and some activity in the extract from the tips of seedling shoots. Hardesty and Elliott (1956) suggest an active inhibiting or stimulating factor to explain the differential post-ripening effects noted among seeds from the same parental spike. Differences in primary root length and percentage germination are related to the sequence of anthesis and maturation on the parental spike. Florets that reach anthesis earlier (1st and 2nd florets from spikelets in centre of spike) have the slowest rates of germination.

S. N. Bhardwaj and I. M. Rao of Agra College reported to the Seminar on 'Modern developments in plant physiology' in Delhi on their long-term research on the use of synthetic substances. Production of straw and grain is increased by soaking seeds for 24 hours in solutions of 10 p.p.m. of NAA and 2,4-D when sowing is delayed by a month. In the rabi season, 1956/7, the influence of soaking in a solution of 10 p.p.m. of 2,4-D on shoot dry weight at maturity and grain yield was compared in normal (1st week November) and late (3rd week December) sowings. A statistically significant increase in both dry weight and grain yield was obtained even in the normal sowing, due mainly to better tillering.

BIBLIOGRAPHY

Roman numerals at right margin indicate the Chapter(s) in which each reference was used; R, general reviews with large bibliographies; Plate, papers from which only illustrations were taken.

AITKEN, Y. (1955). Flower initiation in pasture legumes. *Aust. J. agric. Res.* **6,** 212–64. XI

ALBERDA, TH. (1958). The phytotron of the Institute for Biological and Chemical Research on Field Crops and Herbage at Wageningen. *Acta bot. néer.* **7,** 265–77. IX

ALLARD, H. A., and EVANS, M. W. (1941). Growth and flowering of some tame and wild grasses in response to different photoperiods. *J. agric. Res.* **62,** 193–228. XI

ANDERSON, S. (1952). Methods for determining stages of development in barley and oats. *Physiol. Plant.* **5,** 199–210. II

ANDERSON, S. (1954). A method for determining stages of development in wheat. *Physiol. Plant.* **7,** 513–16. II

ANDREW, R. H., and others (1956). Maturation and yield of corn as influenced by climate and production technique. *Agron. J.* **48,** 231–6. XXII

ARIYANAYAGAM, D. U. (1953). Growth and developmental changes caused by presowing treatment of seed paddy. *Trop. Agriculturalist,* **109,** 4–15. XXII

ARNEY, S. E. (1956 a). Studies on growth and development in the genus *Fragaria.* VIII. The effect of defoliation on leaf initiation and early growth of the leaf initials. *Phyton,* **6,** 109–20. XVIII

ARNEY, S. E. (1956 b). Studies of growth and development in the genus *Fragaria.* IX. An investigation of floral initiation under natural conditions. *Phyton,* **7,** 89–102. XVIII

Asgrow Export Corporation (1956). Bolting of onions: Affected by variety, time of planting and weather. *Asgrow,* **12,** 11. XIV

AUGSTEN, H. (1956). Fermentaktivität und Atmung bei Sommergerste nach Kältebehandlung des Saatgutes. *Dtsch. Akad. LandWiss., Wissenschaftl. Abhandl.* No. 20, Berlin. 87 pp. IV

AVERY, G. S., JOHNSON, E. B., THOMSON, B. F., and ADDOMS, R. (1947). Hormones and Horticulture. McGraw-Hill, New York, 326 pp. R, V

BACH, M. K., MAGEE, W. E., and BURRIS, R. H. (1958). Translocation of photosynthetic products to soybean nodules and their role in nitrogen fixation. *Pl. Physiol.* **33,** 118–24. II

BAKER, H. G. (1955). Self-compatibility and establishment after 'long-distance' dispersal. *Evolution,* **9,** 347–8. II

BAKER, H. G. (1957). Expression of sex in flowering plants. *Nature,* **180,** 614–15. II

BANGA, O. (1948). Krotenstudies. III. Vernalisatie en devernalisatie van bieten. *Meded. Direct. Tuinbouw,* **11,** 324–47. XIII

BAPTIST, E. D. C., and DE JONGE, P. (1955). Stimulation of yield in *Hevea brasiliensis.* 14*th Internat. Hort. Congr.* 1428–36. XII

BARNARD, C. (1955). Histogenesis of the inflorescence and flower of *Triticum aestivum* L. *Aust. J. Bot.* **3,** 1–20. XXII

357

BIBLIOGRAPHY

BARNARD, C. (1957 a). Floral histogenesis in the monocotyledons. I. The Gramineae. *Aust. J. Bot.* **5,** 1–20. II

BARNARD, C. (1957 b). Floral histogenesis in the monocotyledons. II.The Cyperaceae. *Aust. J. Bot.* **5,** 115–28. II

BARTON, L. V. (1956). Growth response of physiological dwarfs of *Malus arnoldiana* Sarg. to gibberellic acid. *Contr. Boyce Thompson Inst.* **18,** 311–18. VI

BEACHELL, H. M. (1945). Effect of photoperiod on rice varieties grown in the field. *J. agric. Res.* **66,** 325–40. XXII

BEIJER, J. J. (1955). The influence of normal and artificially created climatic conditions on the flowering of daffodils. *14th Internat. Hort. Congr.* 188–95. XIV

BELL, G. D. H. (1945). Personal communication, 12 February X, XIII

BENEDICT, H. M. (1941). Growth of some range grasses in reduced light. *Bot. Gaz.* **102,** 582–9. XI

BENTLEY, J. A. (1958). Role of plant hormones in algal metabolism and ecology. *Nature,* **181,** 1499–1502. I

BERNARDES, B. C. (1956). Efeitos da data de semeadura sôbre a duração do ciclo vegetativo do arroz. *Lavour. arroz.* **10,** 232–7. XXII

BERRIE, A. M. M. (1957). Two phytotrons. In: Hudson, J. P., Control of the Plant Environment. Butterworths, London, 171–9. IX

BEST, R. (1959). Photoperiodism in rice. *Field Crop Abstr.* *12,* 85–93. XXII

BIRD, J. N. (1948). Early and late types of red clover. *Sci. Agric.* **28,** 444–53. XI

BLACK, J. N. (1955). The interaction of light and temperature in determining the growth rate of subterranean clover. *Aust. J. biol. Sci.* **8,** 330–43. XI

BLACK, J. N. (1956 a). The distribution of solar radiation over the earth's surface. *Arch. Met. Geophys. Bioklim.,* Ser. B, 7, 165–89. I

BLACK, J. N. (1956 b). Light intensity and plant growth. *Aust.—UNESCO Symp. Arid Zone Clim.* 21a–21f. XI

BLACK, J. N. (1957 a). The influence of varying light intensity on the growth of herbage plants: a review. *Herb. Abstr.* **27,** 89–98. R, XI

BLACK, J. N. (1957 b). Seed size as a factor in the growth of subterranean clover (*Trifolium subterraneum* L.) under spaced and sward conditions. *Aust. J. agric. Res.* **8,** 335–51. XI

BLACKMAN, G. E. (1956). Influence of light and temperature on leaf growth. In: Milthorpe, F. L., The Growth of Leaves. Butterworths, London, 151–69. III

BLACKMAN, G.E., BLACK, J.N., and KEMP, A.W. (1955). Physiological and ecological studies in the analysis of plant environment. X. An analysis of the effects of seasonal variations in daylight and temperature on the growth of *Helianthus annuus* in the vegetative phase. *Ann. Bot., Lond.,* N.S. **19,** 527–48. XX

BLACKMAN, G. E., and WILSON, G. L. (1951). Physiological and ecological studies in the analysis of plant environment. VII. An analysis of the differential effects of light intensity on the net assimilation rate, leaf area ratio and relative growth rate of different species. *Ann. Bot., Lond.,* N.S. **15,** 373–408. XI

BLACKMAN, G. E., and WILSON, G. L. (1954). Physiological and ecological studies in the analysis of plant environment. IX. Adaptive changes in the vegetative growth and development of *Helianthus annuus* induced by an alteration in light level. *Ann. Bot., Lond.,* N.S. **18,** 71–94. III, XX

BLAIR, D.S., MACARTHUR, M., and NELSON, S.H. (1956). Observations in the growth phases of fruit trees. *Proc. Amer. Soc. hort. Sci.* **67,** 75–9. XVII

BLAKE, J. (1955). Photoperiodism in the perpetual-flowering carnation. *14th Internat. Hort. Congr.* 331–6. XV

BLANEY, L. T., and HAMNER, K. C. (1957). Interrelations among effects of temperature, photoperiod, and dark period on floral initiation of Biloxi soybean. *Bot. Gaz.* **119,** 10–24. XXI

BIBLIOGRAPHY

BOLLE-JONES, E. W. (1954). Nutrient levels and flower production in the potato. *Physiol. Plant.* **7**, 698–703. XIII

BOLLE-JONES, E. W. (1956). A glasshouse suitable for physiological investigations on plants grown in the tropics. *Emp. J. exp. Agric.* **24**, 331–9. IX

BONDE, E. K. (1955). The effect of various cycles of light and darkness on the growth of tomato and cocklebur plants. *Physiol. Plant.* **8**, 913–23. XVI

BONDE, E. K. (1956). Further studies on the effect of various cycles of light and darkness on the growth of tomato and cocklebur plants. *Physiol. Plant.* **9**, 51–9. XVI

BONNER, J., and BANDURSKI, R. S. (1952). Studies of the physiology, pharmacology and biochemistry of the auxins. *Annu. Rev. Pl. Physiol.* **3**, 59–86. R, IV

BONNER, J., and BONNER, D. M. (1948). Induction of flowering in *Xanthium. Bot. Gaz.* **110**, 154–6. V

BONNETT, O. T. (1936). The development of the wheat spike. *J. agric. Res.* **53**, 445–51. II

BONNIER, CH., and SIRONVAL, C. (1956). Influence of daylength on nodule formation in *Soja hispida* by a specific *Rhizobium* strain. *Nature*, **177**, 93–4. II, XXI

BORRISS, H. (1952). Die physiologischen Grundlagen der Jàrowisation. *Dtsch. Landw.*, Sonder-Nr. Jarowisation. IV

BORTHWICK, H. A., HENDRICKS, S. B., and PARKER, M. W. (1948). Action spectrum for photoperiodic control of floral initiation of a long-day plant, Wintex barley (*Hordeum vulgare*). *Bot. Gaz.* **110**, 103–18. XXII

BORTHWICK, H. A., HENDRICKS, S. B., and PARKER, M. W. (1952). The reaction controlling floral initiation. *Proc. Nat. Acad. Sci., U.S.A.* **38**, 929–34. IV, XV

BORTHWICK, H. A., HENDRICKS, S. B., and PARKER, M. W. (1956). Photoperiodism. In: Hollaender, A., Radiation Biology. McGraw-Hill, New York. Vol. 3, 479–517. R, I, IV, XXII

BORTHWICK, H. A., HENDRICKS, S. B., TOOLE, E. H., and TOOLE, V. K. (1954). Action of light on lettuce-seed germination. *Bot. Gaz.* **115**, 205–25. XII

BORTHWICK, H. A., and PARKER, M. W. (1952). Light in relation to flowering and vegetative development. *13th Internat. Hort. Congr.* 1–9. IX, XIII, XVIII, XXI

BORTHWICK, H. A., and SCULLY, N. J. (1954). Photoperiodic responses of hemp. *Bot. Gaz.* **116**, 14–29. XII

BOYSEN-JENSEN, P. (1943). Plantefysiologi. 2nd Ed. Ejnar Munksgaards Forlag, København. 487 pp. R, III

BRAAK, J. P. (1955). Effects of some internal and external factors on the embryo and seedling development of the cherry. *14th Internat. Hort. Congr.* 845–52. XVII

BRAAK, J. P., and SMEETS, L. (1956). The phytotron of the Institute of Horticultural Plant Breeding at Wageningen, Netherlands. *Euphytica*, **5**, 205–17. IX

BRADLEY, M.V., and CRANE, J. C. (1957). Effects of auxins on development of apricot seeds and seedlings. *Amer. J. Bot.* **44**, 164–75. XVII

BRANDES, E. W., and COONS, G. H. (1941). Climatic relations of sugar-cane and sugar beet. *Yearb. U.S. Dep. Agric.* 421–38. XIII

BREMER, A. H. (1931). Einfluss der Tageslänge auf die Wachstumsphasen des Salats. Genetische Untersuchungen. I. *GartenbWiss.* **4**, 469–83. XII

BREMER, A. H., and GRANA, J. (1935). Genetische Untersuchungen mit Salat. II. *GartenbWiss.* **9**, 231–42. XII

BREMER-REINDERS, D. E. (1958). The early stages of development in the rye spike. *Acta bot. néerl.* **7**, 223–32. II

BRIAN, P. W. (1958). Role of gibberellin-like hormones in regulation of plant growth and flowering. *Nature*, **181**, 1122–3. IV

BRIAN, P. W., and GROVE, J. F. (1957). Gibberellic acid. *Endeavour*, **16**, 161–71. VI

BRIAN, P. W., and HEMMING, H. G. (1955). The effect of gibberellic acid on shoot growth of pea seedlings. *Physiol. Plant.* **8**, 669–81 VI, XXI

BIBLIOGRAPHY

BRIAN, P. W., and HEMMING, H. G. (1958). Complementary action of gibberellic acid and auxins in pea internode extension. *Ann. Bot., Lond.*, N.S. **22**, 1–17.   VI, XXI

BRIAN, P. W., HEMMING, H. G., and RADLEY, M. (1955). A physiological comparison of gibberellic acid with some auxins. *Physiol. Plant.* **8**, 899–912.   VI

BROERTJES, C. (1955). The forcing of *Forsythia intermedia spectabilis* Khne, 14*th Internat. Hort. Congr.* 1065–71.   XV

BROUGHAM, R. W. (1956 a). The rate of growth of short-rotation ryegrass pastures in the late autumn, winter and early spring. *N.Z. J. Sci. Tech.* **A38**, 78–87.   III

BROUGHAM, R. W. (1956 b). Effect of intensity of defoliation on regrowth of pasture. *Aust. J. agric. Res.* **7**, 377–87.   III

BROUGHAM, R. W. (1958). Interception of light by the foliage of pure and mixed stands of pasture plants. *Aust. J. agric. Res.* **9**, 39–52.   III

BROWN, J. C., TIFFIN, L. O., and HOLMES, R. S. (1958). Carbohydrate and organic acid metabolism with C^{14} distribution affected by copper in Thatcher wheat. *Pl. Physiol.* **33**, 38–42.   Plate

BUKOVAC, M. J., and WITTWER, S. H. (1957). Gibberellin and higher plants. II. Induction of flowering in biennials. *Quart. Bull. Mich. agric. Exp. Sta.* **39**, 650–60.   Plate

BUKOVAC, M. J., WITTWER, S. H., and TEUBNER, F. G. (1957). Gibberellin and higher plants. VII. Flower formation in the tomato (*Lycopersicon esculentum*). *Quart. Bull. Mich. agric. Exp. Sta.* **40**, 207–14.   XVI

BULA, R. J., SMITH, D., and HODGSON, H. J. (1956). Cold resistance in alfalfa at two diverse latitudes. *Agron. J.* **48**, 153–6.   XI

BULA, R. J., SMITH, D., and MILLER, E. E. (1954). Measurements of light beneath a small grain companion crop as related to legume establishment. *Bot. Gaz.* **115**, 271–8.   III

BULLER, R. E., and GONZÁLEZ, M. (1958). Performance of alfalfa varieties, red clover, and alsike clover grown under irrigation at approximately 8,800 feet above sea level in Mexico. *Agron. J.* **50**, 19–22.   XI

BULLER, R. E., PITNER, J. B., and RAMIREZ, M. (1955). Behaviour of alfalfa varieties in the valley of Mexico. *Agron. J.* **47**, 510–12.   XI

BÜNNING, E. (1950). Über die photophile und skotophile Phase der endogenen Tagesrhytmik. *Planta*, **38**, 521–40.   IV

BÜNNING, E. (1956 a). Leaf growth under constant conditions and as influenced by light-dark cycles. In: Milthorpe, F. L., The Growth of Leaves, Butterworths, London, 119–26.   III

BÜNNING, E. (1956 b). Endogenous rhythms in plants. *Annu. Rev. Pl. Physiol.* **7**, 71–90.   R, I

BÜNSOW, R., and HARDER, R. (1956). Blütenbildung von *Bryophyllum* durch Gibberellin. *Naturwissenschaften*, **43**, 479–80.   VI

BUNTING, A. H. (1955). A classification of cultivated groundnuts. *Emp. J. exp. Agric.* **23**, 158–70.   XX

ČAĬLAHJAN, M. H. (1937). On the hormonal theory of plant development. *Izv. Akad. Nauk, SSSR.* 200 pp.   IV

ČAĬLAHJAN, M. H. (1940). Translocation of the flowering hormones in different organs of the plant. *Doklady Akad. Nauk, SSSR*, **27**, 159–62, 253–6, 374–7.   IV

CALVERT, A. (1955). Temperature effects on early growth and development in tomato. 14*th Internat. Hort. Congr.* 560–5.   XVI

Cambridge, Imperial Bureau of Plant Breeding and Genetics. (1943). Photoperiodism in the potato. By Driver, C. M., and Hawkes, J. G. Tech. Communication No. 10. 36 pp.   XIII

CAMPBELL, G. K. G. (1958). Personal communication, 26 June.   XIII

360

BIBLIOGRAPHY

CAMPBELL, R. W., and LINGLE, J. C. (1954). Some effects of low temperatures on the flower primordia of the strawberry. *Proc. Amer. Soc. hort. Sci.* **64**, 259–62.
XVIII

CANHAM, A. E. (1957). Range and characteristics of available lamps. In: Hudson, J. P., Control of the Plant Environment. Butterworths, London, 207–10.
IX

CARR, D. J., and ENG KOK NG (1956). Experimental induction of flower formation in Kikuyu grass (*Pennisetum clandestinum* Hochst. ex Chiov.). *Aust. J. agric. Res.* **7**, 1–6.
XI

CARR, D. J., McCOMB, A. J., and OSBORNE, L. D. (1957). Replacement of the requirement for vernalisation in *Centaurium minus* Moench by gibberellic acid. *Naturwissenschaften*, **44**, 428–9.
VI

CATHEY, H. M. (1954). Chrysanthemum temperature study. *Proc. Amer. Soc. hort. Sci.* **64**, 483–502.
XV

CATHEY, H. M. (1958). Personal communication on 'Changing growth and flowering of chrysanthemums by use of a quaternary ammonium compound, Amo-1618'. 6 May.
VII

CATHEY, H. M., and BORTHWICK, H. A. (1957). Photoreversibility of floral initiation in chrysanthemum. *Bot. Gaz.* **119**, 71–6.
XV

CHAN, A. P. (1955). Some factors affecting flower bud development of chrysanthemums. *14th Internat. Hort. Congr.* 1023–39.
XV

CHANDRARATNA, M. F. (1953). A gene for photoperiod sensitivity in rice linked with apiculus colour. *Nature*, **171**, 1162.
XXII

CHANDRARATNA, M. F. (1954). Photoperiod response in rice (*Oryza sativa* L.). I. Effects on inflorescence initiation and emergence. *New Phytol.* **53**, 397–405.
XXII

CHASE, A. (1908). Notes on cleistogamy of grasses. *Bot. Gaz.* **45**, 135–6.
II

CHAVAN, V. M., and KAJJARI, N. B. (1956). Seasonal behaviour of kharif and rabi jowar types (*Sorghum vulgare* Pers.). *Poona agric. Coll. Mag.* **46**, 99–103.
XXII

CHINOY, J. J. (1950). Effect of vernalization and photoperiodic treatment on growth and development of wheat. *Nature*, **165**, 882.
XXII

CHINOY, J. J. (1956). Determination of photothermic and vernalization quanta for the vegetative period of wheat. *Physiol. Plant.* **9**, 1–18.
XXII

CHINOY, J. J., and NANDA, K. K. (1950). Photoperiodic treatment and nitrogen uptake in wheat. *Curr. Sci.* **19**, 24–5.
XXII

CHINOY, J. J., and NANDA, K. K. (1951). Effect of vernalization and photoperiodic treatments on growth and development of crop plants. I. Varietal differences in flowering of wheat and correlation with length of spike under varying photoinductive and post-photoinductive treatments. *Physiol. Plant.* **4**, 209–23.
XXII

CHINOY, J. J., and NANDA, K. K. (1952). Effect of vernalization and photoperiodic treatments on growth and development of crop plants. IV. Uptake of nitrogen, phosphorus and potassium by wheat plants under varying photoinductive and post-photoinductive treatments. *Physiol. Plant.* **5**, 11–32.
XXII

CHINOY, J. J., NANDA, K. K., and GARG, O. P. (1957). Effect of ascorbic acid on growth and flowering of *Trigonella foenum-graecum* and *Brassica chinensis*. *Physiol. Plant.* **10**, 869–76.
V

CHOLODNY, N. G. (1939). The internal factors of flowering. *Herb. Rev.* **7**, 223–47.
IV

CHOUDHRI, R. S., GARG, O. K., and BORAH, P. C. (1957). Physiological changes in relation to sex in papaya (*Carica papaya* L.) *Phyton*, **9**, 137–41.
XVII

CHOUARD, P. (1955). L'influence des températures basses sur les plantes. *14th Internat. Hort. Congr.* 14–38.
R, I

N
361

BIBLIOGRAPHY

CHOUARD, P., and POIGNANT, P. (1951). Recherches préliminaires sur la vernalisation en présence d'inhibiteurs de germination et de respiration. *C. R. Acad. Sci.*, *Paris*, **232**, 103.   IV

CHROBOCZEK, E. (1955). Influence of the age of plants at the beginning of cold treatment and of the length of cold treatment on seedstalk development and yield of seed of two white cabbage varieties. *14th Internat. Hort. Congr.* 429–39.
XII

CLAES, H. VON (1947). Die Beteiligung des dissimilatorischen Stoffwechsels an der photoperiodischen Reaktion von *Hyoscyamus niger*. *Z. Naturforsch.* **26**, 45–55.   IV

CLAUSEN, J. (1953). The ecological race as a variable biotype compound in dynamic balance with its environment. *I.U.B.S. Sympos. Genet. Popul. Struct.*, Pavia, 105–13.   X

CLAUSEN, J., and HIESEY, W. M. (1958 a). Phenotypic expression of genotypes in contrasting environments. *Rep. Scot. Pl. Breed. Sta.* 41–51.   X

CLAUSEN, J., and HIESEY, W. M. (1958 b). Experimental studies on the nature of species. IV. Genetic structure of ecological races. *Carneg. Inst. Publ.* 615. 312 pp.   X

CLEMENTS, H. F. (1953). Crop logging of sugarcane—principles and practices. *Proc. 8th Congr. Internat. Soc. Sugarcane Technol.* 79–97   XII, XIII

CLEMENTS, H. F., SHIGEURA, G., and AKAMINE, E. K. (1952). Factors affecting the growth of sugarcane. *Hawaii agric. Exp. Sta., Tech. Bull.* 18. 90 pp.   XII

COCKS, B. (1958). The influence of date of sowing and of strain on head production in timothy. *J. Brit. Grassl. Soc.* **13**, 92–8.   XI

COOLHAAS, C. (1955). The influence of environmental factors on the growth and development of tobacco. *14th Internat. Hort. Congr.* 1472–81.   XII

COOLHAAS, C., and WORMER, Th.M. (1953). Developmental differences in rice plants in relation to photoperiodism. *Neth. J. agric. Sci.* **1**, 202–16.   XXII

COOPER, C. C., and WATSON, D. P. (1954). Influence of root temperature and light intensity on flower bud development in *Salvia splendens*. *Proc. Amer. Soc. hort. Sci.* **64**, 437–40.   XV

COOPER, J. P. (1951). Studies on growth and development in *Lolium*. II. Pattern of bud development on the shoot apex and its ecological significance. *J. Ecol.* **39**, 228–70.   III, XI

COOPER, J. P. (1954). Studies on growth and development in *Lolium*. IV. Genetic control of heading responses in local populations. *J. Ecol.* **42**, 521–56.   X

COOPER, J. P. (1956). Developmental analysis of populations in the cereals and herbage grasses. I. Methods and techniques. *J. agric. Sci.* **47**, 262–79.   XXII

COOPER, J. P. (1957). Developmental analysis of populations in the cereals and herbage grasses. II. Response to low-temperature vernalization. *J. agric. Sci.* **49**, 361–83.   XI, XXII

COPEMAN, G. J. F., HEDDLE, R. G., HUNT, I. V., and SAMPFORD, M. R. (1958). Perennial ryegrass strains in Scotland. *Scot. Agric.* **37**, 195–202.   XI

CRAFTS, A. S. (1951). Movement of assimilates, viruses, growth regulators, and chemical indicators in plants. *Bot. Rev.* **17**, 203–84.   IV

CURTH, P. (1955). Temperatur und Licht als blühinduzierende Faktoren bei der Zuckerrübe. *Züchter*, **25**, 14–17.   XIII

DADAY, H. (1954). Gene frequencies in wild populations of *Trifolium repens*. I. Distribution by latitude. *Heredity*, **8**, 61–78.   XI

DADAY, H. (1958). Gene frequencies in wild populations of *Trifolium repens*. III. World distribution. *Heredity*, **12**, 169–84.   XI

DAUBENMIRE, R. F. (1947). Plants and Environment. A textbook of plant autecology. Wiley and Sons, New York. 424 pp.   R

BIBLIOGRAPHY

DAVERN, C. I., PEAK, J. W., and MORLEY, F. H. W. (1957). The inheritance of flowering time in *Trifolium subterraneum* L. *Aust. J. Agric. Res.* **8**, 121–34.   XI

DAVIDSON, J. L. (1954). The effect of density of sowing on the growth of *Trifolium subterraneum* (subterranean clover). *B.Ag.Sci.* (Hons.) Thesis, Univ. Adelaide.   III

DAVIDSON, J. L., and DONALD, C. M. (1958). The growth of swards of subterranean clover with particular reference to leaf area. *Aust. J. agric. Res.* **9**, 53–72.   III

DAVIES, G. M. (1956). The effect of winter and spring defoliation on the subsequent yield of grain and straw of S147 oats. *J. agric. Sci.* **47**, 363–6.   XXII

DE ROPP, R. S., and MARKLEY, E. (1955). The correlation of different aspects of auxin action. *Pl. Physiol.* **30**, 210–14   IV

DE ZEEUW, D. (1952). Literatuurstudie over toepassing van kunstlicht in de tuinbouw. *Meded. LandbHogesch., Wageningen,* **52**, 129–65.   R, XV

DE ZEEUW, D. (1957). Flowering of *Xanthium* under long-day conditions. *Nature,* **180**, 558.   I

DE ZEEUW, D., and LEOPOLD, A. C. (1955). Altering juvenility with auxin. *Science,* **122**, 925–6.   XII

DE ZEEUW, D., and LEOPOLD, A. C. (1956). The promotion of floral initiation by auxin. *Amer. J. Bot.* **43**, 47–50.   V, XXI

DIJKHUIS, F. J. (1956). Computation of heat unit accumulations in maize for practical application. *Euphytica,* **5**, 267–75.   XXII

DONALD, C. M. (1951). Competition among pasture plants. I. Intraspecific competition among annual pasture plants. *Aust. J. agric. Res.* **2**, 355–76.   III, XI

DONALD, C. M., and BLACK, J. N. (1958). The significance of leaf area in pasture growth. *Herb. Abstr.* **28**, 1–6.   R, III

DOORENBOS, J. (1955). Horticultural possibilities of photoperiodism. 14*th Internat. Hort. Congr.* 315–19.   R, XV

DORST, J. C. (1957). Adaptation. *Euphytica,* **6**, 247–54.   X

DOSTAL, R., and HOŠEK, M. (1937). Über den Einfluss von Heteroauxin auf die Morphogenese bei *Circaea. Flora,* **139**, 263–86.   IV

DOWNS, R. J. (1956). Photoreversibility of flower initiation. *Pl. Physiol.* **31**, 279–84.   XV, XXI

DOWNS, R. J., and BORTHWICK, H. A. (1956 a). Effects of photoperiod on growth of trees. *Bot. Gaz.* **117**, 310–26.   XII

DOWNS, R. J., and BORTHWICK, H. A. (1956 b). Effect of photoperiod upon the vegetative growth of *Weigela florida* var. *variegata. Proc. Amer. Soc. hort. Sci.* **68**, 518–21.   XV

DULLFORCE, W. M. (1956). Effects of environmental factors and injury on growth of lettuce seedlings. In: Milthorpe, F. L., The Growth of Leaves. Butterworths, London, 208.   XII

DULLFORCE, W. M. (1957). Timing chrysanthemum flowering. *Grower,* **47**, 1413.   XV

DURRANT, A. (1958). Environmental conditioning of flax. *Nature,* **181**, 928–9.   XII

DYKE, G. V. (1956). The effect of date of planting on the yield of potatoes. *J. agric. Sci.* **47**, 122–8   XIII

EATON, F. M. (1955). Physiology of the cotton plant. *Annu. Rev. Pl. Physiol.* **6**, 299–328.   R, XIX

EVANS, L. T. (1958 a). Notes on the design of the Canberra phytotron. (Mimeographed).   IX

EVANS, L. T. (1958 b). Personal communication of manuscript for: Flower initiation in *Trifolium subterraneum* L. I. Analysis of the partial processes involved. 30 April.   XI

EVANS, L. T. (1958 c). Personal communication of manuscript for: Flower initiation in *Vicia faba* L. 30 April.   XXI

BIBLIOGRAPHY

EVANS, M., and WILSIE, C. P. (1946). Flowering of brome grass, *Bromus inermis*, in the greenhouse as influenced by length of day, temperature and level of fertility. *J. Amer. Soc. Agron.* **38**, 923–32.   XI

EVANS, M. W. (1931). Relation of latitude to time of blooming of timothy. *Ecology*, **12**, 182–7.   X

EVANS, M. W. (1939). Relation of latitude to certain phases of the growth of timothy. *Amer. J. Bot.* **26**, 212–18.   X

EVANS, M. W., and ALLARD, H. A. (1934). Relation of length of day to the growth of timothy. *J. agric. Res.* **48**, 571–86.   XI

EVANS, M. W., ALLARD, H. A., and McCONKEY, O. (1935). Time of heading and flowering of early, medium, and late timothy plants at different latitudes. *Sci. Agric.* **15**, 573–9.   X

EVANS, M. W., and GROVER, F. O. (1940). Developmental morphology of the growing point of the shoot and inflorescence in grasses. *J. agric. Res.* **61**, 481–521.   II, XI

FEDOROV, A. K. (1956). Some characteristics of the light stage of winter plants in relation to their winter hardiness. *Doklady Akad. Nauk, SSSR*, **107**, 605–8.   XXII

FERGUSON, J. H. A. (1957). Photothermographs, a tool for climate studies in relation to the ecology of vegetable varieties. *Euphytica*, **6**, 97–105.   XIII

FINCH, L. R., and CARR, D. J. (1956). Nucleic acid content of Petkus rye embryos in relation to vernalization and devernalization. *Aust. J. biol. Sci.* **9**, 355–63.   XXII

FINNEY, K. F., and FRYER, H. C. (1958). Effect on loaf volume of high temperatures during the fruiting period of wheat. *Agron. J.* **50**, 28–34.   XXII

FISHER, J. E. (1955). Floral induction in soybeans. *Bot. Gaz.* **117**, 156–65.   XXI

FLEMION, F. (1956). Effects of temperature, light and nutrients on physiological dwarfing in peach seedlings. *Pl .Physiol.* **31**—Suppl., iii.   XVII

FRANK, H., and RENNER, O. (1956). Über Verjüngung bei *Hedera helix* L. *Planta*, **47**, 105–14.   II

FRANKEL, O. (1954). Invasion and evolution of plants in Australia and New Zealand. *Caryologia*, **6**—Suppl., 600–19.   X, XI

FRAZIER, J. C., ASCHAM, L., CARDWELL, A. B., FRYER, H. C., and WILLIS, W. W. (1954). Effect of supplemental lighting on the ascorbic acid concentration of greenhouse tomatoes. *Proc. Amer. Soc. hort. Sci.* **64**, 351–9.   XVI

FREY, K. J., and WIGGANS, S. C. (1957). Tillering studies in oats. I. Tillering characteristics of oat varieties. *Agron. J.* **49**, 48–50.   XXII

FRIEND, D. J. C., and GREGORY, F. G. (1953). Acceleration of flowering in partially vernalised grain of Petkus winter rye by subsequent treatment at high temperature. *Nature*, **172**, 667–8.   IV

FUKUI, H. N., WELLER, L. E., WITTWER, S. H., and SELL, H. M. (1958). Natural growth substances in vernalized and non-vernalized lettuce seedlings. *Amer. J. Bot.* **45**, 73–4.   XII

FURR, J. R., and ARMSTRONG, W. W. (1956). Flower induction in marsh grapefruit in the Coachella Valley, California. *Proc. Amer. Soc. hort. Sci.* **67**, 176–82.   XVII

FUSTEC-MATHON, E., and MATHON, C. C. (1958). Lumière et développement. (Influence des radiations de grande longueur d'onde sur la formation des épis chez les Graminées). *Bull. Soc. bot. Fr.* **105**, 323–32.   XXII

GALL, H. J. F. (1947). Flowering of smooth brome grass under certain environmental conditions. *Bot. Gaz.* **109**, 59–71.   XI

GANGULEE, H. C. (1955). Studies on the date of ear emergence in rice. I. Relation between sowing time and date of ear emergence. *Bot. Gaz.* **117**, 1–10.   XXII

BIBLIOGRAPHY

GARDNER, F. P., and LOOMIS, W. E. (1953). Floral induction and development in orchard grass. *Pl. Physiol.* **28**, 201–17.   XI

GARNER, W. W., and ALLARD, H. A. (1920 a). Effect of relative length of day and night and other factors of the environment on growth and reproduction in plants. *J. agric. Res.* **18**, 553–606.   I

GARNER, W. W., and ALLARD, H. A. (1920 b). Effect of relative length of day and night on flowering and fruiting of plants. *Rep. Smithson. Instn.* 569–88.   I

GASSNER, G. (1918). Beiträge zur physiologischen Charakteristik sommer- und winterannueller Gewächse, insbesondere der Getreidepflanzen. *Z. Bot.* **10**, 417–30.   I

GASSNER, G. (1953). Untersuchungen zur physiologischen Charakterisierung unserer Weizensorten. *Züchter*, **23**, 193–206.   XXII

GENTER, C. F., EHEART, J. F., and LINKOUS, W. N. (1956). Effects of location, hybrid, fertilizer, and rate of planting on the oil and protein contents of corn grain. *Agron. J.* **48**, 63–7.   XXII

GHOSE, R. L. M., GHATGE, M. B., and SUBRAHMANYAN, V. (1956). Rice in India. Indian Coun. agric. Res., New Delhi. 507 pp.   R, XXII

GHOSH, B. N. (1955). Photoperiodic response in til (*Sesamum indicum* Linn.). *Curr. Sci.* **24**, 170.   XX

GIBSON, P. B. (1957). Effect of flowering on the persistence of white clover. *Agron. J.* **49**, 213–15.   XI

GIST, G. R., and MOTT, G. O. (1957). Some effects of light intensity, temperature and soil moisture on the growth of alfalfa, red clover and birdsfoot trefoil seedlings. *Agron. J.* **49**, 33–6.   XI

GORTER, C. J. (1955). Photoperiodism of flowering in apple trees. 14*th Internat. Hort. Congr.* 351–4.   XVII

GOTT, M. B. (1957). Vernalisation of green plants of a winter wheat. *Nature*, **180**, 714–15.   XXII

GOTT, M. B., GREGORY, F. G., and PURVIS, O. N. (1955). Studies in vernalisation of cereals. XIII. Photoperiodic control of stages of flowering between initiation and ear formation in vernalised and unvernalised Petkus winter rye. *Ann. Bot., Lond.*, N.S. **19**, 87–126.   IV, XXII

GOWING, D. P. (1956). An hypothesis of the role of naphthaleneacetic acid in flower induction in the pineapple. *Amer. J. Bot.* **43**, 411–18.   XVII

GRAFIUS, J. E. (1956). The interaction of genotype and night temperature in oat and barley varieties. *Agron. J.* **48**, 56–9.   XXII

GREGORY, F. G. (1948). The control of flowering in plants. In: Soc. exp. Biol., Symp. II: Growth in relation to Differentiation and Morphogenesis. C.U.P., 75–103.   R, I, IV

GREGORY, F. G., and HUSSEY, G. G. (1953). Photoperiodic responses of *Arabidopsis thaliana*. *Proc. Linn. Soc., Lond.* **164**, 137–9.   I, VI

GREGORY, F. G., and PURVIS, O. N., (1936). Vernalisation of winter rye during ripening. *Nature*, **138**, 973.   VIII

GREGORY, F. G., and PURVIS, O. N. (1938). Studies in vernalisation of cereals. II. The vernalisation of excised mature embryos, and of developing ears. *Ann. Bot., Lond.*, NS. **2**, 237–51.   VIII

GREGORY, L. E. (1956). Some factors for tuberization in the potato plant. *Amer. J. Bot.* **43**, 281–8.   XIII

GROSCH, H. G. (1956). Weitere photoperiodische Versuche an Kulturkartoffeln. *Z. Acker- u. Pflbau*, **101**, 301–20.   XIII

GROVE, J. F. (1958). Personal communication, 14 April.   VI

GUSTAFSON, F. G. (1936). Inducement of fruit development by growth-promoting chemicals. *Proc. Nat. Acad. Sci., U.S.A.* **22**, 628–36.   V

BIBLIOGRAPHY

GUSTAFSON, F. G. (1939). The cause of natural parthenocarpy. *Amer. J. Bot.* **26**, 135–8. V

GUTTRIDGE, C. G. (1958). Strawberries at any time of the year. *Grower*, **49**, 806–8. XVIII

HABERMANN, H. M., and WALLACE, R. H. (1958). Transfer of flowering stimulus from stock to scion in grafted *Helianthus annuus* L. *Amer. J. Bot.* **45**, 479–82. IV

HAINE, K. E. (1955). The improvement and maintenance of varieties of winter cauliflower. *14th Internat. Hort. Congr.* 479–83. XII

HAMNER, K. C. (1940). Interrelation of light and darkness in photoperiodic induction. *Bot. Gaz.* **101**, 658–87. IV

HAMNER, K. C. (1948). Factors governing the induction and development of reproductive structures in plants. In: Soc. exp. Biol., Symp. II: Growth in relation to Differentiation and Morphogenesis. C.U.P., 104–16. R, I

HAMNER, K. C., and BONNER, J. (1938). Photoperiodism in relation to hormones as factors in floral initiation and development. *Bot. Gaz.* **100**, 388–431. I

HAMNER, K. C., and NANDA, K. K. (1956). A relationship between applications of indoleacetic acid and the high-intensity-light reaction of photoperiodism. *Bot. Gaz.* **118**, 13–18. V

HÄNSEL, H. (1949). Über die Änderung der 'Blühreife' während eines Winterhalbjahres und die Bestimmung einer 'Kältebedarfs-Zahl' bei fünf Wintergerstensorten. *Bodenkultur*, **3**, 1–41. I, XXII

HÄNSEL, H. (1952). Studie über seitliche 'Ausladung' und Anzahl der Keimwurzeln verschiedener Gerstensorten mit besonderer Berücksichtigung ihres Verhaltens nach Vernalisation. *Z. PflZücht.* **31**, 359–80. XXII

HÄNSEL, H. (1953). Vernalisation of winter rye by negative temperatures and the influence of vernalisation upon the lamina length of the first and second leaf in winter rye, spring barley and winter barley. *Ann. Bot., Lond.*, N.S. **17**, 417–32. XXII

HÄNSEL, H. (1954 a). Vergleich der Konstanz verschiedener 'Blühzeit'–Maße im Langtag in Hinblick auf Sortencharakteristik und Erbversuch bei *Pisum sativum*. *Züchter*, **24**, 77–92. I, XXI

HÄNSEL, H. (1954 b). Versuche zur Vererbung der Nodienzahl-Blühzeit-Relation im langen Tag bei Erbsensorten (*Pisum sativum* × *Pisum sativum* ssp. *arvense*). *Züchter*, **24**, 96–115. XXI

HÄNSEL, H. (1954 c). Winterfestigkeit und die Methoden ihrer Überprüfung bei Getreide. *Ber. Arbstag. Saatzuchtleiter*, 96–136. XXII

HÄNSEL, H. (1955 a). Entwicklungs-Relationen ertragbildender Organe von Winterweizen (und Winterroggen) und ihre Bedeutung für Termine zusätzlicher Nährstoff- und Wassergaben. *Z. Acker- u. Pflbau*, **100**, 77–98. XXII

HÄNSEL, H. (1955 b). Mehrjährige Frühjahrs-Saatzeiten-Versuche mit Winterweizen. Ein Beitrag zur entwicklungsphysiologischen Sortencharakteristik von österreichischen und anderen Winterweizen. *Bodenkultur*, **8**, 182–94. XXII

HÄNSEL, H. (1955 c). Entwicklungs-Relationen verschiedener Organe von Winterweizen (*Triticum aestivum* L.) *Z. PflZücht.* **35**, 117–36. XXII

HANSON, R. G., EWING, E. C., and EWING, E. C., Jr. (1956). Effect of environmental factors on fiber properties and yield of Deltapine cottons. *Agron. J.* **48**, 573–81. XIX

HARDER, R., and BODE, O. (1943). Über die Wirkung von Zwischenbelichtungen während der Dunkelperiode auf das Blühen, die Verlaubung und die Blattsukkulenz bei der Kurztagpflanze *Kalanchoe blossfeldiana*. *Planta*, **33**, 469–504. IV

HARDESTY, B., and ELLIOTT, F. C. (1956). Differential post-ripening effects among seeds from the same parental wheat spike. *Agron. J.* **48**, 406–9. XXII

BIBLIOGRAPHY

HARDING, R. B., CHAPMAN, H. D., and WHITING, F. L. (1954). Size fluctuations of the Valencia oranges in major California citrus districts, 1932 to 1952, indicate significance of climate as a cause of small fruit. *Proc. Amer. Soc. hort. Sci.* **64,** 128–38. XVII

HARLAN, J. R. (1945). Cleistogamy and chasmogamy in *Bromus carinatus* Hook. and Arn. *Amer. J. Bot.* **32,** 66–72. II

HARPER, J. L. (1955 a). Problems involved in the extension of maize cultivation into Northern temperate regions. *World Crops,* **7,** 93–6 and 104. XXII

HARPER, J. L. (1955 b). The influence of the environment on seed and seedling mortality. VI. The effects of the interaction of soil moisture and temperature on the mortality of maize grains. *Ann. appl. Biol.* **43,** 696–708. XXII

HARPER, J. L., LANDRAGIN, P. A., and LUDWIG, J. W. (1955). The influence of environment on seed and seedling mortality. I. The influence of time of planting on the germination of maize. *New Phytol.* **54,** 107–18. XXII

HARTMANN, H. T., and PORLINGIS, I. (1957). Effect of different amounts of winter chilling on fruitfulness of several olive varieties. *Bot. Gaz.* **119,** 102–4. XVII

HAUPT, W. (1957). Photoperiodische Reaktion bei einer als tagneutral geltenden Sorte von *Pisum sativum. Ber. dtsch. bot. Ges.* **70,** 191–8. XXI

Hawaii Agricultural Experiment Station (1948). Report for biennium ending June 30, 1948, 125–33. XII

HEDRICK, D. W. (1958). Proper utilization—A problem in evaluating the physiological response of plants to grazing use: a review. *J. Range Mgmt,* **11,** 34–43. XI

HELLMERS, H. (1957). Photoperiodic effects on the growth of Bigcone Douglas-fir and Coulter pine. *Bull. ecol. Soc. Amer.* **38,** 76. XII

HENKELJ, P. A., and others (1955). The effect on maize development and ripening of subjecting the seed to fluctuating temperature. *Fiziol. Rast.* **2,** 447–53. XXII

HESLOP-HARRISON, J. (1956). Auxin and sexuality in *Cannabis sativa. Physiol. Plant.* **9,** 588–97. XII

HESLOP-HARRISON, J. (1957). The experimental modification of sex expression in flowering plants. *Biol. Rev.* **32,** 38–90. R, I, II

HESLOP-HARRISON, J., and HESLOP-HARRISON, Y. (1957 a). Studies on floweringplant growth and organogenesis. *Proc. roy. Soc. Edinb.* (*B*), **66,** 409–34. II

HESLOP-HARRISON, J., and HESLOP-HARRISON, Y. (1957 b). The effect of carbon monoxide on sexuality in *Mercurialis ambigua* L. fils. *New Phytol.* **56,** 352–5. II

HESLOP-HARRISON, J., and HESLOP-HARRISON, Y. (1958 a). Photoperiod, auxin and sex balance in a long-day plant. *Nature,* **181,** 100–2. II

HESLOP-HARRISON, J., and HESLOP-HARRISON, Y. (1958 b). Long-day and auxin induced male sterility in *Silene pendula* L. *Portug. Acta biol.* (*A*), **5,** 79–94. II

HIESEY, W. M. (1953 a). Growth and development of species and hybrids of *Poa* under controlled temperatures. *Amer. J. Bot.* **40,** 205–21. XI

HIESEY, W. M. (1953 b). Comparative growth between and within climatic races of *Achillea* under controlled conditions. *Evolution,* **7,** 297–316. Plate

HIGHKIN, H. R. (1955). Flower promoting activity of pea seed diffusates. *Pl. Physiol.* **30,** 390. XXI

HIGHKIN, H. R. (1956). Vernalization in peas. *Pl. Physiol.* **31,** 399–403. XXI

HIGHKIN, H. R. (1957). Temperature-induced variability in the growth and development of pea plants. *Pl. Physiol.* **32**—Suppl., xlix–1. XXI

HIGHKIN, H. R., and HANSON, J. B. (1954). Possible interaction between light-dark cycles and endogenous daily rhythms on the growth of tomato plants. *Pl. Physiol.* **29,** 301–2. XVI

HILLMAN, W. S. (1956). Injury of tomato plants by continuous light and unfavourable photoperiodic cycles. *Amer. J. Bot.* **43,** 89–96. XVI

367

BIBLIOGRAPHY

HOCKEY, K. C. (1955). Some facts and some problems associated with the production of tomatoes under glass in New Zealand. 14*th Internat. Hort. Congr.* 566–72. XVI

HODGSON, G. L., and BLACKMAN, G. E. (1957). An analsyis of the influence of plant density on the growth of *Vicia faba*. II. The significance of competition for light in relation to plant development at different densities. *J. exp. Bot.* **8**, 195–219. XXI

HOLLAENDER, A. (Ed.) (1956). Radiation Biology. 3. Visible and near-visible light. McGraw-Hill, New York. viii + 765 pp. R, I

HOLLIDAY, R. (1956). Fodder production from winter-sown cereals and its effect upon grain yield. *Field Crop Abstr.* **9**, 129–35 and 207–13. XXII

HOLMES, J. C., and TAHIR, W. M. (1956). The effect of some factors on growth, development and yield of winter wheat. *J. agric. Sci.* **48**, 115–23. XXII

HOPKINS, A. D. (1918). United States Dept. Agric., *Weather Bull., Mon. Weather Rev.*, Suppl. No. 9, 1–42. X

HOUSLEY, S., and BENTLEY, J. A. (1956). Studies in plant growth hormones. IV. Chromatography of hormones and hormone precursors in cabbage. *J. exp. Bot.* **7**, 219–38. XII

HOYLE, D. A. (1955). Preliminary studies on the growth of fruit plants in relation to photoperiod. 14*th Internat. Hort. Congr.* 342–50. XVII

HUDSON, J. P. (1957 a). Control of plant environment for experimental work and notes on environmental control equipment in use in Britain. *Misc. Publ.* 8. Nottingham Univ. Dep. Hort., 30 pp. IX

HUDSON, J. P. (Ed.) (1957 b). Control of the Plant Environment. Proceedings of the University of Nottingham Fourth Easter School in Agricultural Science. Butterworths Sci. Publ., London. xvi + 240 pp. R, IX

HUDSON, P. S., and RICHENS, R. H. (1946). The new genetics in the Soviet Union. *Imp. Bur. Pl. Breed. and Genet., Tech. Comm.* 12. 88 pp. X

HUMPHRIES, E. C. (1958). The effect of removal of the root-system of barley on the production of ears. *Ann. Bot., Lond.*, N.S. **22**, 417–22. XXII

HUMPHRIES, E. C., and KASSANIS, B. (1955). Effects of darkness on the constitution of tobacco leaves and susceptibility to virus infection. *Ann. appl. Biol.* **43**, 686–95. XII

HUSSEY, G., and GREGORY, F. G. (1954). The effect of auxin on the flowering behaviour of Wintex barley and Petkus rye. *Pl. Physiol.* **29**, 292–6. V, XXII

Imperial Agricultural Bureaux (1935). Vernalization and phasic development of plants. Joint Publ. No. 1. R, I

INSELBERG, E. (1956). Factors affecting earshoot development in dent corn. *Diss. Abstr.* **16**, 1572. XXII

JACKSON, T. H. (1955). The reaction of some horticultural crops to climates in East Africa. 14*th Internat. Hort. Congr.* 1463–71. XVII

JEATER, R. S. L. (1956). A method for determining developmental stages in grasses. *J. Brit. Grassl. Soc.* **11**, 139–46. II

JEATER, R. S. L. (1958). The effect of growth-regulating weedkillers on the morphology of grasses. *J. Brit. Grassl. Soc.* **13**, 7–12. XI

JENKINS, J. M., Jr. (1954). Some effects of different daylengths and temperatures upon bulb formation in shallots. *Proc. Amer. Soc. hort. Sci.* **64**, 311–14. XIV

JOHNSON, L. P. V., and OBOLENSKY, G. (1954). Note on the effect of ultrasonic vibration on development of barley. *Canad. J. agric. Sci.* **34**, 651–2. XXII

JOHNSON, S. P. (1956). Influence of growth regulators on setting of tomato fruits: a concept. *Proc. Amer. Soc. hort. Sci.* **67**, 365–8. XVI

JOLIVET, M. E. (1956). Fertilisation azotée du blé d'hiver. *C. R. Acad. Agric. Fr.* **42**, 483–9. XXII

BIBLIOGRAPHY

JONES, J. E. (1956). Growth and development of three population intensities of hybrid corn under irrigation and natural conditions. *Proc. 2nd Ann. Meet. Canad. Soc. Agron.*, **B7**.　　　　　　　　　　　　　　　　　XXII

JONKERS, H. (1958). Accelerated flowering of strawberry seedlings. *Euphytica*, **7**, 41–6.　　　　　　　　　　　　　　　　　　　　　　　　　　　XVIII

JULÉN, G. (1952). Some aspects of the irrigation of temporary leys. I. The influence of water supply, temperature and light upon the rate of growth. *Acta agric. scand.* **2**, 312–20.　　　　　　　　　　　　　　　　　　　　　III

JUNGFER, E. (1955). Kurztagbehandelte Klone in der Roggenzüchtung. *Züchter*, **25**, 255–62.　　　　　　　　　　　　　　　　　　　　　　　　　XXII

KALBFLEISCH, W. (1958). Personal communication, 11 April.　　　　　　IX

KATO, J. (1956). Effect of gibberellin on elongation, water uptake and respiration of pea-stem sections. *Science*, **123**, 1132.　　　　　　　　　　　VI

KELENY, G. P. (1959). Report to the Government of Indonesia on the development of leguminous crops. FAO/ETAP Report No. 1094.　　　　　　　XXI

KINEBUCHI, M., and others (1957). Studies on sterility in lower spikelets of barley. 2. On the environment causing the sterility and on its control. *Proc. Crop Sci. Soc. Japan*, **26**, 33.　　　　　　　　　　　　　　　　　　XXII

KLEBS, G. (1918). Über die Blütenbildung von *Sempervivum*. *Flora*, **111–12**, 128–51.　I

KLOEN, D., and SPECKMANN, G. J. (1956). The creation of tetraploid beets. IV. Morphological and physiological characteristics of C_2 beets. *Euphytica*, **5**, 308–22.　　　　　　　　　　　　　　　　　　　　　　　XIII

KNIGHT, W. E., and BENNETT, H. W. (1953). Preliminary report of the effect of photoperiod and temperature on the flowering and growth of several Southern grasses. *Agron. J.* **45**, 268–9.　　　　　　　　　　　　　　XI

KOLOMIEC, P. T. (1955). Dormancy in red clover. *Izv. Akad. Nauk, SSSR*, **4**, 50–7.　　　　　　　　　　　　　　　　　　　　　　　　XI

KOPECKY, F. (1956). Problems of breeding black poplar in Hungary. *Acta agron. hung.* **6**, 307–20.　　　　　　　　　　　　　　　　　　　XII

KOPETZ, L. M., and STEINECK, O. (1954). Photoperiodische Untersuchungen an Kartoffelsämlingen. *Züchter*, **24**, 69–77.　　　　　　　　　　XIII

KOSTJUČENKO, I. A., and ZARUBAÏLO, T. Ja. (1936). Natural vernalization of grains on the plant during ripening and its significance in practice. *Trudy Prikl. Bot., Genet. i Selek., Ser. A*, **17**, 17–23.　　　　　　　　　　　VIII

KRAUS, E. J., and KRAYBILL, H. R. (1918). Vegetation and reproduction with special reference to the tomato. *Bull. Ore. agric. Exp. Sta.* 149.　　　　　I

KRONENBERG, H. G., GERRITSEN, J. D., and KLINKENBERG, C. H. (1949). De Aardbei. W. E. Tjeenk Willink, Zwolle. 327 pp.　　　　　　　　R, XVIII

KURTH, H. (1955). Die Jarowisation landwirtschaftlicher Kulturpflanzen. Neue Brehm-Bücherei, Wittenberg. 44 pp.　　　　　　　XI, XIII, XX

KURTH, H. (1956 a). Über das Zusammenwirken von Jarowisation und Photoperiodismus bei einigen Leguminosen, insbesondere bei *Vicia villosa* Roth. *Züchter*, **26**, 71–8.　　　　　　　　　　　　　　　　　XI

KURTH, H. (1956 b). The vernalization of some leguminous plants, especially of hairy vetches. *Euphytica*, **5**, 63–70.　　　　　　　　　　XI

LABANAUSKAS, C. K., and DUNGAN, G. H. (1956). Inter-relationship of tillers and main stems in oats. *Agron. J.* **48**, 265–8.　　　　　　　　XXII

LAIBACH, F. (1943). *Arabidopsis thaliana* (L.) Heynh. als Objekt für genetische und entwicklungsphysiologische Untersuchungen. *Bot. Arch.* **44**, 439–55.　　I

LAMP, H. F. (1952). Reproductive activity in *Bromus inermis* in relation to phases of tiller development. *Bot. Gaz.* **113**, 413–38.　　　　　　　　XI

LANA, E. P. (1956). Effects of plant population and seasons on the performance of sweet corn for canning. *Proc. Amer. Soc. hort. Sci.* **67**, 460–7.　　XXII

N*　　　　　　　　　　　　　369

LANDAU, N. (1957). Effect of length of day and temperature on the development of some annual legumes indigenous in Israel. *Bull. Res. Coun. Israel* (*D*), **5**, 245–56.
XI

LANDAU, N. (1958). Vernalization effects in mangold and sugar beet under thermal conditions unfavourable to flowering. *Bull. Res. Coun. Israel* (*D*), **6**, 127–8.
XIII

LANG, A. (1952). Physiology of flowering. *Annu. Rev. Pl. Physiol.* **3**, 265–306.   R

LANG, A. (1956 a). Entwicklungsphysiologie. *Fortschr. Bot.* **18**, 289–328.   R, IV

LANG, A. (1956 b). Induction of flower formation in biennial *Hyoscyamus niger* by treatment with gibberellin. *Naturwissenschaften*, **43**, 284–5.   VI

LANG, A. (1957). The effect of gibberellin upon flower formation. *Proc. Nat. Acad. Sci., U.S.A.* **43**, 709–17.   Plate

LANG, A., and LIVERMAN, J. L. (1954). The role of auxin in the photoperiodic response of long-day plants. 8ᵉ *Congr. Internat. Bot., Rapp. et Comm., Sect.* 11, 330–1.   I

LANG, A., and MELCHERS, G. (1947). Vernalisation and Devernalisation bei einer zweijährigen Pflanze. *Z. Naturforsch.* **26**, 444–9.   IV

LANGER, R. H. M. (1956). Growth and nutrition of timothy (*Phleum pratense*). I. The life history of the individual tillers. *Ann. appl. Biol.* **44**, 166–87.   II, XI

LANGER, R. H. M. (1957). Growth and nutrition of timothy (*Phleum pratense*). II. Growth of the plant in relation to tiller development. *Ann. appl. Biol.* **45**, 528–41.   II, III

LANGER, R. H. M., and RYLE, G. J. A. (1958). Vegetative proliferation in herbage grasses. *J. Brit. Grassl. Soc.* **13**, 29–33.   XI

LANGRIDGE, J. (1955). Biochemical mutations in the crucifer *Arabidopsis thaliana* (L.) Heynh. *Nature*, **176**, 260.   I

LANGRIDGE, J. (1957 a). Effect of day-length and gibberellic acid on the flowering of *Arabidopsis*. *Nature*, **180**, 36–7.   I, VI

LANGRIDGE, J. (1957 b). The aseptic culture of *Arabidopsis thaliana* (L.) Heynh. *Aust. J. biol. Sci.* **10**, 243–52.   I

LANGSTON, R., and LEOPOLD, A. C. (1954 a). Photoperiodic responses of peppermint. *Proc. Amer. Soc. hort. Sci.* **63**, 347–52.   XII

LANGSTON, R., and LEOPOLD, A. C. (1954 b). The dark fixation of carbon dioxide as a factor in photoperiodism. *Pl. Physiol.* **29**, 436–40.   I, V

LARSEN, E. C. (1947). Photoperiodic responses of geographical strains of *Andropogon scoparius*. *Bot. Gaz.* **109**, 132–49.   XI

LAUBE, H. A. (1956). Vergleichende Untersuchungen zur Entwicklungsphysiologie am Petkuser Normalstroh-Roggen (2n) und Petkuser Tetraroggen (4n). *Z. PflZücht.* **36**, 305–62.   XXII

LAUDE, H. M. (1953). The nature of summer dormancy in perennial grasses. *Bot. Gaz.* **114**, 284–92.   XI

LAWRENCE, W. E. (1945). Some ecotypic relations of *Deschampsia caespitosa*. *Amer. J. Bot.* **32**, 298–314.   X

LAWRENCE, W. J. C. (1950). Science and the Glasshouse. Oliver and Boyd, Edinburgh. 171 pp.   IX

LAWRENCE, W. J. C. (1955). Control of glasshouse climate. 14*th Internat. Hort. Congr.* 573–80.   IX

LECRENIER, A., TILKIN, V. E., and RUNCHAINE, J. (1955). Contribution à l'étude morphologique de la chicorée Witloof. 14*th Internat. Hort. Congr.* 581–8.   XII

LEOPOLD, A. C. (1955). Auxins and plant growth. Univ. Calif. Press, Berkeley and Los Angeles. 354 pp.   R, V

LEOPOLD, A. C., and GUERNSEY, F. S. (1953 a). Modification of floral initiation with auxins and temperatures. *Amer. J. Bot.* **40**, 603–7.   V, XXI

370

BIBLIOGRAPHY

LEOPOLD, A. C., and GUERNSEY, F. S. (1953 b). Interaction of auxin and temperatures in floral initiation. *Science*, 118, 215–17.   V, XXI

LEOPOLD, A. C., and GUERNSEY, F. S. (1954). Flower initiation in the Alaska pea. II. Chemical vernalization. *Amer. J. Bot.* 41, 181–5.   V, XXI

LEOPOLD, A. C., and THIMANN, K. V. (1949). The effect of auxin on flower initiation. *Amer. J. Bot.* 36, 342–7.   V, XVII, XXII

LEVI, E. (1955). The inhibition of the growth of perennial grasses by maleic hydrazide. *Aust. J. agric. Res.* 6, 378–87.   VII

LINDSTROM, R. S., WITTWER, S. H., and BUKOVAC, M. J. (1957). Gibberellin and higher plants. IV. Flowering responses of some flower crops. *Quart. Bull. Mich. agric. Exp. Sta.* 39, 673–81.   Plate

LINK, C. B., and SHANKS, J. B. (1954). Studies of the factors involved in terminating the rest period of Hydrangeas. *Proc. Amer. Soc. hort. Sci.* 64, 519–25.   XV

LIVERMAN, J. L. (1955). The physiology of flowering. *Annu. Rev. Pl. Physiol.* 6, 177–210.   R

LIVERMAN, J. L., and BONNER, J. (1953). The interaction of auxin and light in the growth responses of plants. *Proc. Nat. Acad. Sci., U.S.A.* 39, 905–16.   IV

LIVERMAN, J. L., and JOHNSON, S. P. (1957). Control of arrested fruit growth in tomato by gibberellins. *Science*, 125, 1086–7.   XVI

LIVERMAN, J. L., and LANG, A. (1956). Induction of flowering in long day plants by applied indoleacetic acid. *Pl. Physiol.* 31, 147–50.   V

LOCKHART, J. A., and BONNER, J. (1957). Effects of gibberellic acid on the photoperiod-controlled growth of woody plants. *Pl. Physiol.* 32, 492–4.   VI

LOCKHART, J. A., and HAMNER, K. C. (1954). Partial reactions in the formation of the floral stimulus in *Xanthium*. *Pl. Physiol.* 29, 509–13.   I

LONA, F. (1951). Fitofenologia e foto-termoperiodismo. *Nuovo G. bot. ital.* 58, 550–60.   X

LONA, F. (1954 a). Il ciclo di sviluppo della bietola in relazione al termoperiodismo e al fotoperiodismo. *Problemi agric.* 2. 5 pp.   XIII

LONA, F. (1954 b). La vernalizzazione dei cereali autunnali in alta montagna. *Natura Alpina*, 3. 5 pp.   XXII

LONA, F. (1956). L'azione dell'acido gibberellico sull'accrescimento caulinare di talune piante erbacee in condizioni esterne controllate. *Nuovo G. bot. ital.* 63, 61–76.   VI

LONA, F. (1957). Il fenomeno della prefioritura di *Brassica rapa* L. in culture alpine ed il fattore ecologico determinante. *Boll. Soc. ital. Biol. sperim.* 33, 137–40.
                                                                                           Plate

LONA, F., and BOCCHI, A. (1956). Sviluppo vegetativo e riproduttivo di alcune longidiurne in rapporto all'azione dell'acido gibberellico. *Nuovo G. bot. ital.* 63, 469–86.   VI

LONA, F., BRACCI, L., and VALLE, T. (1952). Regime termoperiodico giornaliero e concentrazione endocellulare nelle foglie e nel fusto di *Solanum tuberosum* L. (var. Bianca di Como). *Nuovo G. bot. ital.* 58, 169–71.   XIII

LUDWIG, R. A., BARRALES, H. G., and STEPPLER, H. S. (1953). Studies on the effect of light on the growth and development of red clover. *Canad. J. agric. Sci.* 33, 274–87.   XI

LUND, H. A. (1956). The biosynthesis of indoleacetic acid in the styles and ovaries of tobacco preliminary to the setting of fruit. *Pl. Physiol.* 31, 334–9.   XII

LYSENKO, T. D. (1935). Theoretical basis of vernalization. Moscow.   I

MAATSCH, R. (1955). Die Bedeutung der heimatlichen Standortsbedingungen für die Kultur von Zierpflanzen unter Glas. *14th Internat. Hort. Congr.* 1072–83.   IX

MACARTHUR, M., and CHAN, A. P. (1956). Factors influencing the early blooming of William Pitt tulips. *Proc. Amer. Soc. hort. Sci.* 68, 503–7.   XIV

BIBLIOGRAPHY

McKINNEY, H. H. (1940). Vernalization and the growth-phase concept. *Bot. Rev.* **6**, 25–47.   R, I

McKINNEY, H. H., and SANDO, J. J. (1935). Earliness of sexual reproduction in wheat as influenced by temperature and light. *J. agric. Res.* **51**, 621–39.   VIII

McMILLAN, C. (1956 a). Nature of the plant community. I. Uniform garden and light period studies of five grass taxa in Nebraska. *Ecology*, **37**, 330–40.   XI

McMILLAN, C. (1956 b). Nature of the plant community. II. Variation in flowering behaviour within populations of *Andropogon scoparius*. *Amer. J. Bot.* **43**, 429–36.   XI

McMILLAN, C. (1957). Nature of the plant community. III. Flowering behaviour within two grassland communities under reciprocal transplanting. *Amer. J. Bot.* **44**, 144–53.   XI

MADEC, P., and PERENNEC, P. (1956). Influence de l'origine sur le comportement des plants de pomme de terre. *Ann. Amélior. Pl., Paris*, **6**, 5–26.   XIII

MAGGS, D. H. (1955). The inception of flowering in some apple rootstock varieties. *J. hort. Sci.* **30**, 234–41.   XVII

MANGELSDORF, A. J. (1956). Sugarcane breeding. *Proc. 9th Congr. Internat. Soc. Sugarcane Technol.*, 13–16.   XII

MANNER, R. (1956). Studies on seed setting and seed yield in oil flax. *Medd. Gullak. VäxtförädlAnst.* **12.** 139 pp.   XX

MARGARA, J. (1954). Problèmes que pose l'amélioration de la betterave sucrière en France. *Ann. Amélior. Pl., Paris*, **4**, 147–95.   XIII

MARSDEN RAY, M. P. F. (1958). Formation of Jerusalem artichoke tubers in sterile culture. *Nature*, **181**, 1480–2.   XIII

MARTH, P. C., AUDIA, W. V., and MITCHELL, J. W. (1956). Effects of gibberellic acid on growth and development of plants of various genera and species. *Bot. Gaz.* **118**, 106–11.   VI

MARTH, P. C., PRESTON, W. H., and MITCHELL, J. W. (1953). Growth-controlling effects of some quarternary ammonium compounds on various species of plants. *Bot. Gaz.* **115**, 200–4.   VII

MATHON, C. C. (1955). Recherches sur le développement des céréales. Cinquième note: Les orges. *Bull. Muséum*, 2e sér. **27**, 330–7.   XXII

MATHON, C. C. (1956). Recherches méthodologiques sur l'écologie du développement de diverses variétés de *Triticum turgidum compositum* (blé Poulard branchu). *Bull. Muséum*, 2e sér. **28**, 315–18.   XXII

MATHON, C. C. (1957). La 'greffe' embryonnaire des graminées. *Bull. mens. Soc. Linn. Lyon*, **26**, 66–70.   XXII

MATHON, C. C. (1959). Rythmes de développement, vernalisation, photopériodisme et phytogéographie. Recherches expérimentales. *Bull. mens. Soc. Linn. Lyon*, **28**, 37–49.   XXII

MAXIMOV, N. A. (1934). The theoretical significance of vernalization. *Bull.* 16, *Imp. Bur. Pl. Genet.: Herb. Pl.* 14 pp.   R, I

MELCHERS, G. (1939). Die Blühhormone. *Ber. dtsch. bot. Ges.* **57**, 29–48.   IV

MELCHERS, G. (1954 a). Mechanismus der Vernalisation. *C. R. 8e Congr. Internat. Bot., Sect.* 11, 189–93.   R, IV

MELCHERS, G. (1954 b). Zusammenhang der Vernalisation mit dem Photoperiodismus. *C. R. 8e Congr. Internat. Bot., Sect.* 11, 205–9.   R, I, IV

MELCHERS, G., and LANG, A. (1941). Weitere Untersuchungen zur Frage der Blühhormone. *Biol. Zbl.* **61**, 16–39.   IV

MES, M. G. (1952). The influence of some climatic factors on the growth and seed production of grasses. *VeldGold (S. Afr. Grassl. Conf.)*, 39–51.   XI

MES, M. G. (1957). Studies on the flowering of *Coffea arabica* L. *Portug. Acta biol.* (*A*), **4**, 328–54; **5**, 25–44.   XVII

BIBLIOGRAPHY

MES, M. G., SAUBERT VON HAUSEN, S., and VAN GYLSWYK, N. O. (1957). A comparative study of the growth and yield of a number of *Crotalaria* species suitable for green manuring. And: A comparative study of the nitrogen content of a number of *Crotalaria* species suitable for green manuring. *S. Afr. J. Sci.* **53**, 181–9. XII

MIA, A. J. (1955). The vegetative shoot apex of *Linum usitatissimum* L. and origin and development of leaf and bud primordia and foliar traces. *Pakist. J. sci. Res.* **7**, 159–64. XII

MICHAJLIKOV, V., JUAREZ, G. A., and ALVAREZ HERLEIN, L. A. (1954). El temple de trigo contra la sequía aplicado al gran cultivo. *Meteoros, B. Aires*, **4**, 215–29. XXII

MICHELINI, F. J. (1958). The plastochron index in developmental studies of *Xanthium italicum* Moretti. *Amer. J. Bot.* **45**, 525–33. II

MIHALOVSKIĬ, A. G., and MELJNIK, T. D. (1956). Hastening development and ripening of maize by means of vernalizing the seed. *Zemledelie*, **4**, 91–3. XXII

MIKA, E. S. (1955). Studies on the growth and development and morphine content of opium poppy. *Bot. Gaz.* **116**, 323–39. XX

MILLER, C. O. (1958). The relationship of the kinetin and red-light promotions of lettuce seed germination. *Pl. Physiol.* **33**, 115–17. XII

MILLIKAN, C. R. (1957 a). Phosphate level in the substrate and different day and night temperatures in relation to the growth of flax. *J. Aust. Inst. agric. Sci.* **23**, 51–6. XII

MILLIKAN, C. R. (1957 b). Effects of environmental factors on the growth of two varieties of subterranean clover (*Trifolium subterraneum* L.). *Aust. J. agric. Res.* **8**, 225–45. XI

MILTHORPE, F. L. (Ed.) (1956 a). The Growth of Leaves. Proceedings of the University of Nottingham Third Easter School in Agricultural Science. Butterworths Sci. Publ., London. 223 pp. R, II, III

MILTHORPE, F. L. (1956 b). The relative importance of the different stages of leaf growth in determining the resultant area. In: Milthorpe, F. L., The Growth of Leaves, Butterworths, London, 141–50. III

MISRA, G. (1956). Photoperiodism in rice. IX. Response of an early variety of rice to long photoperiod. *Proc. Indian Acad. Sci.* **44**, 108–13. XXII

MISRA, G., and SAHU, G. (1957). Control of flowering of rice by plant growth substances. *Nature*, **180**, 816. XXII

MISRA, G., and SAHU, G. (1958). Effects of maleic hydrazide on an early variety of rice. *Curr. Sci.* **27**, 64–5. VII

MISRA, G., and SAMANTARAI, B. (1955). Effects of various levels of nitrogen on the vegetative growth and ear emergence of rice plants. *J. Indian bot. Soc.* **34**, 451–4. XXII

Missouri Agricultural Experiment Station (1943). *Res. Bull.* 371. Growth hormone production during sexual reproduction of higher plants with special reference to synapsis and syngamy. By S. H. Wittwer. 58 pp. II

MITCHELL, K. J. (1953 a). Influence of light and temperature on the growth of ryegrass (*Lolium* spp.). I. Pattern of vegetative development. *Physiol. Plant.* **6**, 21–46. III

MITCHELL, K. J. (1953 b). Influence of light and temperature on the growth of ryegrass (*Lolium* spp.). II. The control of lateral bud development. *Physiol. Plant.* **6**, 425–43. III

MITCHELL, K. J. (1954). Growth of pasture species. I. Short-rotation and perennial ryegrass. *N.Z. J. Sci. Technol.* **36A**, 193–206 III

MITCHELL, K. J. (1956). The influence of temperature on the growth of pasture plants. *Aust.-UNESCO Symp. Arid. Zone Clim.* 20/2a–20/2e. III, XI

BIBLIOGRAPHY

MITCHELL, J. W., LIVINGSTON, G. A., and MARTH, P. C. (1958). Test methods with plant-regulating substances. *U.S. Dep. Agric., Agric. Handbook* 126. 68 pp.
R, V

MOLDENHAUER, W. C., and KEATING, F. E. (1958). Relationships between climatic factors and yields of cotton, milo, and kafir on sandy soils in the Southern high plains. *U.S. Dep. Agric.* and *Tex. agric. Exp. Sta., Production Rep.* 19. 13 pp.
XIX

MORGAN, D. G., and MEES, G. C. (1958). Gibberellic acid and the growth of crop plants. *J. agric. Sci.* **50**, 49–59.
VI

MORINAGA, R., and others (1955). Photoperiodic responses of rice varieties. *Proc. Crop Sci. Soc. Japan*, **23**, 258–60.
XXII

MORINAGA, T. (1954). Studies on the photoperiodism in rice. Internat. Rice Comm., 5th Meet., Tokyo, Reports submitted by Japan. Min. Agric. and For., 21–34.
R, XXII

MORINAGA, T., and KURIYAMA, H. (1954). Some experiments on the photoperiodism in rice. Internat. Rice Comm., 5th Meet., Tokyo, Reports submitted by Japan. Min. Agric. and For., 35–63.
XXII

MORLEY, F. H. W., BROCK, R. D., and DAVERN, C. I. (1956). Subspeciation in *Trifolium subterraneum*. *Aust. J. biol. Sci.* **9**, 1–17.
XI

MORLEY, F. H. W., DADAY, H., and PEAK, J. W. (1957). Quantitative inheritance in lucerne, *Medicago sativa* L. I. Inheritance and selection for winter yield. *Aust. J. agric. Res.* **8**, 635–51.
XI

MORLEY, F. H. W., and DAVERN, C. I. (1956). Flowering time in subterranean clover. *Aust. J. agric. Res.* **7**, 388–400.
XI

MORLEY, F. H. W., and EVANS, L. T. (1959). Flower initiation in *Trifolium subterraneum* L. II. Limitations by vernalization, low temperatures, and photoperiod, in the field at Canberra. *Aust. J. agric. Res.* **10**, 17–26.
XI

MURNEEK, A. E. (1926). Effects of correlation between vegetative and reproductive functions in the tomato. *Pl. Physiol.* **1**, 3–56.
II

MURNEEK, A. E. (1939). Physiological factors in reproduction of plants. *Growth*, **3**, 295–315.
II

MURNEEK, A. E. (1951). Growth-regulating substances in relation to reproduction of some horticultural plants. In: Skoog, F., Plant Growth Substances. Univ. Wis. Press, 329–45.
R, V

MURNEEK, A. E., and WHYTE, R. O. (1948). Vernalization and Photoperiodism. Chronica Botanica, Waltham, Mass. 196 pp.
R, XII, XX, XXII

MUZIK, T. J., and CRUZADO, H. J. (1958). Transmission of juvenile rooting ability from seedlings to adults of *Hevea brasiliensis*. *Nature*, **181**, 1288.
II

NAKATA, S. (1955). Floral initiation and fruit-set in lychee, with special reference to the effect of sodium naphthaleneacetate. *Bot. Gaz.* **117**, 126–34.
XVII

NAKAYAMA, H., and SAWAMURA, H. (1955). Effects of high night temperature upon the development of wheat. *Proc. Crop Sci. Soc. Japan*, **23**, 178–82.
XXII

NANDA, K. K. (1958). Effect of photoperiod on stem elongation and lateral bud development in *Panicum miliaceum* and its correlation with flowering. *Phyton*, **10**, 7–16.
XXII

NANDA, K. K., and CHINOY, J. J. (1957). Analysis of factors determining yield in crop plants. *Pl. Physiol.* **32**, 157–69.
XXII

NANDA, K. K., and CHINOY, J. J. (1958). Lateral bud development in 'pearl millet' —*Pennisetum typhoides* Stapf *et* Hubbard, in relation to its flowering. *Curr. Sci.* **27**, 141–43.
XXII

NANDA, K. K., GROVER, R., and CHINOY, J. J. (1957 a). Some observations on lateral bud development in *Panicum miliaceum* and *Setaria italica*. *Phyton*, **8**, 97–108.
XXII

374

BIBLIOGRAPHY

NANDA, K. K., GROVER, R., and CHINOY, J. J. (1957 b). Factors affecting growth and development of some millets. I. Stem elongation and its correlation with flowering as influenced by the time of sowing. *Phyton*, **9**, 15–24.　　　　XXII

NAPP-ZINN, K. (1953). Thermostabile and thermolabile Zwischenstadien im Vernalisationsprozess. *Ber. dtsch. bot. Ges.* **66**, 362.　　　　IV

NAPP-ZINN, K. (1954). Vergleichende Atmungsmessungen an Sommer- und Winterannuellen. Untersuchungen an Caryopsen und Embryonen von *Secale cereale* und Samen von *Arabidopsis thaliana. Z. Naturforsch.* **9b**, 218–29.　　　　IV

NAYLOR, A. W. (1952). Physiology of reproduction in plants. In: Avery, G. S. (Ed.), Survey of Biological Progress, Vol. II. Acad. Press Inc., New York, 259–300.　　　　R, I

NEWELL, L. C. (1951). Controlled life cycles of brome grass (*Bromus inermis*) used in improvement. *Agron. J.* **43**, 417–23.　　　　XI

NICHOLSON, I. A. (1957). The effect of stage of maturity on the yield and chemical composition of oats for haymaking. *J. agric. Sci.* **49**, 129–40.　　　　XXII

NICKELL, L. G. (1952). The control of plant growth by the use of special chemicals, with particular emphasis on plant hormones. In: Avery, G. S. (Ed.), Survey of Biological Progress, Vol. II. Acad. Press Inc., New York, 141–95.　　　　R, V

NOBS, M. A. (1955). Seasonal periodicity in *Mimulus. Yearb. Carneg. Instn.* **54**, 181–2.　　　　XI

NUTMAN, P. S. (1941). Studies in vernalisation of cereals. VII. A study of the conditions of formation and the subsequent growth of dwarf embryos of rye. *Ann. Bot., Lond.,* N.S. **5**, 353 74.　　　　VIII

NUTMAN, P. S. (1956). The influence of the legume in root-nodule symbiosis. A comparative study of host determinants and functions. *Biol. Rev.* **31**, 109–51.　　　　R, II

NUTTONSON, M. Y. (1953). Phenology and thermal environment as a means for a physiological classification of wheat varieties and for predicting maturity dates of wheat. Amer. Inst. Crop Ecol., Washington. 108 pp.　　　　XXII

NUTTONSON, M. Y. (1955). Wheat-climate relationships and the use of phenology in ascertaining the thermal and photothermal requirements of wheat. Amer. Inst. Crop Ecol., Washington. 388 pp.　　　　XXII

OLMSTED, C. E. (1943). Growth and development in range grasses. III. Photoperiodic responses in the genus *Bouteloua. Bot. Gaz.* **105**, 165–81.　　　　XI

OLMSTED, C. E. (1944). Growth and development in range grasses. IV. Photoperiodic responses in twelve geographical strains of side-oats grama. *Bot. Gaz.* **106**, 46–74.　　　　XI

OLMSTED, C. E. (1945). Growth and development in range grasses. V. Photoperiodic responses of clonal divisions of three latitudinal strains of side-oats grama. *Bot. Gaz.* **106**, 382–401.　　　　XI

OLMSTED, C. E. (1952). Photoperiodism in native range grasses. *Proc. 6th Internat. Grassl. Congr.* 676–82.　　　　X, XI

OTTOSSON, L. (1958). Growth and maturity of peas for canning and freezing. *Roy. Sch. Agric. Sweden, Dep. Pl. Husbandry, Publ.* 9, Uppsala. 112 pp.　　　　XXI

PASCALE, A. J., and DAMARIO, E. A. (1954). El índice heliotérmico aplicado a los trigos argentinos. *Meteoros, B. Aires,* **4**, 129–57.　　　　XXII

PATON, D. M. (1957). Thermoperiodic and photoperiodic control of flower initiation in a late pea variety. *Pl. Physiol.* **32**—Suppl., ix.　　　　XXI

PATON, D. M., and BARBER, H. N. (1955). Physiological genetics of *Pisum*. I. Grafting experiments between early and late varieties. *Aust. J. biol. Sci.* **8**, 231–40.　　　　IV, XXI

PATTERSON, J. B. E. (1957). Gibberellins and gibberellic acid. *Quart. Rev. N.A.A.S.* **38**, 139–43.　　　　VI

BIBLIOGRAPHY

Pécaut, P. (1957). Endive. *Rapp. Sta. centr. Amélior. Pl.*, *Versailles*, 76–9.   XII
Penman, H. L. (1956). Weather and water in the growth of grass. In: Milthorpe, F. L., The Growth of Leaves, Butterworths, London, 170–7.   III
Pestalozzi, M. (1956). Vurdering av de klimatiske vilkar for havredyrking i Nordland fylke. Sortforsøk 1938–54. *Forskn. Fors. Landbr.* **7**, 417–39.   XXII
Peterson, M. L., Cooper, J. P., and Vose, P. B. (1958). Non-flowering strains of herbage grasses. *Nature*, **181**, 591–4.   X
Peterson, M. L., and Loomis, W. E. (1949). Effects of photoperiod and temperature on growth and flowering of Kentucky bluegrass. *Pl. Physiol.* **24**, 31–43.   XI
Petinov, N. S., and Ivanov, V. P. (1957). The effect of short day during the sprouting period on the water regime and acceleration of development in maize. *Fiziol. Rast.* **4**, 171–82.   XXII
Philippe, J. (1957). Note sur la biologie florale de l'avocatier et choix des variétés à cultiver sur la base du groupe floral. *Bull. agric. Congo belge*, **48**, 1154–62.   XVII
Phinney, B. O. (1956). Growth response of single-gene dwarf mutants in maize to gibberellic acid. *Proc. Nat. Acad. Sci.*, *U.S.A.* **42**, 185–9.   VI
Piringer, A. A., and Borthwick, H. A. (1954). Photoperiodic responses of coffee. *Turrialba*, **5**, 72–7.   XVII
Pohjakallio, O. (1957). Light climate and crop growth in Finland. *Field Crop Abstr.* **10**, 77–82.   R, XXII
Pohjakallio, O., Salonen, A., and Antila, S. (1957). Analysis of earliness in the potato. *Acta agric. scand.* **7**, 361–88.   XIII
Pope, G. S. (1954). The importance of pasture plant oestrogens in the reproduction and lactation of grazing animals. *Dairy Sci. Abstr.* **16**, 334–55.   XI
Post, K. (1942). Effects of daylength and temperature on growth and flowering of some florist crops. *Cornell Univ. agric. Exp. Sta. Bull.* **787**. 70 pp.   XV
Pretoria University (1955–6). Annual report on the research activities of the Plant Physiological Research Institute. 45 pp.   XI
Pretoria University (1957). Annual report on the research activities of the Plant Physiological Research Institute. 60 pp.   XI, XII
Purvis, O. N. (1934). An analysis of the influence of temperature during germination on the subsequent development of certain winter cereals and its relation to the effect of length of day. *Ann. Bot., Lond.*, **48**, 919–55.   II
Purvis, O. N. (1940). Vernalisation of fragments of embryo tissue. *Nature*, **145**, 462.   IV
Purvis, O. N. (1947). Studies in the vernalisation of cereals. X. The effect of depletion of carbohydrates on the growth and vernalisation response of excised embryos. *Ann. Bot., Lond.*, N.S. **11**, 270–83.   IV
Purvis, O. N. (1948). Studies in vernalisation. XI. The effect of date of sowing and of excising the embryo upon the responses of Petkus winter rye to different periods of vernalisation treatment. *Ann. Bot., Lond.*, N.S. **12**, 183.   IV
Purvis, O. N., and Gregory, F. G. (1937). Studies in vernalisation. I. A comparative study of vernalisation of winter rye by low temperature and by short days. *Ann. Bot., Lond.*, N.S. **1**, 569–92.   II, IV, V
Purvis, O. N., and Gregory, F. G. (1952). Studies in vernalisation of cereals. XII. Reversibility by high temperature of vernalised rye. *Ann. Bot., Lond.*, N.S. **16**, 1–21.   IV, V
Purvis, O. N., and Gregory, F. G. (1953). Acceleration effect of an extract of vernalised embryos of winter rye on flower initiation in unvernalised embryos. *Nature*, **171**, 687.   IV
Quinby, J. R., and Karper, R. E. (1945). The inheritance of three genes that influence the time of floral initiation and maturity date in milo. *J. Amer. Soc. Agron.* **32**, 916–36.   X, XXII

BIBLIOGRAPHY

RADLEY, M. (1958). The distribution of substances similar to gibberellic acid in higher plants. *Ann. Bot., Lond.*, N.S. **22**, 297–307. IV

RAPPAPORT, L. (1957). Effect of gibberellin on growth, flowering and fruiting of the Earlypak tomato, *Lycopersicum esculentum. Pl. Physiol.* **32**, 440–4. XVI

RAPPAPORT, L., and CAROLUS, R. L. (1956). Effects of night temperature at different stages of development on reproduction in the Lima bean. *Proc. Amer. Soc. hort. Sci.* **67**, 421–8. XXI

RAPPAPORT, L., and WITTWER, S. H. (1956 a). Flowering in head lettuce as influenced by seed vernalization, temperature, and photoperiod. *Proc. Amer. Soc. hort. Sci.* **67**, 429–37. XII

RAPPAPORT, L., and WITTWER, S. H. (1956 b). Stimulation of flowering by vernalization of endive seedlings—a preliminary report. *Proc. Amer. Soc. hort. Sci.* **67**, 438–9. XII

REIMERS, F. E. (1957). The effect of photoperiod on the growth and formation of garlic and onion bulbs. *Fiziol. Rast.* **4**, 463–9. XIV

REINHOLD, J. (1955). Fragen des Gewächshausbaues. 14*th Internat. Hort. Congr.* 596–614. IX

RICK, C. M. (1956). Genetic and systematic studies on accessions of *Lycopersicon* from the Galapagos Islands. *Amer. J. Bot.* **43**, 687–96. XVI

RITZEL, M. B. (1957). The distribution and time of occurrence of gibberellin-like substances from flowering plants. *Pl. Physiol.* **32**—Suppl., xxxi–xxxii. XI, XXI

RIVES, M. (1957). Etudes sur la sélection du colza d'hiver. *Ann. Amélior. Pl., Paris*, **7**, 61–80. XX

ROBBINS, W. J. (1957 a). Physiological aspects of aging in plants. *Amer. J. Bot.* **44**, 289–94. II

ROBBINS, W. J. (1957 b). Gibberellic acid and the reversal of adult *Hedera* to a juvenile state. *Amer. J. Bot.* **44**, 743–6. II

ROBERTS, R. H. (1951). The induction of flowering with a plant extract. In: Skoog, F., Plant Growth Substances. Univ. Wis. Press, 347–50. IV, V

ROBINS, J. S., and DOMINGO, C. E. (1956). Moisture deficits in relation to the growth and development of dry beans. *Agron. J.* **48**, 67–70. XXI

ROY, S. K., and SUBRAMANYAM, K. N. (1955). Photoperiodic response of some early varieties of rice of Bihar. *J. Indian bot. Soc.* **34**, 455–8. XXII

RUDORF, W. (1958). Entwicklungsphysiologische Grundlagen der Pflanzenzüchtung. In: Handbuch der Pflanzenzüchtung, 2nd Ed. Edited by H. Kappert and W. Rudorf. Paul Parey, Berlin. Vol. I, 225–306. R, X

SAGAWA, Y. (1957). Nitrogen as a modifying factor in the growth and flowering response of carnations to radiation. *Pl. Physiol.* **32**—Suppl., l. XV

SALISBURY, F. B. (1957). Growth regulators and flowering. I. Survey methods. *Pl. Physiol.* **32**, 600–8. IV

SALISBURY, F. B., and BONNER, J. (1956). The reactions of the photoinductive dark period. *Pl. Physiol.* **31**, 114–7. I

SAMANTARAI, B., and MISRA, G. (1956). Photoperiodic behaviour of 'Thailand'—a Philippinese variety of rice. *Curr. Sci.* **25**, 61–2. XXII

SCHMALZ, H. (1958 a). Der Einfluss alternierender Kurztag- und Dauertag-Perioden verschiedener Länge auf die generative Entwicklung einiger Sommerweizenformen. *Z. PflZücht.* **39**, 97–112. I, XXII

SCHMALZ, H. (1958 b). Die generative Entwicklung von Winterweizensorten mit unterschiedlicher Winterfestigkeit bei Frühjahrsaussaat nach Vernalisation mit Temperaturen unter- und oberhalb des Gefrierpunktes. *Züchter*, **28**, 193–203. XXII

SCHROEDER, C. A., and WIELAND, P. A. (1956). Diurnal fluctuations in size in various parts of the avocado tree and fruit. *Proc. Amer. Soc. hort. Sci.* **68**, 253–8. XVII

BIBLIOGRAPHY

SCHULZ, K. (1958). Der Einfluss der Grösse des Samenkorns auf Entwicklung und Ertrag bei *Lupinus albus. Z. Acker- u. Pflbau*, **106**, 225–44.   XI

SCHULZE, E. (1957). Photoperiodische Versuche an mehrjährigen Futterpflanzen. *Z. Acker- u. Pflbau*, **103**, 198–226.   XI

SCHULZE, E. (1958). Zusammenwirken von Tageslänge und Höhe der Stickstoffgabe bei Kulturkartoffeln. *Z. Acker- u. Pflbau*, **105**, 258–70.   XIII

SCHUPHAN, W. (1958). Biochemische Stoffbildung bei *Brassica oleracea* L. in Abhängigkeit von morphologischen und anatomischen Differenzierungen ihrer Organe. I. Teil: Vegetative Organe. *Z. PflZücht*. **39**, 127–86.   XII

SCHUSTER, W. (1956). Saatzeitenversuche mit der Sonnenblume (*Helianthus annuus* L.). *Z. Acker- u. Pflbau*, **100**, 349–66.   XX

SCHWABE, W. W. (1951). Factors controlling flowering in the chrysanthemum. II. Day-length effects on the future development of inflorescence buds and their experimental reversal and modification. *J. exp. Bot.* **2**, 223–37.   Plate

SCHWABE, W. W. (1955). Factors controlling flowering in the chrysanthemum. V. De-vernalization in relation to high temperature and low light intensity treatments. *J. exp. Bot.* **6**, 435–50.   IV, XV

SCHWABE, W. W. (1956). Evidence for a flowering inhibitor produced in long days in *Kalanchoe blossfeldiana. Ann. Bot., Lond.*, N.S. **20**, 1–14.   IV

SCHWABE, W. W. (1957). Factors controlling flowering in the chrysanthemum. VI. De-vernalization by low light intensity in relation to temperature and carbo-hydrate supply. *J. exp. Bot.* **8**, 220–34.   IV, XV

SCOTT, J. D. (1956). The study of primordial buds and the reaction of roots to defoliation as the basis of grassland management. *Proc. 7th Internat. Grassl. Congr.* 479–87.   XI

SCURFIELD, G., and MOORE, C. W. E. (1958). Effects of gibberellic acid on species of *Eucalyptus. Nature*, **181**, 1276–7.   VI

SEN, P. K., and MITRA, G. N. (1958). Inheritance of photoperiodic reaction in rice. *Nature*, **182**, 119–20.   XXII

SEN, S. P., and LEOPOLD, A. C. (1956). Influence of light and darkness upon carbon dioxide fixation. *Pl. Physiol.* **31**, 323–9.   I

SEN GUPTA, J. C. (1952). Study and research in plant physiology with reference to tropical plants. *Bull. bot. Soc. Bengal*, **6**, 33–9.   R, I

SEN GUPTA, J. C. (1955). The physiology of growth and development of some crop plants. *Bull. bot. Soc. Bengal*, **9**, 62–80.   XII, XX, XXI, XXII

SEN GUPTA, J. C., and TALUKDAR, S. (1955). Investigation on the physiology of growth and development of *Crotolaria juncea* L. C.12. *Indian J. agric. Sci.* **25**, 51–66.   XII

SHARMA, S. L., SRIVASTAVA, R. C., ALAM, M. N., and TRIVEDI, J. P. (1956). Relationship between flowering age and height in *Saccharum spontaneum* Linn. *Curr. Sci.* **25**, 89.   XII

SHARMAN, B. C. (1945). Leaf and bud initiation in the Gramineae. *Bot. Gaz.* **106**, 269–89.   II, XI

SHEN, T. H., and KING, Y. K. (1958). Spring wheat production in Taiwan. *Agron. J.* **50**, 92–4.   XXII

SIEGELMAN, H. W., and HENDRICKS, S. B. (1957). Photocontrol of anthocyanin formation in turnip and red cabbage seedlings. *Pl. Physiol.* **32**, 393–8.   XII

SIMPSON, G. M. (1958). A colorimetric test for gibberellic acid and evidence from a dwarf pea assay for the occurrence of a gibberellin-like substance in wheat seedlings. *Nature*, **182**, 528–9.   XXII

SINGH, L. B., and SINGH, R. N. (1956). Floral induction in axillary buds of mango shoots. *Proc. Amer. Soc. hort. Sci.* **68**, 265–9.   XVII

378

BIBLIOGRAPHY

SINSKAYA, E. N. (1958). Investigations on the composition of ecotypical and varietal populations. (A brief survey of some of our works published in Russian.) *Rep. Scot. Pl. Breed. Sta.* 31–40.   X

SIRCAR, S. M., and KUNDU, M. (1955). Effect of auxins on the flowering behaviour of rice. *Nature*, 176, 840–1.   XXII

SIRONVAL, C. (1957). La photopériode et la sexualisation du fraisier des quatre-saisons à fruits rouges (métabolisme chlorophyllien et hormone florigène). *Trav. Cent. Rech. Hormon. vég.* 18. 229 pp.   XVIII

SIRONVAL, C. (1958). Relation between chlorophyll metabolism and nodule formation in soya bean. *Nature*, 181, 1272–3.   II

SKOK, J., and SCULLY, N. J. (1955). Nature of the photoperiodic responses of buckwheat. *Bot. Gaz.* 117, 134–41.   XXII

SKOOG, F. (Ed.) (1951). Plant Growth Substances. Univ. Wis. Press. 476 pp.   R, V

SKRIPČINSKIĬ, V. V. (1956). Some peculiarities of phasic development in different varieties of barley, ensuring the possibility of their hibernation. *Doklady Akad. Nauk, SSSR,* 109, 1210–13.   XXII

SMEETS, L. (1956). Some effects of the photoperiod on the shoot growth of cherry seedlings. *Euphytica,* 5, 238–44.   XVII

SMEETS, L. (1957). Some effects of temperature on the shoot growth of cherry seedlings. *Euphytica,* 6, 161–8.   XVII

SMITH, B. (1954). Reproductive efficiency in *Arachis hypogea. Amer. J. Bot.* 41, 607–16.   XX

SMITH, D. (1955). Influence of area of seed production on the performance of Ranger alfalfa. *Agron. J.* 47, 201–5.   XI

SMITH, D., LOWE, H. J., STROMMEN, A. M., and BROOKS, G. N. (1954). Establishment of legumes as influenced by the rate of sowing the oat companion crop. *Agron. J.* 46, 449–501.   III, XXII

SMITH, H. H. (1950). Differential photoperiod response from an interspecific gene transfer. *J. Hered.* 41, 199–203.   XII

SOWELL, W. F., and ROUSE, R. D. (1956). Growth and fruiting of the cotton plant under controlled environmental conditions. *Agron. J.* 48, 581–2.   XIX

SPEAR, I., and THIMANN, K. V. (1954). The interrelation between CO_2 metabolism and photoperiodism in *Kalanchoe.* II. Effect of prolonged darkness and high temperatures. *Pl. Physiol.* 29, 414–17.   I

SPRAGUE, G. V. (1948). Relation of supplementary light and soil fertility to heading in the greenhouse of several perennial forage grasses. *J. Amer. Soc. Agron.* 40, 144–54.   XI

SPRENT, J. I., and BARBER, H. N. (1957). Leaching of a flower inhibitor from late varieties of peas. *Nature,* 180, 200–1.   IV, XXI

STACY, S. V., and others (1957). Joint effects of maximum temperatures and rainfall on corn yields, Experiment, Georgia. *Agron. J.* 49, 26–8.   XXII

STAPLEDON, R. G. (1943). The Way of the Land. Faber and Faber, London. 276 pp. X

STEARNS, F., and OLSON, J. (1958). Interaction of photoperiod and temperature affecting seed germination in *Tsuga canadensis. Amer. J. Bot.* 45, 53–8.   XII

STEBBINS, G. L. (1950). Variation and Evolution in Plants. Columbia Univ. Press. 643 pp.   R, I, II

STEBBINS, G. L. (1957). Self fertilization and population variability in the higher plants. *Amer. Nat.* 91, 337–54.   II

STEINECK, O. (1958). Grundlagen der photoperiodischen Reduktionsauslese bei einjährigen Kartoffelsämlingen. *Z. PflZücht.* 39, 403–18.   XIII

STEINECK, O., and CZEIKA, G. (1957). Anatomische und cytologische Untersuchungen über tageslängenbedingte Wachstumsänderungen im Sprossmark der Kartoffel. *Züchter,* 27, 272–8.   XIII

BIBLIOGRAPHY

STOKES, P., and VERKERK, K. (1951). Flower formation in Brussels sprouts. *Meded. LandbHogesch., Wageningen*, **50**, 141–60.   I, XII

STOLWIJK, J. A. J. (1952). Photoperiodic and formative effects of various wavelength regions in *Cosmos bipinnatus, Spinacia oleracea, Sinapis alba* and *Pisum sativum. Proc. Kon. Ned. Akad. Wetensch.* (*C*), **55**, 489–502.   XII, XX

STOUGHTON, R. H. (1955). Light and plant growth. *J. roy. hort. Soc.* **80**, 454–66.   I

STOUGHTON, R. H., and VINCE, D. (1957). Use of artificial light in horticulture. *Agric. Rev., Lond.*, **3**, 8–15.   IX, XIV, XV, XVI

STROUN, M. (1955). A propos du photostade du blé 'Fylgia'. *Bull. Soc. bot. Fr.* **102**, 318–22.   XXII

STROUN, M. (1956). Contribution à l'étude du développement des céréales (le photostade, l'hybridation végétative). Essai mitchourien. Encyclopédie biol., 51, Editions Lechevalier, Paris. 193 pp.   XXII

STRUCKMEYER, B. E. (1950). Biology of flowering in plants. *Sci. Monthly*, **70**, 262–7.
                                                                                        IV

STUART, N. W., GOULD, C. J., and GILL, D. L. (1955). Effect of temperature and other storage conditions on forcing behaviour of Easter lilies, bulbous iris and tulips. *14th Internat. Hort. Congr.* 173–87.   XIV

STUART, N. W., PIRINGER, A. A., and BORTHWICK, H. A. (1955). Photoperiodic responses of hydrangeas. *14th Internat. Hort. Congr.* 337–41.   XV

SULLIVAN, J. T., and ROUTLEY, D. G. (1955). The relation of the protein content of forage grasses to the earliness of flowering. *Agron. J.* **47**, 206–7.   XI

TALUKDAR, S. (1952). Photoperiodic behaviour of *Hibiscus sabdariffa*, L.N.P.5. *Nature*, **170**, 458.   XII

TALUKDAR, S. (1955). Total sugar and nitrogen contents of jute plants, with special reference to the flowering stage. *Nature*, **175**, 210–11.   XII

THIJN, G. A. (1954). Observations on flower induction with potatoes. *Euphytica*, **3**, 28–34.   XIII

THIMANN, K. V. (1941). The hormonal control of plant development. *Amer. Nat.* **75**, 147–53.   R, IV

THIMANN, K. V. (1948). Plant Growth Hormones. The Hormones: Physiology, Chemistry and Applications. Academic Press Inc., New York. 70 pp.   R, V

THIMANN, K. V. (1956). Promotion and inhibition: Twin themes of physiology. *Amer. Nat.* **90**, 145–62.   R, IV

THIMANN, K. V. (1958). (Ed.) The Physiology of Forest Trees. A Symposium held at the Harvard Forest, April 1957. Ronald Press Co., New York. xvi + 678 pp.   XII

THIMANN, K. V., and WENT, F. W. (1934). On the chemical nature of the root-forming hormone. *Proc. Kon. Ned. Akad. Wetensch., Sect. Sci.*, **37**, 456–9.   V

THOMAS, R. G. (1956). Effects of temperature and length of day on the sex expression of monoecious and dioecious angiosperms. *Nature*, **178**, 552.   II

THOMAS, R. G. (1958). Sexuality in diploid and hexaploid races of *Mercurialis annua* L. *Ann. Bot., Lond.*, N.S. **22**, 55–72.   II

THORNE, G. N., and WATSON, D. J. (1955). The effect on yield and leaf area of wheat of applying nitrogen as a top-dressing in April or in sprays at ear emergence. *J. agric. Sci.* **46**, 449–56.   III, XXII

THURBER, G. A., DOUGLAS, J. R., and GALSTON, A. W. (1958). Inhibitory effect of gibberellins on nodulization in dwarf beans, *Phaseolus vulgaris. Nature*, **181**, 1082–3.   VI

THURSTON, J. M. (1957). Morphological and physiological variation in wild oats (*Avena fatua* L. and *A. ludoviciana* Dur.) and in hybrids between wild and cultivated oats. *J. agric. Sci.* **49**, 259–74.   XXII

TINCKER, M. A. H. (1925). The effect of length of day upon the growth and reproduction of some economic plants. *Ann. Bot., Lond.*, **39**, 721–54.   XI

BIBLIOGRAPHY

TONIOLO, L. (1956). Studio sull'accestimento di cultivar di frumento e fattori che lo influenzano. *Ann. Sper. agr.* **10**, 669–709. XXII

TOWERS, G. H. N., HUTCHINSON, A., and ANDREAE, W. A. (1958). Formation of a glycoside of maleic hydrazide in plants. *Nature*, **181**, 1535–6. VII

TRAVIN, I. S., and ŠČERBAČEVA, V. D. (1941). Red Clover. SelHozGiz, Moscow. 392 pp. R, XI

TROLL, H. J. (1952). Viren, deren Schäden und genetische Resistenzfragen bei *Lupinus luteus. Züchter*, **22**, 164–75. XI

TRUMBLE, H. C. (1952). Grassland agronomy in Australia. *Advanc. Agron.* **4**, 1–65. R, XI

TUBBS, F. R. (1955). The control of the vegetative growth and reproduction of perennial plants. *14th Internat. Hort. Congr.* 39–50. I

TUKEY, H. B. (1957). Horticulture is a great green carpet that covers the earth. *Amer. J. Bot.* **44**, 279–89. XVII

TUMANOV, I. I. (1957). Station of artificial climate. *Vestnik Akad. Nauk*, **10**, 111-16. IX

ULLRICH, H. (1939). Photoperiodism and flowering hormones. *Ber. dtsch. bot. Ges.* **57**, 40–52. V

ULRICH, A. (1952). Physiological bases for assessing the nutritional requirements of plants. *Annu. Rev. Pl. Physiol.* **3**, 207–28. R, XIII

ULRICH, A. (1954). Growth and development of sugar beet plants at two nitrogen levels, in a controlled temperature greenhouse. *Proc. Amer. Soc. Sug. Beet Technol.* **8**, 325–38. XIII

ULRICH, A. (1955). Influence of night temperature and nitrogen nutrition on the growth, sucrose accumulation and leaf minerals of sugar beet plants. *Pl. Physiol.* **30**, 250–7. XIII

ULRICH, A. (1956). The influence of antecedent climates upon the subsequent growth and development of the sugar beet plant. *J. Amer. Soc. Sug. Beet Technol.* **9**, 97–109. XIII

VAARTAJA, O. (1957). Photoperiodic responses in tree seedlings. *Canad. J. Bot.* **35**, 133. XII

VAN ONSEM, J. G. (1955). La lumière artificielle et la culture de l'*Aechmea fasciata*. *14th Internat. Hort. Congr.* 1040–7. XV

VAN SCHREVEN, D. A. (1956). On the physiology of tuber formation in potatoes. *Plant and Soil*, **8**, 49–86. XIII

VAN STEVENINCK, R. F. M. (1957 a). Influence of pea-mosaic virus on the reproductive capacity of yellow lupine. *Bot. Gaz.* **119**, 63–70. XI

VAN STEVENINCK, R. F. M. (1957 b). Factors affecting the abscission of reproductive organs in yellow lupins (*Lupinus luteus* L.). I. The effect of different patterns of flower removal. *J. exp. Bot.* **8**, 373–81. XI

VAVILOV, N. I. (1935). Phytogeographical Basis of Plant Breeding. Moscow. *See in:* Vavilov, N. I. (1951). The Origin, Variation, Immunity and Breeding of Cultivated Plants. Chronica Botanica: Ronald Press Co., New York, 13–54. XIII

VELASCO, J. R., and MANUEL, F. C. (1955). The photoperiodic response of Elon-elon rice. *Philipp. Agriculturist*, **39**, 161–75. XXII

VERKERK, K. (1954). De invloed van temperatuur en licht op de tomaat. *Meded. Direct. Tuinbouw*, **17**, 637–47. XVI

VICKERY, H. B. (1956). The capacity of leaves of *Bryophyllum calycinum* to recover from prolonged exposure to darkness or to light. *Pl. Physiol.* **31**, 455–64. I

VIEIRA NATIVIDADE, J. (1957). Juvenilidade na *Olea europaea* L. *Agron. lusit.* **19**, 145–59. XVII

VIGLIERCHIO, D. R., and WENT, F. W. (1957). Plant growth under controlled conditions. IX. Growth and fruiting of the Kentucky Wonder bean (*Phaseolus vulgaris*). *Amer. J. Bot.* **44**, 449–53. XXI

BIBLIOGRAPHY

VISHER, S. S. (1954). Climatic Atlas of the United States. Harvard Univ. Press, Cambridge, Mass. 403 pp.   XI
WARDLAW, C. W. (1952). Morphogenesis in Plants. Methuen, London. 176 pp. R, II
WARDLAW, C. W. (1956). The floral meristem as a reaction system. *Nature*, **178**, 1386.   II
WAREING, P. F. (1954). Experiments on the 'light-break' effect in short-day plants. *Physiol. Plant.* **7**, 157–82.   IV
WAREING, P. F. (1956). Photoperiodism in woody plants. *Annu. Rev. Pl. Physiol.* **7**, 191–214.   R, XI
WAREING, P. F. (1957). Tree physiology. *Nature*, **180**, 77–8.   XII
WAREING, P. F., and CARR, D. J. (1954). Some recent experiments bearing on theories of photoperiodism. *Proc. Linn. Soc. Lond.* **164**, 134.   IV
WASSINK, E. C. (1957). The study of plant growth in controlled environments. In: Hudson, J. P., Control of the Plant Environment. Butterworths, London, 36–57.   I
WASSINK, E. C., and STOLWIJK, J. A. J. (1956). Effects of light quality on plant growth. *Annu. Rev. Pl. Physiol.* **7**, 373–400.   R, I
WASSINK, E. C., STOLWIJK, J. A. J., and BEEMSTER, A. B. R. (1951). Dependence of formative and photoperiodic reactions in *Brassica rapa* var., *Cosmos* and *Lactuca* on wavelength and time of irradiation. *Proc. Kon. Ned. Akad. Wetensch.* (*C*), **54**, 3–14.   XII, XX
WATERSCHOOT, H. F. (1957). Effects of temperature and daylength on flowering in *Dianthus barbatus* L. *Proc. Kon. Ned. Akad. Wetensch.* (*C*), **60**, 318–23.   I, XV
WATSON, D. J. (1947). Comparative physiological studies on the growth of field crops. I. Variation in net assimilation rate and leaf area between species and varieties, and within and between years. *Ann. Bot., Lond.*, N.S. **11**, 41–76.   III
WATSON, D. J. (1956). Leaf growth in relation to crop yield. In: Milthorpe, F. L., The Growth of Leaves. Butterworths, London, 187–91.   III
WATSON, D. J. (1958). The dependence of net assimilation rate on leaf-area index. *Ann. Bot., Lond.*, N.S. **22**, 37–54.   III
WATSON, D. J., THORNE, G. N., and FRENCH, S. A. W. (1958). Physiological causes of differences in grain yield between varieties of barley. *Ann. Bot., Lond.*, N.S. **22**, 321–52.   XXII
WEAVER, R. J. (1956). Plant regulators in grape production. *Calif. agric. Exp. Sta. Bull.* 752. 26 pp.   XVII
WEDDING, R. T., HALL, B. J., and LANCE, E. (1956). Effects of fruit-setting plant growth regulator sprays on storage qualities of tomato fruits. *Proc. Amer. Soc. hort. Sci.* **68**, 459–65.   XVI
WEIBEL, D. E. (1958). Vernalization of immature winter wheat embryos. *Agron. J.* **50**, 267–70.   VIII
WEINBERGER, J. H. (1956). Prolonged dormancy trouble in peaches in the Southeast in relation to winter temperature. *Proc. Amer. Soc. hort. Sci.* **67**, 107–12.   XVII
WELLENSIEK, S. J. (1925). Genetic monograph on *Pisum. Bibliogr. Genet.* **2**, 343.   R, XXI
WELLER, L. E., WITTWER, S. H., BUKOVAC, M. J., and SELL, H. M. (1957). The effect of gibberellic acid on enzyme activity and oxygen uptake in bean plants (*Phaseolus vulgaris*). *Pl. Physiol.* **32**, 371–2.   VI
WENT, F. W. (1928). Wuchsstoff und Wachstum. *Rev. trav. bot. néerl.* **25**, 1–116.   I
WENT, F. W. (1934). A test method for rhizocaline, the root-forming substance. *Proc. Kon. Ned. Akad. Wetensch., Sect. Sci.* **37**, 445–55.   V
WENT, F. W. (1943). Plant growth under controlled conditions. I. The air-conditioned greenhouses at the California Institute of Technology. *Amer. J. Bot.* **30**, 157–63.   I

382

BIBLIOGRAPHY

WENT, F. W. (1944). Personal communication, 9 August.   I
WENT, F. W. (1954). The physiology of the growth of sugar beets. *Proc. Amer. Soc. Sug. Beet Technol.* **8**, 319–24.   XIII
WENT, F. W. (1957). The Experimental Control of Plant Growth. Chronica Botanica Co., Waltham, Mass. 343 pp.   R, I, IX, XII, XVI
WENT, F. W., and THIMANN, K. V. (1937). Phytohormones. Macmillan Co., New York. 305 pp.   R, V
WHYTE, R. O. (1939). Phasic development of plants. *Biol. Rev.* **14**, 51–87.   R, I
WHYTE, R. O. (1958). Plant Exploration, Collection and Introduction. F.A.O. Agric. Study, 41. 117 pp.   R, X, XVI
WHYTE, R. O., and HUDSON, P. S. (1933). Vernalization, or Lysenko's method for the pre-treatment of seed. *Bull.* 9, *Imp. Bur. Pl. Genet.: Herb. Pl.* 27 pp.   R, I
WHYTE, R. O., MOIR, T. R. G., and COOPER, J. P. (1959). Grasses in Agriculture. F.A.O. Agric. Study, 42. 417 pp.   R, XI
WIERSUM, L. K. (1955). Considerations regarding practical and physiological research on yield stimulation of *Hevea brasiliensis*. 14*th Internat. Hort. Congr.* 1437–44.   XII
WIGGANS, S. C. (1956). The effect of seasonal temperatures on maturity of oats planted at different dates. *Agron. J.* **48**, 21–5.   XXII
WIGGANS, S. C., and FREY, K. J. (1957). Tillering studies in oats. II. Effect of photoperiod and date of planting. *Agron. J.* **49**, 215–17.   XXII
WILLIAMS, I. H., and HUDSON, J. P. (1956). Effect of environment upon the growth and development of raspberry canes. *Nature*, **177**, 798–9.   XVII
WILLIAMS, W. (1945). Varieties and strains of red and white clover—British and foreign. *Welsh Pl. Breed. Sta. Bull.* (*H*), **16**, 26.   XI
WILSON, J. W., and WADSWORTH, R. M. (1958). The effect of wind speed on assimilation rate—a re-assessment. *Ann. Bot., Lond.*, N.S. **22**, 285–90.   I
WILTEN, W. (1956). Phaeno-klimogram voor de zomergerst in het Zuidwestlijk kleigebiet. *Jaarb. NaCoBrouw.* 78–82.   XXII
WILTSHIRE, G. H. (1956). The effect of darkening on the susceptibility of plants to infection with viruses. *Ann. appl. Biol.* **44**, 233–55.   XII
WIRWILLIE, J. W., and MITCHELL, J. W. (1950). Six new plant growth-inhibiting compounds. *Bot. Gaz.* **111**, 491–4.   VII
WITTWER, S. H., and BUKOVAC, M. J. (1958). The effects of gibberellin on economic crops. *Econ. Bot.* **12**, 213–55.   VI, XII, XVI, XXI
WITTWER, S. H., BUKOVAC, M. J., and GRIGSBY, B. H. (1957). Gibberellin and higher plants. VI. Effects on the composition of Kentucky blue grass (*Poa pratensis*) grown under field conditions in early spring. *Quart. Bull. Mich. agric. Exp. Sta.* **40**, 203–6.   VI
WITTWER, S. H., and TEUBNER, F. G. (1956). New practices for increasing the fruit crop of greenhouse-grown tomatoes. *Quart. Bull. Mich. agric. Exp. Sta.* **39**, 2–12.   XVI
WITTWER, S. H., and TEUBNER, F. G. (1957). The effects of temperature and nitrogen nutrition on flower formation in the tomato. *Amer. J. Bot.* **44**, 125–9.   XVI
WYCHERLEY, P. R. (1952). Temperature and photoperiod in relation to flowering in three perennial grass species. *Meded. LandbHogesch., Wageningen*, **52**, 75–92.   XI
WYCHERLEY, P. R. (1954). Vegetative proliferation of floral spikelets in British grasses. *Ann. Bot., Lond.*, N.S. **18**, 119–27.   XI
YABUTA, T., SUMIKI, Y., KAZUO, F., and MASAHIKO, H. (1948). Biochemical studies of 'bakanae' fungus. XXII. Chemical composition of rice seedlings treated with gibberellin. *J. agric. chem. Soc. Japan*, **22**, 16–17.   VI

383

BIBLIOGRAPHY

YOSHIDA, S. (1955). Photoperiodic responses of hemp (*Cannabis sativa*) plants, especially their morphogenetic changes in leaf shape. *Proc. Crop Sci. Soc. Japan*, **24**, 213–16.   XII

ZEEVAART, J. A. D. (1958). Flower formation as studied by grafting. Thesis. H. Veenman en Zonen, Wageningen. 88 pp.   IV

ŽURBICKIĬ, Z. I., and VARTAPETJAN, S. M. (1956). The influence of the polar summer day on assimilation and tuber formation in potato. *Fiziol. Rast.* **3**, 58–65.   XII

INDEX OF SUBJECTS AND PLANT NAMES

INDEX

INDEX

389

INDEX

Pawpaw (*Carica papaya*), 298
Pea (*Pisum*), 25, 42, 71–2, 98–9, 104, 106, 115–16, 120, 122–4, 317–21
Peach (*Prunus persica*), 290, 298
Pear (*Pyrus communis*), 67–8, 290
Pecan (*Carya*), 59
Pelargonium hortorum, 270
Pennisetum clandestinum, 201; *P. typhoideum*, 340
Pepper (vegetable) (*Capsicum* spp.), 121
Peppermint (*Mentha piperita*), 229
Perennials, physiological characteristics, 44, 50, 60–1, 65, 98, 200, 210, 309
Perilla, 42, 99, 102
Persea gratissima, 292–3
Petunia hybrida, 269–70
Peucedanum graveolens, 221
Phalaris arundinacea, 192, 194, 199; *Ph. canariensis*, 51; *Ph. minor*, 200; *Ph. tuberosa*, 157; *Ph. tuberosa* var. *stenoptera*, 202
Pharbitis nil, 101
Phaseolus, 72; *Ph. aureus*, 316; *Ph. vulgaris*, 106, 120–3, 129, 314–15
Phases, in reproductive development, 14, 16, 20, 34, 38, 40, 47, 96, 179, 180, 251, 268, 282, 290, 293, 302, 311, 320, 328, 332, 340, 355
Phenoclimogram, 326
Phleum pratense, 51, 53, 60, 78, 81, 83, 169–73, 192, 194, 196, 198–9, 201–2
Phosphate(orus), as nutrient, 207, 234, 245–6, 310, 314, 353
Photoperiod: after-effect, 25; and sex expression, 64; and temperature, 31, 39–40, 263, 268–70, 284, 321–2, 325, 347; and vernalization, 24, 27, 39–40, 56, 91; perception, 18, 25, 31, 74, 81, 237–8, 273; requirements, response, types, 26–7, 34, 41, 56, 72, 77, 106–7, 172, 193–4, 204–7, 209–10, 217, 225–8, 232–3, 236–7, 240, 243–5, 247–8, 268–9, 271, 274, 276–8, 294–5, 303–5, 310–11, 321, 333–4, 339, 342–9, 353–4
Photoperiodism, 14, 18, 20, 25, 33, 103, 181, 193, 240–1, 253, 268, 329, 342; and thermoperiodism, 25
Photophase, 38, 40, 175, 282, 302–3, 328, 333, 352
Photosynthesis, 17, 25, 75–6, 281, 329–30
Photothermal summation, 325–7, 337, 349
Photothermograph, 255–8

Phyllotaxis, 45, 59
Phytotron(s), 147–60
Picea, 239; *P. glauca*, 240
Pigeon pea, see *Cajanus cajan*
Pigment(s), 25, 32, 59, 195, 223, 275, 303, 334
Pineapple (*Ananas comosus*), 111, 113, 290, 299
Pinus, 239; *P. banksiana*, 240; *P. coulteri*, 241; *P. resinosa*, 240; *P. silvestris*, 239; *P. taeda*, 238
Pisum, see Pea
Plastochrone, 58–9, 283–4
Plum (*Prunus domestica*), 290
Poa, 197; *P. ampla*, 195; *P. bulbosa*, 194; *P. compressa*, 194–5; *P. pratensis*, 126–7, 194, 199, 201; *P. scabrella*, 202; *P. trivialis*, 127, 202
Poppy, see *Papaver somniferum*
Population variability, 65
Populus, 239, 240; *P. serotina*, 240; *P. tremula*, 239
Potash, as nutrient, 245–6, 353
Potato (*Solanum tuberosum*), 25, 113, 121, 181, 243–8
Primordia: flower, 34–5, 47–57, 87–8, 92–3, 115–16, 190, 193, 221–2, 231, 234, 236, 269, 283, 297, 301, 320, 332, 348, 353; leaf, 47, 49, 54–5, 57, 77–8, 87, 193, 231, 234, 269, 283, 297, 300, 348
Privet, see *Ligustrum vulgare*
Protein content, and reproduction, 192, 204, 341
Prunus armeniaca, 59, 122, 290; *P. avium*, see Cherry; *P. domestica*, 290; *P. persica*, 290, 298
Pseudotsuga douglasii, 241
Pteridophyta, 16, 45
Pyrus communis, see Pear; *P. malus*, see Apple

Quercus, 59, 238

Radiation: biology, 25; solar, 28–9, 75
Radio-isotopes, in plant nutrition, 17
Radish (*Raphanus sativus*), 122
Rape, see *Brassica napus*
Raspberry (*Rubus idaeus*), 299
Rejuvenation, 18, 32, 60
Reproduction (= reproductive development): and growth, 13, 15, 17, 18, 38, 40, 45, 48–9, 51, 66, 297–8
Resistance, drought, salt, 17

INDEX

Retardation, growth and flowering, see also inhibition, 129–32

Rhododendron, 240

Rhubarb (*Rheum officinale*), 122

Rhythm(s), endogenous and other, 26, 32, 282, 293–4, 308, 322, 329

Ribes nigrum, 296

Rice (*Oryza sativa*), 123, 132, 342–6

Ripeness-to-flower, 20, 22–4, 27, 34, 37, 41, 48, 55–6, 181, 283, 331–2, 345

Root(ing), 113, 120, 190, 204, 278, 299, 330–1, 356; crops, 248–61; environment, 21–2

Rosa, 113, 121

Rubber, see *Hevea brasiliensis*

Rubus idaeus, 299

Rye (*Secale cereale*), 19, 23, 24, 36, 39, 40, 49, 50, 52, 56, 87–95, 116, 138–40, 174, 177, 326, 329, 347

Ryegrass, see *Lolium*

Saccharum officinarum, see Sugar-cane; *S. spontaneum*, 231

Salvia splendens, 278

Sarson (*Brassica campestris* var. *sarson*), 310

Secale, 66, 169; *S. cereale*, see Rye

Seed: characters, 207, 308, 314, 337; production, 184, 216, 223–4, 250

Sempervivum funkii, 20, 35–6

Senescence, 18, 58, 77, 79, 289–90, 340

Sesamum indicum, 311–12

Setaria italica, 338–9; *S. tenuiseta*, 195

Sexuality, physiology, 61–5, 68–9, 227, 235–6, 293, 298

Shallot, see *Allium ascalonicum*

Short day, see Photoperiod, response types

Silene armeria, 117; *S. pendula*, 64

Sinapis alba, 309–10

Sisal (*Agave sisalana*), 120

Sodium-naphthaleneacetate, 297, 299

Soil, moisture, temperature, 21, 22

Solanum demissum, 244; *S. tuberosum*, see Potato

Sorghum halepense, 194–5; *S. vulgare*, 176, 347–8

Soybean (*Glycine soja*), 19, 42, 71–3, 107, 115–17, 165, 244, 274, 321–4, 334

Spectrum, 26, 27, 31, 32, 35, 106, 165, 227, 309–10, 317, 329, 333

Spinacia oleracea, 67, 227

Spruce (*Picea*), 239

Sterility, 218–19, 301, 309, 316, 330, 340

Stipa, 65; *S. cernua*, 202

Stock (*Matthiola incana*), 121, 268, 270

Stolon, characters, 244, 247

Strawberry (*Fragaria vesca*), 21, 69, 300–4

Streptocarpus, 99

Sugar-beet (*Beta vulgaris*), 75, 77, 114, 165, 180, 184, 248–60

Sugar-cane (*Saccharum officinarum*), 167, 229–32, 249, 251

Sugar content, 36, 248–60, 281

Sunflower (*Helianthus annuus*), 77, 97, 129, 175, 312–13

Synecology, 13

Temperature: and photoperiod, 31, 39, 40, 195, 284, 321–2, 325, 347; during germination, 20; response, requirement, 22, 36–7, 79, 87–94, 187–8, 199, 201, 208–9, 222, 225–6, 234, 248, 262, 272, 275, 296–8, 307, 321–2, 325, 332, 341–3, 348–54; summation, 42, 319–20, 326–7, 337–8, 349

Teosinte (*Euchlaena mexicana*), 51, 115

Tetragon palaestinus, 205

Thermoperiodism, 22, 25, 34, 125, 238–9, 247, 281, 294, 319, 321–2, 335

Thermophase, 24, 40, 282–3, 333

Thiamine, 116

Thorns, 59, 290

Thuja plicata, 241

Tiller(s), physiology, development, 53, 57, 60–1, 78–80, 83, 86–7, 106, 201, 234, 335, 338–42, 346, 348, 353

Time-to-flowering, measurement, 42, 320–1, 344

Timothy, see *Phleum pratense*

Tobacco (*Nicotiana tabacum*), 39, 98, 157, 167, 227–9, 244

Tolylphthalamic acid, 285

Tomato (*Lycopersicon esculentum*), 21, 25, 106, 114–15, 121–3, 164, 180, 280–7

Traumatic acid, 86

Trifolium, 65; *T. lappaceum*, 205; *T. palaestinum*, 205; *T. pratense*, 71–2, 81, 188, 203–4, 206, 216; *T. purpureum*, 205; *T. repens*, 81–2, 186–8, 210–14; *T. scabrum*, 205; *T. spumosum*, 205; *T. stellatum*, 205; *T. subterraneum*, 72, 80, 82–3, 157, 186–7, 191, 206–10; *T. vavilovii*, 205; *T. xerocephalum*, 205

391